FALLOW DEER

Their history, distribution and biology

by

DONALD AND NORMA CHAPMAN

with photographs by
John K. Fawcett

COCH-Y-BONDDU BOOKS

First published in 1975 by Terence Dalton Ltd.

New edition 1997.
Published by Coch-y-bonddu Books, Machynlleth.
Copyright Norma Chapman 1997.
All rights reserved.

ISBN 0 9528510 5 9

Dedicated to
Colonel V. S. Laurie, C.B.E., T.D., D.L. of South Weald
who kindly gave us the freedom of his estate to watch the wild deer.

Published & distributed by
COCH-Y-BONDDU BOOKS
MACHYNLLETH, POWYS, SY20 8DJ
Tel 01654 702837   Fax 01654 702857

Preface to 1997 Reprint

When this book was published in 1975 Donald and I hoped that it would stimulate interest and further study of a species which was giving us so much pleasure but about which there was much yet to be learned. We were not disappointed. Many researchers, in England and abroad, took up the challenge of field studies and laboratory investigations. Observations during the rut were of special interest, proving that under some circumstances fallow deer form leks. The advent of farming fallow deer catalysed much research, especially in New Zealand where female reproductive physiology was thoroughly investigated and hybridisation of the two sub-species of fallow deer followed.

It is a gratifying tribute to my late husband, who was the senior author, that the book is still sought by fallow deer enthusiasts in many countries, despite the recent advances in knowledge. When Paul Morgan suggested a reprinting I was delighted to acquiesce.

Further Reading (post 1975 references) has been added. This is not a complete list of publications on fallow deer over the last twenty-two years but should direct readers to the major new sources of information on a wide range of topics.

Norma Chapman
Barton Mills,
Suffolk.

August 1997.

ERRATA

page 58	Under Bulgaria: change Bourges to *Burgas*
page 59	Under Austria: insert *numerous* before Austria
page 64	Under Nebraska: change Geeley to *Greely*
page 65	Under Argentina: change Peryra to *Per Eyra*
page 94	Figure 4. Vertical section of a molar. There has been conflicting information on the presence of cementum over the crown. It now seems that this coronal cementum is normally absent in fallow deer apart from occasional small patches over the enamel at the base of the crown.
page 111	In caption: change menil to *common coloured*
page 131	line 11: change beat to *bear*
page 143	line 19: change five to *six* in list of data: change 6 weeks to *7 weeks* change 7 weeks, 3.5g to *8 weeks, 7.0g*
page 178	line 15: change page 77 to *page 179*
pages 197, 198 and 199: add key to the Figures: black = males, white = females
page 210	line 1: change spring to *autumn*
page 220	paragraph 2, line 4: change just east to *north east*
page 229	Under Cumbria: change Dallas to *Dallam*
page 243	lines 2–3: these should be at the top of page 255.

Contents

Index of Illustrations

Index of Figures

Acknowledgements

A BOOK such as this relies on the work of many people. Over the years we have received continued friendship and help in our studies of fallow deer from Brian Barton, David Corke, Bob Cowlin, Ron Critchley, Brian Eastcott, Jeanne and John Fawcett and their sons Raymond and Vernon, Stephen Harris, Cate Hickling, Ken Hoy, Diane Hughes, Chris Hutchings, Ron Newbery and Peter Stothert. We thank them for being ever ready to erect deer netting, catch animals, collect specimens, search for fawns or tramp the countryside recording the distribution of deer, and for making their observations available to us. Very many other people, too numerous to name, have helped on occasions with these activities: to them also we extend our thanks.

The Superintendent of Epping Forest, A. Qvist; the Superintendent of Richmond Park, M. B. Brown, and his predecessor, G. J. Thomson; and Col. V. S. Laurie of South Weald graciously allowed us to study the deer in their care.

Our studies have been financed by grants from The Carnegie United Kingdom Trust, The Essex Field Club, The Essex Naturalists' Trust, The Nature Conservancy and The Natural Environment Research Council. Many companies supplied equipment and materials. Dr R. K. Archer, Director of the Equine Research Station, generously made laboratory facilities available to us. We are most grateful to all of them for their support.

The following have assisted by providing specimens: J. Bowers, W. N. Brown, J. W. Clark, M. Clark, D. Davis, R. Eden, I. Edwards, Essex Constabulary, E. Gwilliam, D. Hart-Davis, J. Humby, Metropolitan Police, D. Pedler, B. Smith, D. Talbot, The Hon. Vincent Weir, the late H. Wonham, R. West and G. Woods.

We are indebted to John Fawcett who not only dealt with all the photographs but, with his wife, Jeanne, read the entire manuscript, made many valuable suggestions and checked the proofs.

For reading and commenting on certain sections of the manuscript and for providing information from their particular fields of study, we thank Professor A. Azzaroli, A. Batty, Dr J. Clevedon Brown, W. Buckingham, Dr G. R. Coope, Dr G. B. Corbet, F. Courtier, Dr S. Hess, J. Hotchkis, Dr J. E. Jackson, Dr G. A. Lincoln, Dr A. McDiarmid, Dr B. Mitchell, R. Prior, H. Selle and Dr Elizabeth Shillito.

The following people kindly made their unpublished theses available to us: K. Baker, Dr B. K. Gilbert, Dr G. Heidemann, Dr J. E. Jackson and Gillian Puttick.

Information about fallow deer and their distribution has been provided by many people throughout the world: *Argentina*, B. Affolter, Jose Maria Gallardo, S. Safontás; *Australia: Northern Territory*, F. R. Gnauck; *Queensland*, W. Saunders;

South Australia, J. Conquest, M. R. Irving; *Tasmania*, P. Murrell; *Victoria*, G. M. O'Brien; *Western Australia*, J. L. Long; *Austria*, K. Bauer, H. Frey; *Barbuda*, J. L. Robinson; *Belgium*, S. de Crombrugghe, L. J. Petyt; *Bulgaria*, E. Clay; *Canada*, G. W. Smith, J. H. Todd; *Chile*, J. Rottman; *Cyprus*, L. I. Leontlades; *Czechoslovakia*, V. Mimra; *Denmark*, B. Jensen, U. Møhl, H. Strandgaard; *Finland*, M. Montonen; *France*, E. Heil, J-P. Rieb; *Greece*, Maud Psarris, Anne Yannoulis; *Hungary*, L. Bencze; *Ireland*, C. D. Deane, F. Mulloy, Lord Revelstoke; *Israel*, G. Ilany; *Italy*, P. L. Florio, C. Petronio; *Japan*, T. Ito; *Jugoslavia*, B. Andrej; *Liechtenstein*, B. Konrad; *Luxembourg*, R. Van den Kerchove, A. Strauss; *Malagasy*, R. Albignac, J. M. Andriamampianina; *Morocco*, A. Elkadiri; *Netherlands*, W. A. Weyland; *New Zealand*, L. T. Pracy; *Norway*, J. A. Pedersen; *Peru*, C. F. del Prado; *Poland*, K. Caboń-Raczyńska, Z. Pucek; *Portugal*, G. B. Gooch; *Romania*, M. Bodea; *Scotland*, A. Allison, A. B. Cooper, P. A. Joynson; *South Africa*, R. C. Bigalke, J. David, H. J. Richards; *Spain*, J. Castroviego, J. de la Pena Payá; *Sweden*, K. Curry-Lindahl; *Switzerland*, R. Schloeth; *Turkey*, C. Holloway; *United States of America; Alabama*, R. H. Allen; *California*, W. G. Macgregor; *Colorado*, A. E. Anderson; *Georgia*, T. Kile; *Illinois*, W. D. Klimstra; *Indiana*, L. Johnson; *Kentucky*, J. S. Durrell; *Louisiana*, J. W. Farrar; *Maryland*, R. L. Miller; *Massachusetts*, J. J. McDonough; *Michigan* and *Minnesota*, W. R. Jones; *Nebraska*, K. Menel, R. E. Woodruff; *New Mexico*, W. A. Synder; *Tennessee*, R. W. Nall; *Texas*, J. L. Cooke; *U.S.S.R.*, V. G. Heptner.

Translations of papers and letters were kindly undertaken by Kate Adrian, D. Archer, Hilary Footitt, Jean Hawkins, Dr F. Holmes, Jean Ingles, R. McCready, I. Perkins, C. C. Pond, Dr W. R. Rybotycki and K. A. Toye. We are grateful also to many park owners, museums, organisations and libraries for having supplied information and facilities for study.

We thank Dr Diane Hughes for preparing Figures 1, 2, 4, 5 and 7. The following provided photographs: Aerofilms Ltd.; British Museum (Natural History); Cambridge University Library; R. A. Cowlin; Greek Tourist Office, Rhodes; Dr S. Hess; K. E. Hoy; Dr Diane Hughes; C. W. Hutchings; Dr L. B. Jeffcott; J. R. Mercer; A. Qvist; G. B. Thompson; and S. R. Worsfold. All the other monochrome plates and the colour photographs are by J. K. Fawcett; L. Preston kindly allowed his perruque fallow antlers to be photographed and J. Aplin, Head Keeper, facilitated the photography in Petworth Park. J.K.F. is grateful to Carl Zeiss Jena Ltd. for the loan of equipment for some of the photographs.

Valerie Brooks, Susan Marshall and Barbara Marsham typed the manuscript.

Finally, we thank the Leverhulme Trust Fund for the award of a Research Grant to Norma which enabled the book to be written.

Donald and Norma Chapman   September 1975.
Barton Mills, Suffolk.

Fit to grace any stately home.

CHAPTER ONE

Introduction

OUR INTERESTS in fallow deer began in 1950 when one of us, living on the borders of Epping Forest, used to spend weekends and holidays rambling through the woods and watching the deer. Indeed, it was a proud boast that a full day was never spent in the Forest without deer being seen. Unfortunately, the same could not be said today, because few deer remain in the main areas of the Forest, others having found more peaceful homes on the surrounding estates and in outlying woods. However, it was not until 1963 that our studies took a more serious turn when, after seeing the corpse of a doe lying beside the busy London to Norwich trunk road which bisects the Forest, we realised that little was known of the natural history of this ancient herd of black fallow deer. With the very helpful co-operation of Mr A. Qvist, the Superintendent of Epping Forest, and of the late Mr K. Marshall, at that time Curator of the Passmore Edwards Museum, the headquarters of the Essex Field Club, we were able to examine this corpse and, subsequently, those of many more killed in road traffic accidents in the area.

Fallow are the most widely distributed deer in the British Isles, having been recorded in nearly all the counties of England, most counties in Wales, several in Scotland and most in Ireland. They have been present for many centuries and are the species most favoured in deer parks. The disbandment of many parks in the last one hundred years has led, in part, to the present widespread occurrence of this deer in the British countryside. Largely as a result of man's influence, some would say interference, fallow are also one of the most widely distributed species of deer in the world, being found now in 35 countries.

Despite the interest shown in fallow, their natural history has been much less extensively studied than that of the other two species of deer common in Britain and Europe, the red deer and the roe deer. Millais in *British Deer and their Horns*, published in 1897, allocated only 28 pages to fallow deer compared with 91 pages to red deer and 54 pages to the roe. Whereas books such as Darling's *A Herd of Red Deer* and Tegner's *The Roe Deer* have been devoted to those species, no monograph in the English language has yet been published on fallow deer. Two German monographs on fallow have appeared: *Das Damwild* by Ueckermann and Hansen, and *Zur Biologie des Damwildes* by Heidemann.

Nevertheless, the study of the natural history of fallow has not been neglected entirely. Over 200 years ago, Russell described in *The Oeconomy of Nature in*

Epping Forest. Fallow buck of the black variety standing amidst tall grass. *A. Qvist*

Acute and Chronical Diseases of the Glands that the buck's antlers are cast from the middle of April to the end of May and that the velvet was shed about the end of August, facts which are just as true today. He also described accurately the effect of castration on a buck's antlers although he was probably wrong when he stated that fallow rutted about the middle of September; the middle of October is usual now. In 1840, Gulliver studied certain features of the reproductive organs of fallow and, since the middle of the nineteenth century, there has been a trickle of scientific papers on various aspects of both fossil and living fallow, as well as numerous anecdotal articles. In the last 25 years, much more interest has been directed to fallow deer and serious studies have been made in several countries. In particular the last decade has seen a great increase in factual knowledge of the animal living in its natural surroundings.

14

Epping Forest in Essex, one of the ancient royal hunting grounds, has held fallow deer for centuries. A document of 1495 distinguished between red deer and fallow in the Forest. The latter are less numerous now and red deer have not been present since early in the nineteenth century. The Forest is a long, narrow crescent-shaped tract of deciduous woodland and grassland about 20 kilometres long and in few places more than four kilometres wide. It is situated on a ridge of higher ground, rising to 120 metres, between the valleys of the Lea and Roding; it extends southwards to within 10 kilometres of St Paul's Cathedral in the City of London. The southern part consists mainly of grassy plains, much grazed by commoners' cattle, and scattered patches of woodland. Busy roads intersect this part of the Forest and it is almost surrounded by built-up areas. The northern part of the Forest is mainly deciduous woodland with fairly large areas of bracken, much less urbanised than the southern part, and bordered largely by agricultural land.

South Weald. Three conspicuous white deer with a well-camouflaged menil fawn and common doe in the centre and a black doe to the right, between the oak trees. *C. W. Hutchins.*

Aerial view of the South Weald estate, which is left of centre in the picture, taken in October 1970. The main London to Colchester trunk road runs diagonally across the photograph with the edge of Brentwood to the east, the railway to the south and the golf course to the west. Part of Weald Park can be seen in the top centre. The deer frequent most the small wood adjacent to the roundabout and the fields immediately to the north.

Aerofilms Limited.

The Forest is used widely for recreation, is visited by thousands of people each year and innumerable motor vehicles use the roads through it. The deer have been pushed further and further north as urbanisation and disturbance have increased. By 1963, they had confined themselves entirely to the northern part of the Forest, with the exception of a single animal killed in the southern-most part of the Forest in November of that year.

Ornithologists have long recognised the necessity to mark birds in studies where individual identification is essential and bird-ringing is now well established. Unfortunately, many naturalists, including even some mammalogists, have been slow to recognise that these requirements apply just as much to mammals as to birds. We were exceedingly fortunate in that Colonel V. S. Laurie gave us freedom to study and to mark the wild fallow on his estate at South Weald near Brentwood in south-west Essex, only 15 kilometres east of Epping Forest. These deer are almost certainly descendants of animals which escaped from Weald Park when the fences were breached about 30 years ago. They inhabit an area of small deciduous woods and small fields, both pasture and arable, on the edge of the Thames valley and rising to 85 metres. The woods are young and, apart from the areas of coppiced hornbeam, have a dense ground flora. One of the most fascinating characteristics of the estate is that it is in a cul-de-sac of urbanisation. It is bordered by the town of Brentwood to the east, a golf course and the council estates of Harold Hill to the west and the main London to Colchester trunk road and railway to the south, as shown in the aerial photograph (Page 16). The Brentwood by-pass, a road of almost motorway standard, an electric pylon line and an oil pipe line have all been put through the estate in the past 15 years and yet still the deer remain, often feeding and resting within metres of the by-pass. The estate is frequented by people riding horses, local villagers exercising their dogs, members of a local pigeon control society and, of course, us to watch the deer. In Britain, deer are being subjected more and more to this type of disturbance and we thought that information on the natural history of wild fallow living so close to civilisation might prove interesting.

Fallow deer in Britain have no natural predators and consequently large numbers have to be culled, the Forestry Commission alone shooting almost 900 fallow deer in 1973-74. To investigate certain aspects of the biology of fallow, particularly methods of estimating their age, we needed to mark a large number of animals and to collect specimens when the deer were culled. Again we found good friends in Mr G. J. Thomson, then Superintendent of Richmond Park, and Mr M. B. Brown, the present Superintendent, who allowed us to study the deer in the Park. This Park, like Epping Forest, was once a royal hunting ground although, unlike the Forest, the Park was enclosed by 1637, the present 300 to 400 head of fallow and 250 to 350 head of red deer being confined to about 950 hectares. This Royal Park is situated on ground, rising to 50 metres, overlooking the River Thames only 15 kilometres south west of London. The fertility of the soil, overlying London

Menil fallow doe in Richmond Park. The well-grazed plain, characteristic of parkland, presents a striking contrast to the dense ground flora seen in parts of Epping Forest and the South Weald woods.

Clay with occasional gravel outcrops, is low because reserves of plant nutrients are small and drainage is poor. Apart from the plantations, most of the area is grassland but much of the higher ground has been invaded by bracken which provides shelter for the deer. It is one of the most natural public parks that we know and, although it is much frequented by people, wild life including badgers, foxes, rabbits and grey squirrels still abound. In summer, the deer share the grazing with sheep. Culling of the deer takes place twice a year, fallow bucks and red deer stags in August and September and fallow does and red deer hinds from November to January.

Altogether, almost 200 fallow deer have been caught and marked with coloured, plastic, numbered ear-tags of the type used on cattle and sheep. These tags are readily inserted with a pair of special pliers which enable the cartilage of the deer's ear to be pierced and the tag applied single handed in one swift movement. We put a numbered tag in the left ear, using a different colour for each year, and a plain, coloured tag in the right ear, the two halves of this tag generally being of different colours. The various colour combinations enable each individual animal to be identified and its age known at a glance, even when the number on the tag cannot be read. The tags have proved extremely satisfactory, some of the deer having carried them for ten years.

Newly born fawns have been found by diligent searching; they can be restrained readily by hand when only a few days old. Marking, weighing and examining the animals take only a few moments and, in our experience, handling the fawn does not cause desertion by the doe. Even so, one's aim should be to

Wild deer at South Weald. The buck, ear-tagged as a newly born fawn, is 27 months of age and has his second head of antlers. *C. W. Hutchins.*

disturb the animal and the surrounding area as little as possible. Excessive disturbance and moving the fawn to another area may cause the doe to lose contact with it. Young fawns are left alone by their mothers for long periods and so-called "abandoned" fawns are best left where found; the doe will not return while someone waits around to see that the fawn is all right. Their chance of survival is far better in the wild than in somebody's sitting room!

Adult deer were caught by walking them into nets, placed along the edges of rides and so arranged that a complete block of woodland was surrounded. These nets, each 100 metres long and 2½ metres high, were made of black polyethylene with 15cm between the strands: their breaking strain was in excess of 130 kg. They were suspended on poles with the bottom 30cm of netting lying flat on the ground. Deer meeting the netting were restrained immediately by people hiding in the edge of the wood. When the head of the deer was covered, even bucks were easily held and ear-tagged. The deer were released as soon as all the netting had been removed to avoid the possibility of their being caught again. This method of catching deer requires a knowledge of their habits in the woods and large numbers of people to ensure that deer do not struggle in the nets. Under the terms of the Deer Act 1963, a special licence is required to catch deer in England and Wales.

This extensive programme of catching and marking deer has enabled numerous observations to be made on individual deer that could be recognised without ambiguity. Unless deer are clearly marked, there is no guarantee that the buck seen one day is the same animal as that seen the day before. Prior, in *The Roe Deer of Cranborne Chase,* tells how he shot a roe buck with a pair of poor and rather crooked antlers only to see him in the usual place again next morning! On shooting this second buck and comparing the two heads, he found them to be almost indistinguishable.

Several of our marked fallow deer have been culled: specimens from 60 of these deer of known age have been examined. Altogether, specimens from 896 fallow deer have been examined, about one third of them after post-mortem investigation of the entire carcase. These deer were obtained from herds of both park and wild animals from 12 localities in England and Scotland.

In this book, we have attempted to relate our studies on the natural history of fallow deer to those by other people in different parts of the world. Although a thorough revision of fossil fallow is clearly needed, an attempt has been made to give a brief outline of the origins and history of present-day fallow deer, and an overall picture of what is known of their natural history. In a book of this size and nature, it is impossible to include all that is known about fallow. The choice of what to include, or omit, has been difficult and undoubtedly has been influenced by our special interests. We hope, however, that by using the bibliography the reader interested in knowing more about any aspect of the natural history of fallow deer will be encouraged to delve deeper.

CHAPTER TWO

Classification and General Characteristics

DEER ARE among the most attractive, graceful and cosmopolitan of the world's mammals. Zoologists classify them in the Order Artiodactyla, or even-toed ungulates, with the other plant-eating mammals that have an even number of hooved toes on each foot. These ungulates are a very successful and large group, with some 200 living species, the exact number depending upon the classification scheme followed. Three suborders are distinguished: the ruminants; the pigs, peccaries and hippopotamuses; and the camels and llamas. Ruminants are the cud-chewing mammals, which are divided into five families, one of which is the Cervidae or Deer family.

Classification

The main characteristic which separates the 40 or so species of deer from other ruminants is that the adult males have antlers, as distinct from horns, which most other species of ruminants have. Deer are divided into four subfamilies, namely the musk deer, the muntjacs, the Eurasian deer and the Odocoileinae, which comprise mostly American deer. The Eurasian subfamily, the Cervinae, includes fallow deer, Père David's, axis, sika and red deer. Fallow deer form the genus *Dama* but are closely related to red deer and sika which belong to the genus *Cervus:* some authorities still place the fallow in this, the genus in which Linnaeus placed it when he first described the fallow. In several ways, however, fallow deer can be distinguished from members of the genus *Cervus.* The most obvious difference is that mature male fallow have a broad, flat palm on each antler. They have no mane and adults usually have no upper canine teeth. Male deer belonging to the genus *Cervus* have antlers with spike-like branches but no flat palm; they have a mane and in both sexes upper canine teeth are present. The Japanese sika deer, *Cervus nippon,* an Asiatic species now well-established in some European countries including parts of England, Scotland and Ireland, is sometimes misidentified as fallow, or *vice versa,* by people unfamiliar with either species. The two are very close in size and have rump markings with some similarities. The sika's rich brown and white-spotted summer coat could be confused with a common coloured fallow and, in its completely different winter coat, it is not unlike the black variety of fallow. The antlers of mature males of the two species are quite distinct, so any confusion is more likely to be between females or young males. In Britain it is customary to place fallow in the genus *Dama* and this practice is followed here. The classification of the genus *Dama* is summarised below.

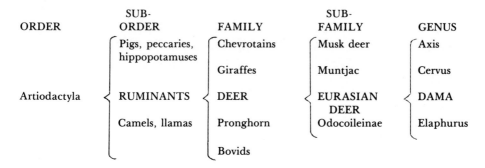

ORDER	SUB-ORDER	FAMILY	SUB-FAMILY	GENUS
	Pigs, peccaries, hippopotamuses	Chevrotains	Musk deer	Axis
		Giraffes	Muntjac	Cervus
Artiodactyla	RUMINANTS	DEER	EURASIAN DEER	DAMA
	Camels, llamas	Pronghorn	Odocoileinae	Elaphurus
		Bovids		

Formerly, the same generic name was used also for the American white-tailed or Virginian deer, named *Dama virginiana,* which is sufficiently different from fallow to be in a separate subfamily. This led to much confusion, especially in North America, where white-tailed deer are native whereas fallow are introduced. Long discussions raged in international committees on nomenclature from 1916 until the matter was finally settled in 1960, following a petition by many eminent zoologists to retain the widely-used name *Dama* for fallow deer but, for the white-tailed deer, to revert to the name *Odocoileus virginianus,* first given in 1832. At various times other names have been used or proposed for *Dama,* including *Platyceros, Dactylocerus, Machlis* and *Palmatus:* none of these is accepted now. The genus comprises several fossil species and two living forms, the European fallow and the Persian or Mesopotamian fallow.

European and Persian Fallow

The Persian follow is larger and typically its antlers have palms nearer the base whereas they are at the top in the European fallow; the tail colouring of the two forms differs slightly. These are the most obvious differences on which the fallow deer are separated into the two species, the European *Dama dama* and the Persian *Dama mesopotamica.* The contrary view is that the differences are insufficient to warrant two separate species but sufficient only to divide the one species, *Dama dama,* into two subspecies. *Dama dama dama,* and *Dama dama mesopotamica.* As more antlers of Persian bucks are examined they are showing that, as in the European animals, there is a wide range of individual variation and the flat palm is not always at the base: indeed some Persian antlers are like some, though perhaps not typical, European antlers. The summer coat of the Persian fallow is not dissimilar to a heavily spotted summer coat of a common-coloured European fallow and the tail colour differences are minor. Any differences in coat between the European and Persian deer are small when one considers the extremely wide range of colours found within the European fallow. That the present distribution is totally different cannot be questioned but fossil and historical evidence suggests that in former times the distribution of the two types either over-lapped or was contiguous. Once the two populations had become completely separated any differences would become more pronounced. Present-day Persian fallow can be likened to an island fauna, cut off from contact with the mainland population of the same species; therefore any genetic change must come from within that isolated population and, if not detrimental to the species, is likely to be perpetuated. The two forms have inter-bred in captivity and produced fertile young: such hybridisation points to a very close relationship. Instances of one species breeding with another to produce fertile offspring are known but are the rare exceptions rather than the rule: within the deer family hybridisation between sika and red deer has been reported several times. The differences between the Persian and European fallow are relatively minor and the animals are best regarded as two subspecies of *Dama dama*. Except for Chapter Thirteen, which is devoted to Persian fallow, this book is concerned with the European fallow.

Colour Varieties

Fallow deer are sleek, long-legged animals similar in size to a domestic goat: their Welsh name, *gafrdanas,* means Danish goat. Of all the deer species, the fallow exhibits the greatest variation in coat colour, ranging from white to almost black. Similar variations are familiar in many domestic animals from pet mice to cats and cattle; they are associated with domestication and inbreeding, which favour and perpetuate mutations.

Wild as well as park herds of fallow show a wide colour range which must be associated with the long history of semi-domestication of this species. The four main colour varieties are the common, which is sometimes regarded as the typical fallow colour, menil, white and black. In 1874, formal names were given by Fitzinger to each of those varieties, a practice now reserved for geographical races only.

In summer the common-coloured fallow is rich brown over the head, upper side of the neck, back, flanks and the upper, outer sides of the legs (Page 24). This background is liberally splattered with white spots on the back and upper flanks, with fewer on the neck and none on the head or legs. Along the mid-line of the flanks and at an oblique angle across the rump the spots give way to a continuous white line. A black stripe runs down the mid-line of the back from the nape to the rump and continues, and broadens, so that the upper surface of the tail is black but underneath it is white. The underside of the head and neck and the lower legs are pale, almost white, and the chest and belly distinctly white. The buttocks are also white but are partly bordered by a black line, shaped like an inverted horse-shoe: this distinctively marked area is known as the speculum. In winter this variety assumes a darker, duller and greyer brown appearance and the spots, whilst not disappearing, become barely detectable unless the animal is seen at close quarters.

Buck just over three years old, common variety in summer coat, and growing his third head of antlers. The prominent Adam's apple, the long tail and the palmate antlers are characteristic of the species.

The vertebral stripe is much less distinct as it merges into the now darker surrounding hairs. The belly, speculum and tail more or less retain their summer colouration, becoming a little creamier rather than pure white. It seems that this colour variety gave the species its English name, for *fealou* was an old English word meaning pale brown or reddish yellow.

The menil fallow is basically a paler variety of the common fallow. Its light fawn coloured coat is heavily spotted with white and these spots remain distinct in winter when the background coat becomes duller. The markings down the back, bordering the speculum and on the tail are light-brown lines, a little darker than the background colour. The distinction between the common and menil varieties in summer is best seen from behind, the common variety showing the black markings but the menil having a deeper shade of fawn on the tail and round the buttocks. The name menil is used widely although not listed in the Oxford English Dictionary. It seems to be a corruption of Manilla, the capital of the Philippine Islands, from where deer of this type are said, erroneously, to have been imported about 1730. These islands are well beyond the natural range of fallow and the imported deer, if from the East Indies at all, were probably the Philippine spotted deer, a subspecies of sambar which is less spotted than the menil fallow. Erroneous claims have also been made for the menil fallow's importation from Bengal. Here the confusion is with the heavily spotted axis deer, a native of India.

24

The white variety is not uncommon although one would expect such a conspicuous animal to be at a disadvantage in the wild. Probably it first arose in park-bred herds. At birth these animals are sandy or dark cream, sometimes with very slight, paler spotting. They become progressively paler at each moult until the deer is milk-white. The head and neck remain off-white for longer than the rest of the body but there are no brown or black markings at all. The time taken to attain the white coat appears to vary from about one year to several years. A sandy fawn born and ear-tagged in Richmond Park in June 1968 did not gain a fully white coat until it was three years old. In *The Deer Parks and Paddocks of England,* however, Whitaker stated that the white deer of Welbeck Park were white from birth.

This variety must not be confused with total albinism which is rare in fallow, for these white deer, unlike albinos, have normal pigmentation of the eyes although the hooves are less pigmented and more yellow-orange than the usual black or tawny colour and the nose is pale. In the wild the presence of a white animal frequently betrays to the human observer the whereabouts of the rest of the well-camouflaged herd (Page 15). White bucks, being distinctive, sometimes become the subject of local legends and consequently their memory is perpetuated over a yarn and a pint in country inns. The popularity of the *White Hart,* one of the commonest names for an inn in Britain, is probably associated with Richard II, a popular monarch who adopted a white hart emblem on a badge. The carved figure of such a beast was the centre-piece for the most elaborate inn sign ever made in Britain, that erected at Scole in Norfolk in the mid-seventeenth century for the vast sum of £1,000. In hunting terms a hart was a six-year old red deer stag but many inns bearing this name display a sign showing a fallow buck: too many signs depict an artist's hybrid of the two!

Sika deer. Yearling stag with antlers in velvet.

The darkest fallow deer are those of the so-called black variety. Unlike the spotted varieties, this is darker in summer than in winter but even then it is not the jet black of a cat or panther. The glossy summer coat is black on the back, buttocks and tail, with barely detectable grey-brown spots. Many writers have reported this variety as being unspotted but spots are present on fawns and adults although they may not be seen at a distance or in poor light. The neck, lower flanks and under-parts are mushroom. In winter the coat is duller and browner but still very dark, particularly on the rump and tail. There are no white or very light coloured parts although occasionally a scattering of white hairs occurs just above the hooves. The terminal hairs of the tail of this type are sometimes copper coloured. The hairs and skin over the growing antlers of the male are also very dark whereas in other varieties they are sometimes, but not always, a pale colour. Some deer of this colour were brought to Britain by James I from his father-in-law, the King of Denmark, around 1612 but fallow of this colour were already present in England. As early as 1465 Baron von Rozmital remarked about black, as well as white and spotted, fallow in Windsor Park and about 1535 Leland mentioned a park herd of black deer in Lincolnshire.

In addition to these four main colours there are very many minor variations and gradations which occur in wild and park herds. The names of the colours are almost as numerous as the number of authors who have described them but even this multiplicity of names fails to describe all the shades which sometimes occur. In *Deer Breeding for Fine Heads,* Winans invented ten names for what he regarded as distinct varieties, including spotted, light bay, brown, chestnut, grey, white, cream and black. Reports of parti-coloured roe deer occur occasionally but pied fallow deer seem to be an extreme rarity. Nevertheless they evidently have occurred for the two rarest of Winans' ten varieties were listed as "black with white spots" and "black with white legs". Even more bizarre must have been the fallow in Brockhampton Park in 1892 which was said to be "pied like a badger".

Some of the basically common coloured fallow are more ginger-brown and some have sooty patches on the shoulders, neck, saddle or rump. In most fallow varieties the hairs immediately round the nose and mouth are a little paler than the rest of the face but some individuals have very light, almost white, faces giving the impression of a "bald-face", a term more usually applied to red stags and hinds, especially on inn signs. The bald-faced fallow was regarded as a distinct variety by Shirley who thought that it originated in Bosworth Park in Leicestershire. It is not only the common colour which shows such variation. The variety known as the sooty-dun is very similar to the black fallow but the summer coat is liver-coloured rather than black. Blue roan fallow have an almost white coat with silver-grey hairs, giving a pale blue effect, or blue-grey hairs intermingled with brown. In the late nineteenth century Bushey Park had some fallow of this type, described as lavender or bluish. Woburn is one deer park where this unusual variety is still bred: indeed,

Whitaker referred to white fallow with bluish-grey shoulders and rumps as "Woburn deer".

A variety unusual in hair length rather than colour occurs in Mortimer Forest in Salop. Twenty years ago approximately five per cent of the herd of about 200 wild fallow, which are mostly black or common coloured, were noticed to have a long, shaggy coat, the winter coat being made up of hairs about three times as long as most of the hairs on other fallow. Ten years ago it was estimated that the proportion had risen to 25 per cent and the area within which they were found had increased to include part of the adjacent county of Herefordshire. The long curly hairs on the forehead resemble the top-knot of a Hereford bull and buff or ginger hairs up to 13cm long flow from the ears. The long hairs on the tail almost double its apparent length. The females have tufts of hairs about 5cm long on the head, in the equivalent position to the males pedicles. In summer much of the long body hair is lost but the hairs of the ears, forehead and tail remain long. Fawns and yearlings appear shaggier than older animals. Some intermediate forms, with a coat of mixed normal and long hairs, have been recorded and are distinct from the usual fallow coat in which there is a sparse scattering of long hairs.

Although wild herds of fallow deer of mixed colours are not uncommon, in some localities one variety predominates. The deer of Epping Forest were all of the black variety. The first common-coloured fallow was reported in this Forest by Buxton in 1953 and by 1964 it was estimated that about 20 per cent were not of the black variety. Adjacent to the Forest there is a deer sanctuary, about 44 hectares of woodland and arable land, in which the dark variety live and breed under more or less natural conditions. As a further precaution to maintain this stock some Epping Forest fallow were sent to the Zoological Society of London's park at Whipsnade in Bedfordshire.

Early this century Lascelles described the New Forest fallow as being all of the same variety, apart from an occasional white animal. He commented on their marked seasonal change of coat, from the rich, bright, red-brown with white spots in summer to a dark brown in winter; this has been described as the dun variety. Now the New Forest fallow are of mixed colours.

At Ashbridge, on the Hertfordshire and Buckinghamshire border, the wild fallow are of mixed colours. In 1969 the herd was estimated to be composed of about 50 per cent common variety, 40 per cent black and the remainder menil and white. Herds of mixed colours occur in many places in Britain and also on the Continent but the common variety is usually the most frequent. Most fallow in New Zealand, all descendants of introduced animals, are of the black variety but the herd in the Blue Mountains is unusual in having mixed colours: in 1972 about five per cent of the herd were common or white. In Tasmania the fallow population on one side of a major road is common-coloured whilst on the other side it is black, apart from 5 to 10 per cent of white animals. In California, the introduced fallow in Marin

Black fallow buck rutting. Mature bucks feed little during the peak of the rut.

County are said to be white, common and black but in Mendocino County all the fallow, several hundred, are white.

In parks, selection for or against particular colours is practised frequently. At Houghton Park in Norfolk the large herd of about 200 white fallow presents a striking sight. In former times white herds were maintained in several English parks including Welbeck in Nottinghamshire, Sledmere in Humberside and Brockhampton in Gloucestershire. A small herd, about 34, remains at Grange Con in Co. Wicklow, Ireland. The Houghton herd was originally of mixed colours but with a high proportion of white animals. Selective culling has led to the establishment of the all-white herd which has been maintained for the past two or three decades. Some owners regard the menil type as the most attractive to grace their parkland: the herd at Holker Hall in Cumbria certainly presents a pretty sight which prompts recollection of the line in Gerard Manley Hopkins' poem, *Pied Beauty*, "Glory be to God for dappled things". A few parks, such as Levens Hall also in Cumbria, maintain all-black herds. Mixed herds, exhibiting the main colours and some of their variations, can be seen in numerous parks in Britain including Holkham Park in Norfolk, Helmingham in Suffolk, Lydney Park in Gloucestershire and Phoenix Park in Dublin.

There has been discussion for generations about which of the colour varieties was the ancestral type. Early historical representations of fallow, both European and Persian, which seem to have diverged into distinct forms by prehistoric times, usually depict well-spotted animals. The Persian fallow remains spotted and shows little variation in colour today whereas the European fallow has many colour mutants. A mutation to a melanistic form, the black variety, should not be regarded as peculiar. When coat-colour mutations do occur in wild mammals it is not

White, menil and common fallow bucks in winter showing differences in rump markings.

infrequently to a melanistic form. Melanistic grey squirrels are not a great rarity, nor are melanistic forms of the brown rat, rabbit or, in the northern part of its range, the red fox. Once such a mutation in coat colour has arisen naturally it will be perpetuated if it is an advantage, or at least no disadvantage, to the species and in semi-domestication in parks its survival value becomes almost irrelevant because man, rather than natural factors, will be the main influence on the population.

Some people believe the black variety to be the original type and refer to it as the "old forest breed". Undoubtedly this form is well-camouflaged in woodland and since, in ancient times, much of Europe was more extensively wooded, one can see the argument for suggesting the dark form to be the ancestral type. Fallow are not exclusively forest animals however: their structure suits them to open habitats as well as woodland. In any case, the common variety is at least equally well camouflaged: in summer its dappled coat merges with sun-splattered leaves and in winter its duller, plainer coat merges with tree trunks and bare shrubs. The black variety has been said to be the hardiest variety and Winans claimed that it grew to the largest size: but Shirley stated that it was smaller than the lighter-coloured varieties. We know of no evidence to support either of those contradictory claims. The weights of culled or accidentally killed deer from Richmond Park and Essex show no correlation with colour.

It is known that does may give birth to fawns of different colour from themselves, but the genetic study of inheritance of coat colour in deer, and indeed of antler characteristics, is a wide-open untouched field. With a species that breeds only once a year any studies would, of necessity, be long-term and would require marked animals for certain identification, and separate breeding enclosures for different colour-cross experiments. Winans advised anyone wishing to establish an all-spotted herd to shoot all black deer as those are "the most antagonistic to the spotted type". By this he presumably meant that black colouring was dominant to spotted, that is, menil. He also believed that a white buck brought lightness and spots into the herd. Over sixty years later there are no recorded facts on which to discuss the genetics of coat colour inheritance, nor firm evidence about which was the original colour variety.

As the photographs show, in all colour varieties except uniformly white animals, the lower side of the neck, the belly, insides of the legs, the under side of the lower jaw and the lowest part of the cheeks are all of a lighter shade than the rest of the body. This is a typical example of counter-shading which, against a background of the same tone, make a standing deer appear flat, an even colour all over and therefore inconspicuous, especially at a distance. The ability to "freeze" in a motionless position is further support to the camouflage effect of coat colour. White deer are conspicuous, except in snow, but all the other colour varieties are well disguised against various backgrounds such as tree trunks, leaf litter and ploughed fields. The dull winter coat merges well with leafless trees and bushes whereas the more heavily spotted summer coat blends especially well with the sun-dappled surrounding of a leafy woodland. On very young fawns lying on dead bracken litter or on dry leaves, the spots break up the outline of the vulnerable animal and so provide cryptic colouration even at close quarters. When not lying against a background with which they merge they are invariably well concealed, perhaps in a bed of stinging nettles or under bramble bushes. Only those who have searched diligently for fawns can appreciate the effectiveness of their camouflage or concealment.

Weight and Size

When speaking of body weights, naturalists think of the whole animal. The hunting fraternity, who collectively have weighed more adult deer than any other group of people, generally record the weight after the beast has been bled and gralloched and call this the "clean" weight. Obviously the stalker does not wish to cart home the weighty but unwanted gut, perhaps 15 to 25 per cent of his burden. When it comes to consulting records of weight, complications arise. At the gralloch, the stomach and intestines are always removed but some stalkers may also remove the liver, lungs, heart, reproductive organs, antlers, skin or even the head before weighing the beast. Various terms such as "quite clean", "clean without liver" and "hog-dressed" are used according to which viscera are removed. Deer park records frequently show only the weight of dressed carcases, when the body is eviscerated, usually leaving the kidneys, and bereft of skin, head and lower leg bones. Thus, although there are many published weights for shot deer, few can be used in a comparative study because of the differences in the preparation of the carcases and the terms used are rarely fully defined. An argument against using the weight of the complete animal, as is usual for many other species, is that, because of the large rumen, the amount of stomach contents may vary greatly and will influence the overall weight of the deer. With few exceptions, the fallow we have examined have had well-filled stomachs but, even so, the proportions varied from 4 to 20 per cent of their body weight. Of 46 stomachs and contents the heaviest, 8.7kg, was from a seven year old buck and represented 15 per cent of his weight. Rutting bucks had the least-filled stomachs. Nevertheless, Jackson found a linear relationship between the weight of New Forest fallow deer and the weight after gralloching in which the entire alimentary tract, except the oesophagus, was removed.

The type, quality and availability of food is of prime importance when considering body weight. In some parks supplementary food is provided in winter whereas in other parks poor pasture or lack of supplementary food may prevent the animals reaching their full potential. Even within one park two types of management can lead to very different results. For Eastwell Park in Kent, which is disbanded now, Whitaker gave the average weight of paddock fed bucks as 55kg and of park fed bucks as 41kg. Table 1 gives some examples of whole body weights for bucks from various places.

Table 1. Weights of male fallow deer

Locality	Age in years (approximate)	Number of animals	Weight, kg. Mean	Range
Dalkeith Park, Scotland	—	8	70	71-90
Richmond Park, Greater London	1-4	30	52	21-73
Essex	1-4	22	60	31-80
Essex	5 and over	3	64	63-66
Hampshire	1-4	16	59	46-75
Hampshire	5 and over	6	82	75-98
Germany	1-4	225	43	16-78
Germany	5 and over	143	70	43-103

The German bucks, taken from several localities and listed in *Das Damwild*, present the largest samples available. As they were divided into bucks aged one to four years and those over five, the same division has been applied to the English bucks; the ages of those for Essex and Hampshire are only approximate, being estimated using the criteria which apply to Richmond Park fallow. The German bucks show wider ranges in weight than the much smaller English samples and their mean weights are lower than those for park or wild English fallow, apart from the very small sample of older Essex bucks. The average weight of German bucks under five years is equalled by Richmond Park bucks when they are about two years old. Although some German bucks reach more than 100kg, such a weight is regarded as a rarity but it would be even more unusual in Britain, although Whitaker gave the average weight of an unspecified number of bucks in Rickmansworth Park as 110kg. The heaviest Scottish park fallow recorded by Millais, 91kg, was from Drummond Park where the feeding was particularly luxuriant but some bucks from Dalkeith Park approached this weight. In Victoria, Australia, bucks are said rarely to exceed 119kg, a high figure compared with weights from other countries. A buck from Turkey, shot about 1905 south-west of the Sea of Marmara in an area where fallow no longer occur, was, at 153kg, about half as heavy again as a top-weight German buck. Its identity is not in doubt: a photograph was published in *The Field*, on 13th January, 1955. One cannot but wonder whether it was weighed on a fisherman's scales! Even allowing for some error in the balance this animal must have been exceptionally heavy.

In *Deer and Their Management* Whitehead reports, with understandable scepticism, on two exceptionally heavy bucks. One was a wild Sussex buck, shot in 1947, which was said to have weighed 120kg "clean" weight, so the whole body weight would have been much more. The other was a stall-fed buck from Woburn Park which, in 1892, was said to tip the scales at 140kg, and that was *after* it had been gralloched and the head and lower leg bones removed! As these weights can be neither verified nor disproved, one can place no reliance on them since they are much in excess of a normal weight for a prime buck: the accuracy of the scales must be under suspicion.

Female fallow are lighter than males and show a smaller range of weights. Hunters pay more attention to information about bucks than about does, so figures for the latter are less well recorded. The weights of 130 does, culled from late November to mid January between 1964 and 1973 in Richmond Park, ranged from 29 to 54kg, with 39kg as the mean. These were whole body weights, apart from blood lost at the time of shooting. The ages ranged from 18 months to at least seven and a half years. In the same park, thirty does of comparable ages, whose deaths resulted from accidents or natural causes in any month of the year, had an average weight of 35kg; their range was from 25 to 50kg. Twelve does from Essex ranged from 34 to 52kg, with 42kg as the average, and twenty from Hampshire averaged 40kg, ranging from 31 to 52kg. Not many does, even when pregnant, reach the upper end of these ranges.

Few measurements are available for the size of fallow deer. Baker has measured the carcases of deer of various ages culled in the Blue Mountains in New Zealand and his figures for body length, shoulder height and tail length of adult deer are summarised in Table 2. The length of the body was measured over the curvature of the dorsal surface from the nose to the tip of the last tail bone, with the animal on its side. The shoulder height was the distance in a straight line between the tip of the hoof and a point level with the mid-line between the shoulders. The tail was measured on the dorsal surface from its base to the end of the last tail vertebra, thus excluding the long terminal hairs. Although there is a surprisingly wide variation in the measurements, which probably results from combining figures from animals of different ages, the greater size of bucks compared with does is apparent.

Table 2. Sizes of fallow deer over two years of age from the Blue Mountains in New Zealand

	Number of animals	Mean cm	Range*
Body length			
Males	23	157	139-175
Females	42	139	119-159
Shoulder height			
Males	20	89	81-97
Females	42	78	72-84
Tail length			
Males	22	19	15-23
Females	46	16	13-19

*Range is the mean size plus and minus two standard deviations.

Young bucks. Common, white and black varieties.

34

CHAPTER THREE

Fossil and Early History

FALLOW deer have a history extending back several million years but their evolution is imperfectly known. Portions of antlers, limb bones and teeth are the most usual fossils from which their history can be traced but these remains are rarely complete. Studies are complicated by the use of different names for specimens of the same species found in different localities or by different people. The palaeontologist concerned with deer has the bonus of antlers as raw material. However, this seeming advantage could well become a pitfall if the tremendous variation which occurs in the shape and size of antlers at different ages or even among similarly aged animals of the same species from the same locality is forgotten. Individual variation must always have occurred; indeed, without it evolution would not be possible. The limitations of antlers must therefore be remembered when identifying or tracing relationships amongst deer. When only a portion of a fossil antler is available, the problem is much intensified and the resulting uncertainty means that frequent adjustments must be made to our ideas as new information becomes available. Perusal of the literature on fossil deer is further complicated by the continuing revision of the ages of geological strata in the light of improved dating techniques. Dates given in old reports may not agree with present views. When remains are from sites of prehistoric man, the dating terminology becomes complicated further by the multiplicity of names used for the various stages of man's culture in different parts of the world. The main terminology for geological and archaeological periods, their approximate dates and the occurrence of fallow deer fossils in Britain are given in Table 3.

Early Fossil Fallow

The true antler-shedding deer first appear in the fossil record of Eurasia and North America some 20 million years ago, during the Miocene, a period unrepresented in Britain. The greatest evolution of the deer occurred during the following period, the Pliocene, which was the final period of the Tertiary Era or "Age of Mammals" and which lasted from about ten to three million years ago. Early in the period, according to Azzaroli, the deer were represented by animals of several main types one of which, a Chinese deer with three tines on each antler, probably gave rise to the subfamily to which fallow deer belong. This may explain the presence of remains attributed, by Teilhard de Chardin and Trassaert, to a fallow deer, *Dama sericus,* in late Pliocene or early Pleistocene deposits in south-eastern

Shansi in China, which is well outside the natural range of later fallow deer. The two well-preserved antlers differed from those of present day European fallow in having the broad palm spread symmetrically on both sides of the axis of the beam and the brow tine was higher up the beam.

Table 3. Approximate dates of the main climatic and cultural periods and the occurrence of fallow deer in Britain

Era	Epoch	Years Before Present (approximate)	Climate	Culture	Fallow deer in Britain
				Present day	D. dama
		1,000		Medieval	D. dama
	HOLOCENE	1,500		Saxon	
	or	2,000		Roman	
	RECENT	4,000		Bronze Age	
		5,000		Neolithic	
		10,000	Postglacial	Mesolithic	
QUATERNARY			Würm Glaciation	Upper Palaeolithic	
		100,000	Last Interglacial (Ipswichian or Eemian)		D. dama
			Riss Glaciation		
		250,000	Second Inter-glacial (Hoxnian or Holsteinian)	Middle Palaeolithic	D. clactoniana
	PLEISTOCENE		Mindel Glaciation		
		500,000	First Interglacial (Cromerian)		D. nestii
		590,000	Günz Glaciation	Lower Palaeolithic	
		3 million			
TERTIARY	PLIOCENE	10 million			(D. sericus in China)
	MIOCENE	23 million			(First true deer in Eurasia and North America)

The Pleistocene, the first epoch of the Quartenary Era, began about three million years ago. The second epoch of this Era, the Holocene or Recent, started about 10,000 years ago and extends to the present day. The major evolutionary occurrence during the Pleistocene was the establishment of most present-day mammal species, including man. Environmentally it was characterised by a sequence of Ice Ages, which affected not only northern Eurasia and North America but also New Zealand and Antarctica. Although about 32 per cent of the present-day land area of the world was ice-covered during the glacial periods, compared with about ten per cent now, the ice coverage was not continuous and considerable ice-free areas occurred in northern Eurasia and North America. The cold glacial periods alternated with relatively shorter and warmer interglacials. Furthermore, each glacial period comprised two or more cold phases separated by milder periods when climatic conditions ameliorated but were on the whole less warm than in the interglacial periods. In Britain, still attached to the continent of Europe, there were four glacial periods, Günz, Mindel, Riss, and Würm, and three interglacial periods. The maximum extent of the ice occurred during the Second, or Mindel, Glacial period and it covered all but the south of Britain, roughly to the River Thames which was then a tributary of the Rhine.

In Europe, bones of an early Pleistocene fallow deer, *Dama nestii*, have been found in several localities, best known of which are Valdarno and Olivola in Italy and Oltenia in Romania. Two subspecies from Italy, *Dama nestii nestii* and *Dama nestii eurygonus* were described by Azzaroli and antler fragments, attributed to the former, have been found in England, in the Weybourn Crag of Norfolk. Azzaroli believes that the following deer are closely related to *Dama nestii: Cervus philisi* from France and Spain, *Cervus punjabensis* from the Siwalik Hills of India and the poorly known *Cervus perolensis* from France and *Cervus rhenanus* from the Netherlands. Apparently none of these species had palmate antlers. The names "Dama" and "Cervus" are used here in a wider sense than in modern zoological nomenclature.

Clacton Fallow

The best known of the fossil fallow at once showing very close similarities to present day European fallow, is the Clacton deer of the early Second Interglacial, (or Hoxnian), some 250,000 years ago. Portions of antlers were found by a farmer, John Brown, at Clacton-on-Sea, Essex in the 1860s and were first described briefly by Falconer. At various times this animal has been known as *Cervus clactonianus*, *Cervus browni* and, since 1937, *Dama clactoniana*. The antlers of the Clacton fallow, portions of 41 of which were found at the original site, have a third tine on the distal part of the anterior edge: mainly on this character a new species was named distinct from *Dama dama*. However, modern European fallow may occasionally have a third anterior tine and Falconer himself, when he first saw the Clacton deer's antlers, regarded them as belonging to the same species as the modern deer. Even Dawkins, who named it *Cervus browni*, stressed that as far as the second tine the antlers of the two were indistinguishable in form. Almost complete, well-palmed antlers still attached to the skull were found later at Swanscombe and show the very close likeness to modern European fallow, greater size being the main distinction (Page 38).

(*Above*) Clacton fallow deer. Skull and antlers from Second Interglacial deposits at Swanscombe in Kent, now in the British Museum (Natural History). (*Below*) Antlers of a six and a quarter year old fallow buck from Richmond Park, showing similarity to those of Clacton fallow.

Remains of Clacton fallow deer found in the Lower Loams and Lower and Middle Gravels at Swanscombe, Kent, the site of the famous Swanscombe man's skull, were identified by Sutcliffe. Over 500 specimens were discovered and it was the most numerous of the mammalian remains which included rhinoceros, elephant, bison and Giant deer, all of which indicated temperate climatic conditions. Leg bones of Clacton fallow from Swanscombe have been compared by Sutcliffe with those of modern European fallow. Ironically, there were fewer present-day fallow bones available than fossil ones. The lengths of the various fossil bones were from 17 to 34 per cent greater. This wide variation may be due, in part, to comparing bones of different sex rather than the same sex, an unavoidable problem when dealing with fossil deer, unless one is lucky enough to find a complete skeleton. This suggests that the Clacton fallow was about a fifth to a third as tall again as the modern fallow. The animal must have been about the size of a modern red deer, but not the red deer contemporary with it. Like many other Pleistocene mammals, red and fallow deer from the interglacials were larger than their present-day descendants.

Other sites where this fallow deer has been reported include Jaywick, close to Clacton; Trafalgar Square and nearby Charing Cross Road and Turnham Green, all in London. Its distribution in England therefore appears to have been in the south-east, but it must be remembered that interglacial sites are uncommon outside this area. The Clacton fallow has been listed also amongst the fauna of the Forest Bed on the Norfolk coast. This material is scanty but is closely comparable with specimens from Swanscombe.

At the time of the discovery of the first Clacton remains, antlers obviously akin to them were unknown on the continent. However, Sickenberg's recent examination of a shed antler from Edesheim in North Germany, where Pleistocene conditions were very like those in East Anglia, showed it to be from a Clacton fallow, not from a Giant deer as previously believed. This fallow deer has also been found at Torralba in Spain and recently Leonardi and Petronio informed us that, at Riano in Italy, they had found a fine skeleton of Clacton fallow in deposits of Third Glacial period, possibly from one of the milder phases.

Fragments of antlers of another fallow, *Dama somonensis*, were found first in Lower Pleistocene deposits in Northern France, near the mouth of the Somme, close to Abbéville. The specimens named by Desmarest in 1820, and described by Cuvier, puzzled Falconer when he inspected them in 1863. There was no pedicle, the antler base was very close to the eye socket and the top was a misfit, joined with plaster and either turned the wrong way or not even belonging to the same species! The beam flattened immediately above the brow tine, not remaining cylindrical until above the second tine as in modern European fallow. The use of this name is dubious in view of the poor specimen on which it is based. Nevertheless bones, portions of antlers and teeth found at several other French sites, including Pedemar, the Limagne, the Velay and Languedoc have been attributed to the Somme fallow. Boule reported this species from caves at Grimaldi but Azzaroli believes that these remains belong to a variety of red deer.

Many specimens thought to be of a fallow-like deer have been recorded from the Pleistocene of Europe and at least 18 species of fossil fallow have been named. Some of these, such as *Dama quirinus* from Rome and *Dama gastaldi* from the Po valley, are reasonably well described and are probably synonymous with Clacton fallow. Certain other species are no longer regarded as being fallow deer. *Dama priscus* from Le Puy de Dome is synonymous with *Cervus solilhacus* and has been placed in the genus *Megaloceros,* as has *Dama savini* from the Forest Bed of Norfolk, for both these deer are now thought to be related to the Giant deer. Many of the other fossil fallow species may be invalid too. When a species extends over a wide geographical range, variations will occur and these will be most marked in specimens from the extreme ends of that range. If only animals from the extremities are known, their differences may suggest that they are two distinct species. When examined alongside specimens from intermediate places, however, they are seen as part of a series, a cline, with each form grading into its neighbouring types. Today, wide differences, due to the influence of habitat, can occur in the body and skeletal sizes of deer without raising the question of separate species. A red deer stag living in the harsh Scottish Highlands may weigh only 90 kg and his antlers are regarded as good if they have 12 points. Some Highland deer were among the original stock at Warnham Park in southern England. After a few generations in this Park on good, calcium-rich pasture, stags averaged about 195 kg and had up to 47 points. Similarly, when British red deer were taken to New Zealand their descendants showed marked increases in body and antler weights.

The overall sizes of the Clacton and so-called Somme fallow seem to have been similar although the number of specimens from the latter which are available for comparison is small. As a result of his studies on those and other fossil fallow, Sickenberg considered that the Somme fallow from Abbéville and from La Grotte des Enfants, Monaco and also the Gastaldi fallow from Italy, were the same as the Clacton fallow from Edesheim. It seems likely, therefore, that the Clacton and Somme fallow as well as the Gastaldi fallow are all one species, different only in minor details, principally size, from the present-day European fallow, and are best regarded as subspecies of *Dama dama.* Cuvier himself saw no reason to think the original Somme specimens were different from those of modern fallow.

Last Interglacial Fallow

As the Clacton fallow has not been found in English deposits later than the Second Interglacial, the fallow deer was believed to have become extinct during the Third or Riss Glacial period, during which ice covered much of northern Europe and in England extended approximately as far south as a line drawn from the River Severn to East Anglia. In 1905, fallow deer remains were found in a cavern at Hoe

Grange quarry near Brassington, Derbyshire. The molar teeth and some bones were intermediate in size between present-day fallow and Clacton fallow. Here in central England was the first evidence of the presence of fallow in Last Interglacial, (or Ipswichian), times. Later, in 1931, came the first of several reports of fallow deer antlers from the Burtle Sand Beds of mid-Somerset. Examination of broadly-palmed whole, or almost complete, antlers showed that they were smaller than those of Clacton fallow and lacked the characteristic third anterior tine. Of the other bones found, a shoulder blade agreed in size with one from Hoe Grange. The teeth and some portions of leg bones agreed with those reported from the Milton Hill fissure, near Wells, also in Somerset, which had been described a few years earlier. These findings indicate the presence of a fallow deer, at most slightly larger than that of to-day, in deposits believed to be of Last Interglacial age.

Further evidence of the fallow deer's return to England during this period came with excavations, begun in 1939, of some Devonshire caves. The most exciting of these was, and still is, the Joint Mitnor Cave at Buckfastleigh. The present entrance is part way up the cliff-face of the disused Higher Kiln quarry. In prehistoric times there was a natural opening from the ground above the cave, level with the top of the quarry. Below the opening there was a natural shaft about 12 metres deep. From the floor of the cave, extending up the shaft, is a cone of fallen earth, stones and mammal bones. The animals probably fell down the shaft and were buried in the rubble. No other bone cave in Britain compares with this one for the richness of its fauna. The bones were studied by Sutcliffe in the 1950s. He examined over 4,000 specimens comprising at least 127 individual animals of 16 species including red and fallow deer, wolf, fox, wild cat, cave lion, hyaena, badger, bear, straight-tusked elephant, rhinoceros, hippopotamus and bison. The remains are belived to date from the warmest part of the Last Interglacial, as were the Derbyshire and Somerset bones. The Joint Mitnor excavations were performed with such skill and forethought that one half of the lower part of the cone of fallen rocks and bones has been left intact. The caves are administered jointly by the William Pengelly Cave Studies Trust and the Devon Trust for Nature Conservation. By prior arrangement, visitors still can see bones *in situ,* where they have lain for 100,000 years within this Aladdin's cave of fossil treasure. Of the deer bones from the Joint Mitnor cave about 300 specimens were tentatively named as *Dama dama,* and represented at least seven adults and several juveniles. Unfortunately no antlers were found. Measurements of the adult bones by Sutcliffe showed that they were intermediate in size between Clacton and present-day fallow. His average measurements of seven different limb bones from Joint Mitnor cave and present-day fallow show that the former were seven to 18 per cent longer.

Other Devonshire caves also have yielded Last Interglacial mammalian remains in smaller quantities. Tornewton Cave at Torbryan, once used as a den by hyaenas, contained a fallow antler base and a few bones. These deposits have been disturbed by frost action attributed to the peripheral effects of the Last Glaciation.

At Yealhampton, antler bases from fallow deer were amongst the remains found in Eastern Torrs Quarry cave where disturbance by freezing and thawing has also occurred. Other sites, all thought to be Last Interglacial, at which fallow have been recorded in England include Brentford and Trafalgar Square in London, Selsey on the south coast and Barrington in Cambridgeshire.

Remains of Last Interglacial fallow deer have been found in Denmark, Germany, Poland, the U.S.S.R., Greece, Italy, France and Gibraltar. The finding of fallow bones in south-west Jutland is of very special importance because Møhl-Hansen has found that many of the limb bones had been split by man, presumably for the extraction of marrow. This provided the first evidence of human activity in Denmark before Postglacial times. At Egtved the greater part of a single fallow skeleton was unearthed and bones have also been found at Hollerup, Ejstrup, Scest and Raagelund. The German sites for Last Interglacial fallow include Gross Wusterwitz, Mosbach, Belzig and Ehringsdorf. Caves in the Kracow area, in Wierzchow, at Wrzoshy and Lower Wesia in Poland also contained fallow bones. Until 1960, the European fallow had never been identified with certainty from the Pleistocene of the U.S.S.R.; then, in the Drnansk region of the Upper Orozman in South Georgia, in Middle and Upper Pleistocene deposits, several fragments were found, including two of cannon bones which Vekna thought were indistinguishable from those of modern European fallow apart from being slightly larger. A deer's jaw bone, believed to be of fallow, has been reported also, from a site near Yerevan in Armenia, not far from Turkey. There is also evidence in the Mediterranean countries of fallow in Last Interglacial times. Fallow bones larger than those of the present-day animals have been found in the Genista and Poco Roco caves at Gibraltar and also in the Romanelli cave near Otranto, Italy. At Buxo in Spain a cave painting shows a deer with broadly palmed antlers, suggesting that fallow deer were known to men of the Old Stone Age who lived there. In Greece, remains of fallow from the Last Interglacial have been found at Mussakla in the Megalopolis Basin of the Peloponnes. Although these are similar in size to the English and Danish fallow of the same age these Greek animals were named by Melentis as *Dama somonensis*. Here the name is being applied differently from elsewhere in Europe where it is used for the still larger and earlier fallow, typical of the Second Interglacial and where Last Interglacial are usually named as *Dama dama*. Similarly, at Fontechèvade in the Charente region of France, fallow bones of the Last Interglacial have been named as Clacton fallow. The sizes of some bones fall within the range of those of Clacton fallow but others are similar in size to those of the Joint Mitnor deer. Examples such as these emphasise the weakness of distinguishing between species primarily on size, especially when the sex of specimens is unknown.

Origins of Modern Fallow

The widespread finds of the Last Interglacial period suggest that deer slightly larger than modern fallow lived in much of Europe some 100,000 years ago. Although some of these sites where Last Interglacial fallow lived were not ice-covered during the Last Glaciation, much of northern and central Europe would have been in the grip of arctic-style climatic conditions. With the onset of this severe climate Sutcliffe believes that the hippopotamus would have been the first member of the Interglacial fauna to go, followed by the fallow deer. Fallow deer remains have not been found in Mesolithic or Neolithic sites in Britain, which suggests that the species became extinct during the Last Glaciation, at the end of the Pleistocene epoch. However, there is one report of fallow from a British Neolithic site, the Giants' Hill long barrow at Skendleby in Lincolnshire. The specimen, part of a shed antler, cannot now be traced and was probably misidentified or was an artifact imported from elsewhere.

In contrast to the lack of fallow remains, red deer have been recorded at Neolithic sites from Dorset to the Orkneys and roe deer were common at sites in southern England. Jarman has shown that at 158 of 165 Neolithic sites in Europe, the red deer was the most common vertebrate but the fallow deer was not found, suggesting its absence from those areas too. Its apparent extinction over much of Europe during the Last Glaciation must have been associated with unfavourable climatic conditions. The ice sheets were fringed by extensive belts of tundra with partly frozen ground devoid of trees, except for a few dwarf arctic species. Such a habitat was suitable for reindeer but not for fallow. Although the Scandinavian and British ice sheets covered only the north of Europe, in southern Europe there were ice caps in the Pyrenees and the Alps and also many centres of mountain glaciation, particularly in northern Spain, central Italy and Greece. The surrounding areas were mainly forest steppe beyond which lay grassy steppe. Even in the Mediterranean Basin conditions were cool or cold during the Last Glaciation, and woodland was restricted. The Ice Age caused a general impoverishment of the whole European fauna. Almost all groups of mammals were affected, especially the largest species, many of which, such as rhinoceros, apparently were unable to survive in the warmer but small refuges in southern Europe.

Did the fallow deer become extinct over the whole of Europe during the Last Glaciation? This is the age-old problem in discussions of the origin of present-day fallow deer. Obviously it survived somewhere. The possibilities are that it remained in a few areas of southern Europe, along the northern coast of the Mediterranean or that it survived only in the east in the area now called Turkey or Anatolia and through this region into the countries on the east of the Mediterranean which were beyond the direct influences of glaciation. There is some evidence for its survival in a few refuges in southern Europe for at least part of the last phase of the Pleistocene. Fallow bones found at Parpalló in Valencia, Spain have been dated as just before the end of the Last Glaciation. In the foot of Italy too, fallow bones have been identified in deposits of Last Glacial age at the caves of Cirello and Scalea in

Cosenza. However, these findings do not prove the fallow's survival in Europe right through to the end of the Last Glaciation, about 10,000 years ago.

If the fallow did survive in southern Europe one would expect to find bones not only in deposits of Last Glacial age but also in archaeological sites dating from the early Postglacial period. Last century a number of fragmentary remains were reported from various parts of north and central Europe but in each case either the identification or the age of the deposits was in doubt, if not actually proved incorrect. However, more recently, fallow deer bones have been described by Bökönyi from a prehistoric settlement at Photolivos in East Macedonia, Greece, which man occupied from the Neolithic to the Early Bronze Age, a period from approximately 4,600 to 1,900 B.C. Also at Saliagos, in the Cyclades islands in the Aegean Sea, fallow deer bones have been found at an early Neolithic site. Bones from these sites were marginally larger than those of present-day fallow but distinct from red deer bones. Teeth of fallow have been reported also from Kavo Kapelo on the island of Kirthira, off the southernmost tip of Greece. At Mihelič in south-east Bulgaria fallow remains of similar age have been recorded. These specimens suggest that fallow deer survived in southern Europe through the Last Glaciation into Postglacial times. However, the evidence is not conclusive since importation, even in prehistoric times, cannot be ruled out.

Certainly in historical times man has played a major role in the dispersal of fallow deer within and beyond Europe. If the fallow deer did become extinct in the whole of Europe during the Last Glaciation, it must have been imported from countries in which it survived, beyond the influence of glaciation. This means Asia Minor, now called Turkey, or further south, on the eastern side of the Mediterranean. In ancient times much of Asia Minor was occupied by the Hittites, many of whose monuments, rock carvings and treasures still survive and depict the people and fauna of the age. Deer feature in some of these works of art and in some cases probably had a religious significance, male deer, like bulls, being used as symbols of divinities. The literature on Hittite art is extensive and well illustrated. The representations of the deer are somewhat heavy-bodied and the tail is not always distinct; but in some examples a European fallow buck is probably being portrayed, for the antlers have a palm at the far end but not the base. The body, as on some other beasts, is often incised with decorative motifs, not the natural markings of the animal. A god standing on a male deer is a regularly occurring theme depicted on seals and other objects from various places. Some, such as a stele from Yenikoy and a relief from Alaca Hoynik in central Turkey, date from the second millenium B.C. and show antlers with definite palms. Also from Alaca Hoynik, on the walls near the city gate, a series of reliefs in basalt show several deer with rather horse-like hind quarters but palmate antlers. A relief from Carchemish in southern Turkey, near the border with Syria, shows a similar figure of a buck. These are but a few of the examples of representations of fallow deer in the art of Turkey, a country in which this animal was widespread until fairly recently but is now very localised and rare. With such artistic evidence to suggest the presence of European fallow in ancient Turkey it seems plausible that the deer could have been exported to other countries. Even if fallow survived the Last Glaciation in a few areas in southern Europe, their numbers and natural distribution could have been supplemented by importations from Turkey at various times.

The evidence is insufficient to come to any firm conclusion as to whether fallow survived the Last Glaciation in southern Europe. Consequently, the origins of the European fallow deer will probably remain controversial and unresolved unless further fossil and archaeological specimens are found. The only other kind of fallow deer now living is the Persian subspecies whose fossil remains are known in Middle and Late Pleistocene deposits from countries on the east side of the Mediterranean. Their remains can be distinguished from European fallow with confidence only by differences in their antlers. The two subspecies must have evolved from the same stock, so at some time they must have lived in the same area or at least have had adjacent ranges. There are claims, based on various forms of art, that the people of ancient Iraq knew both fallow deer. Portions of two antlers from Tell Asmar, in Iraq, have been identified as European fallow but their fragmentary condition must be emphasised as, too, must the range in form shown by antlers of both subspecies of present-day fallow. Iraq could well have seen the divergence of the two forms but stronger evidence of the co-existence of the two subspecies is required. The Persian fallow evidently became the typical fallow of the Middle East whereas the European fallow was the form that became established westward, in Turkey and Europe.

Early History

The early history of the fallow deer, after the close of the Pleistocene, is shrouded in speculation, being hedged with doubts concerning its survival or extinction in Europe during the time of the Last Glaciation. If the fallow deer survived in at least parts of southern Europe throughout the Pleistocene, there is obviously no need to postulate its re-introduction to the continent as a whole, only to particular countries such as Britain where its extinction during the Last Glacial period seems certain. Had the fallow, if it survived in southern Europe, advanced northwards as forests developed after the final retreat of the ice at the end of the Pleistocene, about 10,000 years ago, the deer could have arrived in Britain before it became an island, some 8,000 years ago. However, the absence of fallow remains in both Mesolithic and Neolithic sites in Britain strongly suggests that the deer did not spread in this way. Therefore in Britain, at least, it must have been introduced. The question is, by whom? Although Phoenicians, Gauls, Romans and Normans have all been suggested as having introduced the fallow, the first conclusive evidence we have of these animals in Britain is in medieval times.

The Phoenicians, whose land on the eastern side of the Mediterranean corresponded to modern Lebanon and adjoining parts of Syria and Israel, may have kept fallow deer in semi-domestication as a sacrificial beast for Baal. The fallow remains from Palaeolithic sites in Phoenicia, however, were of Persian fallow. The Phoenicians may have obtained the European fallow from neighbouring areas. They were skilled in shipbuilding and many other crafts, had colonies and trade routes all round the Mediterranean and are thought to have come across Gaul to Britain for tin, although archaeological evidence is lacking. For what purpose ancient Britons would have wanted another species of deer, when red and roe deer were indigenous, is hard to imagine.

In the Mediterranean region the trade in live fallow, if initiated by the Phoenicians, is believed to have been continued by the Greeks and Romans, with the spread of various religious cults. The presence of fallow on the island of Rhodes is usually attributed to the ancient Greeks. Mythology accounts for its arrival there by decree of the Oracle at Delphi, to fight a serpent with its hooves. Fallow deer featured on ancient coins of the island and also from Greek colonies in Asia Minor. Roman writers and artists left numerous records concerning the catching, taming, harnessing, emparking and exhibiting of deer. In many instances the species is clearly red deer but in some representations the palmed antlers or dappled markings suggest fallow. In the lists of species appearing in the vast shows put on by emperors, *dammae* are mentioned frequently but whether these were fallow deer or gazelles is not known. Whatever their identity, in company with 1,000 head each of ostriches, stags, boars and numerous other animals they must have presented an incredible spectacle. Pausanian recorded seeing white deer in Rome but gave no details of their origin: although white fallow are relatively common, a white variety of red deer does occur, so their species is undetermined. Firmer evidence of the Romans' knowledge of fallow deer comes in the third century A.D. with the description of 200 *cervi palmati* in Gordian's collection, their antlers being like "palms of a hand". These particular animals were claimed to have come from Britain, somewhat surprising if the Romans had introduced the deer to these islands.

A prominent brush is characteristic of fallow bucks.

Representations of antelopes and deer symbolising gods, such as Diana, as "Preservers of the Emperor" occur on Roman coins, some of which were probably minted at Antioch in Syria. One from the reign of Gallienus, about 267 A.D., shows a deer which is probably a fallow doe: the tail is far too long for a red deer.

Introduction to Britain

At the time of the Roman occupation of Gaul, which comprised present-day France, Belgium and parts of the Netherlands, Switzerland and Germany, there were some large parks for sporting purposes. One, established by Pompeius in Transalpine Gaul, occupied about 4,000 hectares and according to Columella, a Roman writer on agricultural affairs in the first century A.D., fallow deer, stags, roe deer and boars were among the animals emparked. He believed that the chieftains of ancient Gaul had established some of these parks. The Belgic tribes of Gaul, themselves much influenced by Roman civilisation, certainly settled in Britain on more than one occasion during the last century and a half B.C. and in some respects paved the way for the later Roman invasion. The Belgic people had a marked influence on the native Iron Age Britons of south-east England, as is known from their wheel-made pottery at settlements such as Wheathampstead and Prae Wood in Hertfordshire. Their import and export trade across the Channel with the Roman Empire was considerable and varied but there is no evidence to indicate that they brought the fallow deer to Britain even if this deer was emparked in their native land at that time.

The introduction of the fallow deer to Britain is attributed most frequently to the Romans. At least they were settled here for some 400 years, established important trade routes and worshipped gods to whom the sacrifice of a fallow deer may have been appropriate. If fallow deer were present at this time, it is surprising that such few remains have been identified, considering the numerous excavations of Roman sites and the wealth of other material found throughout Britain. The presence of fallow remains at Roman sites has been reported from places such as London, Colchester, Irchester and St Albans. In each case there appears to be doubt about either the identity of the specimens or, more usually, their age: Roman remains may be mixed with more recent material. The only supposedly Roman fallow bone from St Albans was a single shed antler base found by Helen O'Neil. Bones cannot be identified with certainty as Roman unless their stratification is known. Unfortunately, many early archaeologists failed to appreciate both the importance of animal bones and the importance of recording their level. The bones from many excavations have never been identified and reported, but lie gathering dust in the cellars of museums. Recently a small number of fallow bones have been found at Portchester Castle in Hampshire. The site, dating from 290 A.D., includes Roman, Saxon, Medieval and eighteenth century remains. Anne Grant informed us that she is fairly confident that the fallow remains are of Roman origin, having examined bones only from contexts where there was little likelihood of contamination. Nevertheless, there is still no evidence to support the idea of an extensive Roman introduction of fallow in Britain.

The Romans have been credited with taking the fallow deer to France, Germany, Spain and Switzerland as well as to Britain although, as we have seen, the Gauls are thought to have had fallow in their parks. However, in the Swiss town of Augusta Raurica, three fallow deer leg bones were identified by Elisabeth Schmid among thousands of bones at the site of a Roman guesthouse for merchants. Even if the Romans did take the animal to Switzerland, as seems probable, this did not result in wild populations of the deer, which do not occur in Switzerland at the present time and probably never did.

After the departure of the Romans, Britain had several unsettled centuries and there is no evidence of the presence of fallow deer at these times. A vague mention last century of fallow remains in a Celtic or Saxon barrow cannot be accepted as relevant details were not published. Edward the Confessor, who reigned prior to 1066, is purported to have made an agreement with Randolph Peperking in which "doe and bocke" as well as "hoerte and hinde" were named. Although the latter terms refer to red deer the former cannot be taken as proof of the presence of fallow deer, for the same words are used for the roe deer. The same criticism applies to some of the earliest documents after the Conquest of England by the Normans. In 1086, just twenty years after William's invasion, a wonderfully comprehensive survey was carried out, the results comprising the Domesday Book. This shows that there were 31 parks, usually termed "parcus bestium silvaticarum" or "parcus ferarum silvaticarum", in nine counties of England. It is often supposed that these were parks for fallow deer but the wording for the entries does not actually say so: the beasts may have been the native British deer, the red and roe, and wild boars.

One of the first pieces of definite evidence of the presence of fallow in Britain since Last Interglacial times is the *Colloquies of Aelfric* written in the eleventh century. In the *Colloquies,* discussed by Fisher in *The Forest of Essex,* mention is made of the hunting of "dammas" with hounds and also chasing them into nets. In the twelfth century, according to Fitzstephen's description of London, the forest which lay to the north of the city was well-stocked with stags and fallow deer. By the thirteenth century there is more documentary evidence about the presence of fallow deer. In 1223 William Briwer was allowed to chase bucks in the New Forest with his hounds which were described as "canes *damericos* currentes". Their name clearly suggests that they were used on fallow deer. Furthermore, this breed is mentioned again in 1227 together with other hounds named as "canes *cervericiis* currentes" which were permitted to chase red deer. These were just two of the many varieties of dogs bred for sporting purposes in medieval times and named according to the quarry they pursued.

In 1247 the Earl of Winchester and Roger de Somery made a formal agreement concerning their hunting rights in Charnwood Forest and Bradgate Park in Leicestershire. This document refers to bucks and does, which were almost certainly fallow rather than roe deer. A clue to their identity lies in the dates stipulated for the hunting seasons. Bucks were to be taken between 1 August and 14 September. The latter date was that given in the next century as the close of the fallow buck season, but the roe buck season continued until 29th September. More important, a fallow buck is in his best condition in August and September, which was known then, as now, as the fat buck season. A fascinating contribution to the history of hunting literature was written about 1300 by Twici, the King's huntsman. His book dealt with each of the beasts of the chase including fallow deer. The treatment was thorough: the detection of game from tracks and droppings, the protocol of the hunt and the appropriate seasons were all given. The complex and colourful vocabulary associated with hunting in medieval times is revealed in all its splendour. Terms such as "sorrell" and "soar", for a buck in his third and fourth years, although little used now, do still survive, with modified spelling. Further evidence of the presence of fallow in England in the Middle Ages is provided by remains found during archaeological excavations such as those recorded by Kenyon at Jewry Wall, Leicester. Here incomplete fallow antlers were found in medieval deposits overlying a Roman building. A twelfth to fourteenth century moated site at Ellington was another of the places that yielded a fallow antler.

The evidence available at present strongly suggests that fallow deer were introduced into Britain in the early Middle Ages, possibly by the Normans. The Norman kings, William and his son William Rufus, and their nobles were passionately fond of hunting and sited many of their residences close to the Royal Forests. They ruled Sicily and southern Italy, where there may have been fallow in parks since Roman times, as well as their province in northern France. So here we have a people with a reason for introducing another species of deer to Britain and a supply of animals. Even if they had not established fallow in their parks by the time of the Domesday survey, they are nevertheless the strongest contenders for the introduction of fallow deer to Britain.

Denmark has early medieval documents which record the introduction of fallow deer to several islands about the year 1200. At Naesholm, just 16 kilometres from one of the points of release, many medieval fallow bones have been identified by Møhl from the site of a castle dating from 1240 to 1340. Introductions of fallow to Germany are also thought to have been made in the Middle Ages but probably not for the first time as a German glossary of the eighth century already gave a word for this animal.

Whoever did introduce this elegant and graceful animal to Britain is owed a debt of thanks. For centuries now it has provided pleasure, sport, meat and fine skins to generations of park-owners, naturalists, sportsmen and consumers of its products.

Common doe in winter.

CHAPTER FOUR

Distribution, Past and Present

THE popularity of fallow deer from medieval times onwards has influenced greatly the distribution of these animals. Few other large mammals, apart from truly domestic stock, can have been transported about the world as much as the fallow. In parts of its former range it has become extinct but man has taken this deer across the globe and its distribution now spans six continents: Europe, Asia, North America, South America, Africa and Australasia. Usually its importation has been to provide either an additional animal for sporting purposes or an aesthetic attraction to beautify an estate.

British Isles

The fallow is the most widely distributed of the six species of deer living wild in England and also the deer most commonly kept in parks. Red deer, fallow deer, boar and, until the fourteenth century, roe deer were "beasts of the forest" and belonged to the king. Royal permission was granted to some noblemen to create chases on their estates. These were private forests or hunting grounds but even here they could not hunt the royal beasts without the monarch's authority. Not surprisingly, therefore, many of the nobility wished to enclose their own parks where they had control over all the game. The sizes of these parks ranged from about 80 to 400 hectares; usually they were enclosed by a ditch and a bank surmounted by palings. As Cantor has shown in Leicestershire, traces of these earthworks still remain in many places.

Most medieval deer parks, unlike those of today, were tracts of woodland or wasteland, often distant from the owner's house. Consequently quite elaborate hunting lodges were built, examples of which still survive—including Queen Elizabeth's, now a museum, in Epping Forest and James I's in Thetford. The number of parks and their area in the whole country at that time are not known but contemporary accounts for certain counties give some indication of their importance. In 1512, the Percy family alone had 21 parks and chases with nearly 6,000 deer, many if not all being fallow, within the former counties of Northumberland, Cumberland and Yorkshire. Even so, the number of parks already was declining. In Cornwall, Henry VIII disbanded four parks at one time, to make way for cattle. In his time, it was estimated that a twentieth of the realm was employed upon deer and

Common, white and black does feeding at dawn.

rabbits. Over 700 parks were shown on Saxton's maps published between 1575 and 1580 when Elizabeth I was on the throne. She too was a keen follower of field sports even though the fashionable buck-hunting degenerated into a colourful spectacle in which she sat in an elaborate bower in a park and shot arrows at the deer that were driven past. Deer parks and hunting were clearly important elements in the pattern and life of the English countryside in the sixteenth century.

By the eighteenth century, the fashion was changing in favour of a smaller park or paddock in landscaped grounds surrounding the mansion. The waste lands formerly used as deer parks were brought into economic use with the modern methods of agriculture being expounded by Coke and others. Also, it was becoming fashionable for the gentry to satisfy their instinct for hunting by chasing the fox which did not require specially maintained enclosures.

When Whitaker wrote *The Deer Parks and Paddocks of England* in 1892 he described 390 parks having fallow deer and 86 with red deer. In 1950, Whitehead recorded 130 parks with fallow but today there are under 100. Despite the general decline in deer parks it is very pleasing that a few former parks have been re-established recently, as at Ashton Court near Bristol, Welbeck Park in Nottinghamshire and Knebworth in Hertfordshire.

The numbers and fortunes of wild fallow deer in England have fluctuated over the centuries. In the late seventeenth and the eighteenth centuries they were numerous in many areas, as shown by Cox in *The Royal Forests of England*. Cranborne Chase in Dorset is reputed to have contained over 10,000 fallow around 1800 and Wychwood Forest in Oxfordshire held about 1,000. The fallow population of the New Forest was estimated by the Regarders in 1670 as 7,593. Several thousand fallow still lived in the New Forest in the 1840s when conflict between Crown and commoners over enclosure of grazing land for forestry led to the New

Forest Deer Removal Act of 1851. This Act gave the Crown power to enclose and plant vast areas for timber but in return the right to keep deer in the Forest was surrendered: the deer, which competed for grazing with the commoners' stock, were to be removed within two years. Although the deer were not eliminated, at least 6,000 were killed officially during the two years following the passing of the Act; the number killed unofficially is unknown. Those deer that were not netted, snared or shot fled to outlying estates, only to re-establish themselves in the Forest later. By 1900, the fallow in the Forest had increased to about 200 and are now about 1,000. Similar attempts were made to exterminate the deer in Whittlebury Forest in Northamptonshire about 1850 but again were probably unsuccessful.

The Forest of Dean in Gloucestershire is another of the ancient haunts of fallow. In the 1840s the population was reckoned to be over 800. As they were encouraging poachers, the deer were destroyed until, as recorded by Nicholls, by 1855 none remained. A few outlying stragglers and escapees from parks subsequently re-established themselves in the Forest.

A remnant of the extensive Essex forests still remains as Epping Forest. Here the fallow declined from over 200 in 1846, when the Forest comprised about 2,400 hectares, to less than 10 in 1860 when it was being enclosed, destroyed and built upon. Fortunately the Epping Forest Act of 1878 prevented its entire destruction; it was disafforested and placed in the charge of the Corporation of the City of London. Hainault Forest, also a remnant of the great Essex forests, was turned over, with the sanction of Parliament, to agricultural use in the 1850s.

The reasons for the change of attitude towards deer were that royal interest in hunting had declined and the Forest Laws, originally to protect vert and venison, were no longer enforced rigidly. Some people in authority saw more profit in breaking the law than in keeping it. Although many of the Forest Laws had long fallen into disuse, some were not repealed until as recently as 1971 when the Wild Creatures and Forest Laws Act was passed. This Act abolished "any prerogative of

Petworth Park, a National Trust property in Sussex.

Her Majesty to wild creatures (except royal fish and swans), together with any prerogative right to set aside land or water for the breeding, support or taking of wild creatures: and any franchises of forest, free chase, park or free warren". Thus no less than 62 Acts made from 1297 to 1961 were rescinded in whole or part, but appointment of verderers for the ancient royal forests is still permitted.

As a result of attempts to exterminate the deer, wild fallow were far from numerous in the latter years of the nineteenth century compared with one or two hundred years earlier. Of 31 English county faunas published between 1871 and 1911, wild fallow are mentioned in only seven, namely those of Essex, Hampshire, Leicestershire, Northamptonshire, Shropshire, Staffordshire and Sussex, confirming that wild fallow were scarce in England at that time. Had they been common, they would have been mentioned as they were in earlier centuries but lack of a mention does not necessarily mean that the deer were completely absent: it would be surprising if a few escapees from parks were not roaming the countryside in other counties.

By the early 1960s wild fallow had been reported from every county of England and they are probably more widespread today than they have been for many decades. What has caused this tremendous increase in the population of wild fallow in the last sixty or so years?

The disbanding of deer parks has occurred at different times over the centuries for various economic or social reasons and escapees undoubtedly have contributed to the present distribution of fallow. In this century a great number of disbandments occurred during the war years, particularly the Second World War. By order of the War Agricultural Executive Committee, many parks came under the plough. Other parks were requisitioned for a variety of purposes, particularly for the billeting and training of troops, with the consequent loss of deer. Once the war was over, there was still a desperate need to utilise all available land. Furthermore, raw materials were in demand for essential buildings and manpower was required for tasks more important than renewing park fences. By the time supplies of food and materials were readily available, the economic situation was such that most landowners preferred to continue farming the land rather than indulge in the luxury of a deer park. Even 35 parks which survived the war years were disbanded between 1950 and the early '60s. Some parks had been turned over to cattle and sheep even before the war, thus earning the owners some reduction in taxation. The Deer Herd Book Society of Great Britain in its report for 1932 referred to the difficult times that landowners were facing and in the circumstances it was considered satisfactory that only 46 parks had registered herds, 43 of which were fallow.

A good example of the influence of the disbanding of parks on deer distribution is shown by the present situation of wild fallow deer in Essex, where a comprehensive survey was carried out from 1964 to 1970. In 1867 Essex had 13 fallow parks; by 1892 this figure had dropped to ten and by 1950 to two. In *The*

Mammals, Reptiles and Fishes of Essex, written in 1898, Laver refers to the fallow as a feral animal in Epping Forest: in the rest of the county it was known only as a park animal. The recent survey showed that fallow deer were widely distributed. Although they were encountered in many woods, there were some areas where their concentration was greater than others. With the exception of the countryside close to Epping Forest, all the large populations of fallow, such as that at South Weald, were centred on areas close to a former deer park. At St Osyth Priory near Clacton-on-Sea a deer park was established in 1960 and escapees soon led to the presence of fallow in the local woods from which they were absent formerly. In other counties too, present-day fallow distribution can be related at least partly to the former presence of parks.

Once liberated, the future of the deer depends upon the reception they meet. The absence of many gamekeepers, stalkers and landowners during the two world wars must have helped the fallow to become established in some areas. The decimation of much mature woodland by the hasty removal of timber during the First World War and the extensive fellings during and after the Second caused the rapid growth of ground flora and scrub which provided an excellent habitat for fallow. The proportion of woodland in Great Britain that was productive high forest fell from 72 per cent in 1913-14 to 48 per cent by 1924, whereas the proportion of unproductive woodland, namely scrub, devastated woods and felled areas, increased from 9 to 34 per cent in this period. The proportion of productive coppice remained unchanged at about 19 per cent. Moreover in 1919, after the First World War, the Government, realising the need for home-grown timber, constituted the Forestry Commission with the aim of increasing the area of productive woodland. Consequently, from that time onwards many tree-less areas were afforested.

The distribution of fallow does not depend entirely upon escapes from parks for, as we have seen, there are some forests which have held fallow for many centuries. Dispersal of fallow from these forests has helped to populate the adjoining counryside. The conditions which proved so suitable for the spread of fallow escapees from parks also favoured the dispersal of these wild, forest deer.

The fallow's distribution in the British Isles, so dependent on man's activities, is not static and is at present still far from perfectly known. Felling of woodland, construction of a motorway, building a new estate or other changes in land use all destroy the habitat used by fallow whereas elsewhere a young plantation may provide a new suitable environment.

In *The Deer of Great Britain and Ireland,* published in 1964, Whitehead gave a county by county account of the history and distribution of fallow deer. One cannot do better than refer to this monumental work for detailed information, for there is no more recent, comparably thorough account.

England. The parts of England most populated with fallow lie south of a line drawn from The Wash to the Severn estuary. Within this area many counties have large resident populations. In Suffolk and Essex, fallow are widely dispersed and across the Thames they are common in central Kent. Along the south coast, East Sussex, West Sussex, Hampshire, Dorset and Devon are well populated. About 80 years ago East and West Sussex together had 19 parks with fallow and Ashdown Forest has held this species for centuries. Although Hampshire has not had more than four fallow deer parks during the last century, the New Forest lies within it and accounts for the largest population of fallow. Cranborne Chase still holds fallow and park escapees have also become established in other parts of Dorset. Mid-Devon has plenty of fallow in the Teign Valley and Haldon Hills and some occur in the south-west but they are rarely reported in north Devon although some occur near Dunster and elsewhere in neighbouring Somerset. In Gloucestershire they are common and about 100 live in or around the Forest of Dean in the Wye Valley. Wiltshire has many fallow, particularly in Savernake Forest which has been a stronghold for centuries. Berkshire has fallow in many woods, as does Oxfordshire, where they are well established on the Chiltern Hills. Near where Buckinghamshire, Bedfordshire and Hertfordshire meet, around 200 wild fallow are resident close to Ashridge, an extensive National Trust property. Small herds of fallow live in many other parts of Hertfordshire but much of Cambridgeshire and Lincolnshire is too open for fallow, which occur only in a few wooded areas.

Fallow are well-scattered in the central counties of England. Amid the industrial Midlands, Cannock Chase in Staffordshire is a stronghold for fallow as it has been since the thirteenth century, except for a few periods when numbers dropped. The present-day Forests of Rockingham in Northamptonshire, and Sherwood in Nottinghamshire are also remnants of ancient forests which still have fallow. Again, correlation between parks and wild herds can be seen, as in the Edge Hill district of south Warwickshire where war-time escapees from Ettington Park led to a wild population. The picture is similar in the northern counties but there are greater areas free of fallow. North Yorkshire has quite a number in the eastern part, which is not surprising since, less than a hundred years ago, Yorkshire as a whole had fallow in 40 parks. In recent years escapees from Studley Royal Park and Ripley Castle Park have settled in the Harrogate area. A few places on the border of Lancashire and Cumbria have fallow but in the other northern counties they are few and localised.

Of the counties which border Wales, Cheshire has few fallow but Salop has many, Mortimer Forest alone probably having over 200. Many are also resident in the county of Hereford and Worcester: Wyre Forest, on the west of the River Severn, has held fallow since a whole herd escaped from Mawley Park in 1880; now there are about 200.

Wales. Relatively few deer live in Wales but the fallow is again the most widespread, reported in recent years from six of the eight counties; there are no reports from Mid or South Glamorgan. In south Wales there are fallow in Gwent near the border with England and, in West Glamorgan, within sight of Port Talbot's steelworks some roam Margam Forest, having originated from the adjacent park. Near Llandeilo, where there are two parks, and south-west of Carmarthen are the main fallow areas in Dyfed. In Gwynedd they are more widely scattered; in the south-west a mass escape of 90 from Nannau Park near Dolgellau was witnessed in 1963. By 1971 about 100 fallow were reported in the vicinity and another 30 had established themselves to the north in Coed-y-Brenin Forest which centres on the Ganllwyd Valley. Others ranged southwards to the Dovey Valley. Adjacent to the Menai Strait, near Vaynol where there was formerly a park herd, fallow are present also. On Anglesey a small population of fallow exists in the Newborough area, having originated from Bodorgan Park. Clwyd, in the north-east of Wales, has fallow in the Denbigh to Colwyn Bay area. In Powys the main localities are around Welshpool, near the border with Salop.

Scotland. Scotland is primarily the land of red and roe deer but nevertheless fallow occur in a few areas. Parks with fallow have been known at least since 1283 when Stirling Park was in existence. In 1949 Taylor reported fallow in small numbers or as occasional visitors to eight Forestry Commission woodlands scattered within the five counties of Argyllshire, Dumfries-shire, Inverness-shire, Perthshire, and Ross and Cromarty. In southern Scotland in recent years fallow have been reported from west Kircudbrightshire and the Moffat area of Dumfries-shire. Fallow have been present on the island of Inchlonaig in Loch Lomond since the seventeenth century. From there, deer have swum to other islands such as Inchcailloch and to the shores of the Loch, so fallow are now present in both Dunbartonshire and Stirlingshire. Probably there are now no established fallow populations further north than Perthshire in central Scotland where, early last century, they were introduced to the Duke of Atholl's estate. They frequent mainly the east side of the River Tay near Dunkeld. Wanderers from this area have been reported near Loch Lintratten in the neighbouring county of Angus. Of 11 islands off the west coast of Scotland to which fallow either were introduced or reached by swimming, they survive only on Mull, Islay and Scarba.

Ireland. The earliest recorded introduction of fallow to Ireland was by the Normans in 1244 when a park was established at Glencree in Co. Wicklow. By the mid-seventeenth century fallow were present in many parks and, according to Mulloy, no less than 118 places in Ireland still bear a name meaning "deer park". As elsewhere, disbandment of parks has given rise to wild populations and now fallow have been recorded in almost every county. They are far more widely spread than the native red deer or the sika deer introduced over 100 years ago. In the middle of last century, 500 fallow were reported within a 20 kilometre radius of Clonmell, having escaped from Gurteen Park, Co. Waterford. Today this county and neighbouring Co. Tipperary have fallow in many places. In the west, fallow occur in Co. Clare and in Co. Galway, particularly between Portumna and Longhrea. Offaly, Leix and Co. Wicklow have fallow in many places but the south-east tip of Ireland has few. Off the coast of Dublin, fallow were released on Lambay Island in 1880; a herd, maintained at about 30, still roams the island. In the north of Ireland the largest populations of fallow are where the three counties of Tyrone, Co. Monaghan and Co. Armagh meet. Three estates alone in the Caledon and Glaslough area were estimated to hold over 400 falllow in 1971. In Co. Down fallow occur on the Clandeboye Estate. Randalstown Forest, on the northern shore of Lough Neagh, Co. Antrim, holds about 60 black fallow which originated from Shane's Castle Park.

The following account of the world distribution of fallow has been compiled from information kindly provided by many people. A brief historical introduction is given for each continent after which the distribution in that continent is discussed by countries in alphabetical order.

EUROPE

In many ways the history of fallow deer in much of Europe parallels that in England. In some countries fallow have been present for centuries, medieval remains having been found in Denmark and in Germany. As early as 1305, fallow hides were exported to England from Norway but the records do not indicate whether the skins were merely in transit or had originated from Norway. However, continental countries generally did not have deer parks on the same scale as those in England.

The fortunes of fallow in Europe have fluctuated widely from country to country and many introductions have taken place over the years. They were formerly abundant in Sardinia, in the nineteenth century even as many as 3,000 being killed in some years, but by 1969 Reinhardt and Schenk believed only a dozen survived. In the U.S.S.R., fallow appear never to have been widely distributed whilst Switzerland probably never had wild fallow at all, for, although they were recorded there in 1561, later writers doubted this account.

Wild fallow deer are now widespread in Europe, occurring in at least two-thirds of the countries, but they are generally not as numerous as roe and red deer. Fallow occur mainly in a central belt from Britain, Denmark and Sweden in the north, through Germany, Poland and the western part of the U.S.S.R. to Italy, Jugoslavia and Bulgaria in the south. The occurrence of fallow deer in many of these countries, together with details of their trophy antlers, are given by Sartorius in *Stärkste Damschaufler der Welt.* Of the European countries which lack wild fallow, namely Finland, the Grand Duchy of Luxembourg, Switzerland, Liechtenstein and Iceland, all but the last two have them in parks or reserves. Even in countries where fallow are abundant many are kept enclosed and escapees have helped to populate the countryside just as they have done in Britain. The position of fallow in Albania, Andorra, and Turkey-in-Europe is unknown.

Austria. Fallow are not in Austria, the only two sizeable wild herds being those in the Horn district, near Therasburg, and near Anthering in Salzburg province.

Belgium. In Belgium, wild fallow are rare; less than 100 inhabit about 1,500 hectares of the Royal Forest of Ciergnon, west of Rochefort.

Bulgaria. Fallow are widely dispersed in Bulgaria: they are most numerous just north of Sofia, on Mount Vitosha and south of Vitosha city near Pazardzhik; on the boundaries of the Khaskovo and Kurdzhali districts, south of Bourges and near Shabla, both of which are on the Black Sea coast; south-east of Kubrad and to the north of Yambol, Stara Zagora and Novi Pazar.

Czechoslovakia. Recently just over 5,000 fallow were estimated to be living in Czechoslovakia, over half of them in fenced hunting reserves. Some fine trophy heads have been produced by bucks at Breclav, near the Austrian border, and at Stara-Obora and Obora-Brezka.

Denmark. The Jutland peninsula and all the major islands of Denmark have scattered, mostly small, populations of fallow. In Jutland, they occur from the Aalborg district in the north as far south as Vejle. Alex-Hansen did not report fallow further south in his 1965 survey, which is surprising because they are numerous in the adjacent German province of Schleswig-Holstein. On Zealand over 2,000 fallow are enclosed in the well-wooded Jaegerborg Deer Park at Copenhagen and small herds of wild deer occur mainly in the south. Lolland also has several localities favoured by fallow but on the narrow island of Langeland they are reported only from Tranekaer. Fyn, between Jutland and Zealand, is noted for its fine bucks many of which, especially those from Wedellsborg, have produced trophy heads.

France. Wild fallow now have a very restricted distribution in France, being found wild only in Alsace where they frequent some 20,000 hectares along the River Ill between Strasbourg and Colmar. Of the estimated population of 300, about half are thought to be in the Illwald Forest.

Germany. Fallow are widespread in the German Federal Republic and their increase has been particularly noticeable since the late 1950s, especially in Saxony and North-Rhein Westfalen. In Schleswig-Holstein, fallow, introduced from neighbouring Denmark and from England, have been at large since 1800. According to Heidemann, an introduction of ten deer to the Schleswig district in 1939 succeeded so well that 30 years later the population could withstand a cull of 800 in one year. Fallow are most common in Hesse, Holstein, Lower Saxony,

Schleswig-Holstein and Westfalen. Smaller numbers live in Baden-Wurttemberg, Bavaria, Rhineland-Palatinate and a few in Hamburg.

The German Democratic Republic too has fallow widely dispersed. Their main localities in the north are around Rostock, near the Baltic coast; Schwerin and Neubrandenberg. In the central part of the country they frequent areas near Potsdam, Magdeburg, Halle, Cottbus and, further south, Erfurt. On the border with Poland fallow occur near Frankfurt-an-der-Oder.

Greece. On the mainland of Greece, wild fallow deer probably have been extinct since early this century, but several hundred still flourish on the Island of Rhodes. Visitors arriving at the Aegean island are greeted at Mandraki harbour by statues of fallow, erected on the sites of the feet of the Colossus of Rhodes, the Wonder of the Ancient World which formerly straddled the harbour (see below).

Hungary. Hungary is famous for the fine quality of its fallow, particularly those from Gyulaj, the national forest and hunting area near Tamasi, where world record heads of antlers have come from. This area has a fallow population of around 3,000; smaller numbers live in several other scattered areas, some having spread into the surrounding countryside from reserves such as Gyarmatpuszta, west of Budapest, and Gyula in the south-east.

Entrance to Mandraki Harbour on the island of Rhodes.
Greek Tourist Office, Rhodes.

Italy. The main Italian localities for fallow are the woods of Maremma in Tuscany and Latium; three state-owned forests in the Appenines; the Presidential Reserve of Castel Porziano and other woodland in central Italy; the National Park of Circeo and the state-owned forest of Sila in southern Italy. In Sicily fallow were formerly numerous but have become extinct.

Jugoslavia. In Jugoslavia fallow occur near Kozina and Sežana, on the Pohorje mountains near the country's northern border, and in two hunting reserves on the banks of the River Sava, between Trbovje and Litija, the latter being about 100 kilometres north-west of Zagreb. All these populations are derived from stock brought from the island of Brioni in the Adriatic Sea. A few fallow have been introduced also to reserves at Boranja and Majdon-Kučajna.

Netherlands. In the Netherlands most fallow live in enclosed forests but during the past decade some escapees from a park have established themselves in the wild near Leersum, Overberg. In the east too, near the coast at Kennemerduinen and further south on the dunes near Haamstede, some are living wild.

Norway. Early this century seven fallow from Denmark were released on the small Norwegian island of Hankö, at the entrance to Oslo Fjord, where about 40 now live. Attempts to introduce the species to other parts of southern and western Norway have failed.

Poland. Fallow deer were widespread in Poland according to the survey carried out in 1965 by Caboń-Raczyńska. The main areas for fallow were within the provinces of Bydgoszcz, Katowice, Lodz, Lublin, Opole, Poznan, Radom, Siedlce and Wroclaw with fewer animals in the more peripheral regions. Fallow occur also at the extreme western edge of the country, against the border with Germany, about 80 kilometres north-east of Berlin.

Portugal. Early this century in Portugal fallow apparently occurred only in game reserves near Lisbon and Evora. Little is known of the situation since then but tracks possibly of fallow have been seen recently in woodland near Ovar, south of Oporto.

Romania. Fallow are widespread in Romania, mainly inhabiting the Muresul Valley in the west, the valleys of the Oltul and La Domita in the south and near the River Prut in the north-east of the country. Fallow also occur in two valleys just east of the Carpathian Mountains.

Spain. About 60 years ago in Spain, fallow were reported only in central Cáceres but since then new stock has been introduced and now wild herds are widespread, mainly in reserves in the provinces of Cuenca, Oviedo, Jaén and Navarra which are administered by the Instituto Nacional Para la Conservacion de la Naturaleza. Fallow also occur in the Pardo Mountains in the province of Madrid and at Rio Frio in Segovia and also are enclosed on many private estates. A population estimated at about 1800 inhabits the Coto Doñana, south-west of Seville.

Sweden. In Sweden fallow are well-distributed in about 12 of the southern provinces, namely Skåne, Halland, Småland, Öland, Västergötland, Dalsland, Östergötland, Södermanland, Närke, Västmanland, Uppland and possibly also Värmland and Dalarna.

U.S.S.R. In the 1950s Heptner and his colleagues reported fallow from five localities in western Russia. In the Molodetschno region, where they were introduced from Germany in 1932, only five were counted in 1955 and none survives now. The population in the western parts of the Lithuanian Republic, estimated at 137 in 1957, has gone also. On the island of Chortiza, near Zaporozhye, fallow have become extinct during the last 20 years too. Askanya Nova, in the Carpathian region, has an enclosed population from which some were taken in the 1940s to Biryuch Island, in the Azov Sea, where more than a hundred now live. In Moldavia, there are about 40 fallow at Kishinev, near Donbass, close to the great forest of Khakov in the Ukraine; fallow were seen in 1959 but their subsequent fate is unknown.

ASIA

Although it seems likely that the European fallow may have originated in the Near East, they are rare in Asia and have not been widely introduced. At present, a few still occur in Turkey-in-Asia. Fallow do not appear to have been introduced into the Indian sub-continent despite the extensive British influence there in the past. It must be remembered, however, that in the nineteenth century, when fallow were being introduced to many countries, India had numerous wild deer of her own such as axis, barasingha, hog, muntjac and sambar as well as other large game mammals like blackbuck, gaur, leopard and tiger.

Turkey. In the middle of the last century fallow were widespread in Turkey-in-Asia. There were reports from Maritza in the extreme west to Patnos which lies north of Lake Van in the far east; at least fourteen other localities, mostly spread in a southerly arc, lay between them. In the late 1800s they still survived in the mountains north-east of Lake Tuz in central Turkey and until about 1905 they occurred near Karaboga, south of the Sea of Marmara which lies south of the Bosporus. By 1934 fallow were thought to survive only in the northern and southern foothills of the Western Taurus Range. Now fallow are very rare in Turkey, only being known for certain to occur in two areas. In the southern part of Monavgat Forest, where there is intensive illegal hunting and also heavy grazing by domestic stock, about 25 fallow were estimated to be present in 1967, some in an area which is now an enclosed reserve. In the second locality, the Duzlercani Forest, only a handful of fallow existed in 1967 but now illegal hunting and grazing by domestic stock has been eliminated there is hope that the herd will increase.

AFRICA

Until late last century there were reports of fallow deer in north-east Africa, from the wooded coastal area near la Calle on the border between Algeria and Tunisia, and extending eastwards to Tripoli. None remains today and their origin is unknown. Some people believe the fallow were indigenous as is the Barbary red deer which evidently crossed the former Gibraltar land-bridge from Europe. Others think they were introduced by either the Phoenicians or the Romans. Stones bearing Phoenician lists of sacrificial animals and dating from the fifth to seventh centuries B.C. have been found at Carthage, on the North African coast, and also in France. One of the words listed, *'yl,* Joleaud interpreted as fallow deer.

South Africa. Cecil Rhodes was responsible for the first introduction of fallow deer to South Africa, when he released some in 1897 on the Groote Schuur Estate on the slopes of Table Mountain near Cape Town. The population here was recently estimated at about 350. Elsewhere in Cape Province, about 1,000 fallow deer are present on the grassveld and karoo, especially in the districts of Middelburg, Sutherland, Bedford, Somerset East, Bredasdorp, Paarl and Colesburg, according to a recent survey by Professor Bigalke. In the Orange Free State fallow have been present for over 60 years on the Vereeniging Estates and they occur also in the Harrismith district. The province of Transvaal too has had fallow since the early part of this century. At Volksrust in 1968 over 350 fallow were present on one farm which sells about 150 each year as breeding stock to other South African farmers who shoot some for sport.

Malagasy. Fallow were imported to Malagasy, formerly Madagascar, from Czechoslovakia in 1932. They live on the high, wooded plateau in the centre of the island, about 60 kilometres south of Tananarive, but the present number is unknown.

NORTH AMERICA

North America has five indigenous species of deer, namely moose, mule deer, reindeer also known as caribou, wapiti and white-tailed deer, as well as other large game animals such as bighorn sheep, musk ox, pronghorn antelope and Rocky Mountain goat. Nevertheless, alien ungulates such as fallow, axis, barasingha, sambar and sika deer, blackbuck, nilgai and sable antelope have all been imported, mostly this century. Exotic animals, which were introduced both privately and by official departments, are now widely distributed, particularly in the United States of America. The release of exotic species is highly controversial and many professional biologists involved in wildlife management are opposed to the idea. They fear that introduced animals will affect adversely the native fauna and flora. Others see no harm in the practice and have released more animals in the past decade. A few years ago fallow were introduced into Indiana but they were soon shot after blundering into the suburbs of towns; further introductions, however, are being considered. In Louisiana, where fallow exist only as captive or semi-captive animals, recent attempts to establish them as a game animal for archers were terminated by poachers. Wild fallow deer are now present in Canada, the West Indies as well as nine of the 50 States. In addition to truly wild populations, some fallow are kept as semi-captive animals on farms and ranches in various States.

Alabama. About 1930 in Alabama, 20 fallow escaped from captivity at Miller's Ferry, County Wilcox and formed the nucleus of a wild population which now numbers 200 to 300 and has spread over 30 kilometres along the Alabama River. Fallow also occur in Dallas County and possibly in Mobile County where 30 escaped in 1946.

California. In California there are four populations of wild fallow deer. The largest herd, about 300, is on Point Reyes National Seashore where some were introduced about 1947 from San Francisco Zoo. An all-white herd of similar size lives on the North Coast Range in central Mendocino County. Small herds are established south of Proberta, Tehama County and at Pomponio Ranch in San Mateo County.

Colorado. Fallow were introduced to Conejos County, Colarado in the 1920s, to Conejos and Larimer Counties in the 1930s and to Rio Blanco County in 1944. In 1958 the wild population in the State was estimated as 50 to 75 but their present status is unknown.

Georgia. In Georgia, fallow were released on Little St Simons Island near Brunswick in the early 1950s and they now number 500 to 600.

Kentucky. Kentucky supports a sizeable population of wild fallow in the west, in the area which was formerly the Woodlands National Wildlife Range. This is probably the oldest established population in the U.S.A., the original stock having been introduced about 1900. In 1974 their strength was estimated at over 700. Recently a few fallow were released at the Grayson Lake Wildlife Area in Carter County.

Massachusetts. Fallow have been introduced to the islands of Nantucket and Martha's Vineyard in Massachusetts. The latter received its first few fallow in 1932 and 150 were present by 1962; another seven animals were introduced more recently.

Nebraska. In the 1930s, 60 white fallow were introduced into Nebraska, being liberated near Petersburg in the Beaver River Valley in Boone County; by 1955 their range had extended into adjacent Geely and Hall Counties. The highest count from an aerial survey, in 1959, was 157. In 1966, the severe crop damage was no longer tolerated and consequently the population was reduced; only about 55 deer remained in 1973 and were almost entirely restricted to two ranches in Boone and Wheeler Counties.

New Mexico. A wild population of fallow is established in the Sacromento Mountains in New Mexico, but little is known of them.

Texas. Between 1930 and 1936 over 500 fallow were liberated in the coastal Prairie Region of Texas but by 1938 only 22 deer were thought to be present. When the area was purchased by the Government, the former owners were allowed to remove the remaining deer to other properties. A detailed survey in 1971 by the Texas Parks and Wildlife Department assessed the population at 2,617. Although they were spread through 54 counties, over 60 per cent were in the Edwards Plateau region on the eastern side of the State. The next most populous areas were the adjacent South Texas Plains with 13 per cent and the Cross Timbers and Prairies with ten per cent.

Canada. In Canada, fallow are present on three islands in the province of British Columbia. Deer from the Duke of Devonshire's estate at Chatsworth in Derbyshire, England were released on James Island in 1907. Some stock was transferred to nearby Saltspring and Pender Islands and to the Alberni District of Vancouver Island in the 1930s. Apart from individuals which occasionally swim to Vancouver Island, they now survive only on James, Sidney and Saltspring Islands, which lie at the southern end of the Strait of Georgia. The 150 fallow now on Sidney Island originated from animals which swam from James Island, two kilometres away, about 20 years ago.

West Indies. In the West Indies, fallow have been introduced to the small island of Barbuda, north of Antigua in the Leeward Chain. Probably they were imported between 1700 and 1772. Darwin sent one black and two common coloured skins from here to the Natural History Museum in London but little else is recorded about them. Although protected by a close season, these deer now are said to be relatively scarce.

SOUTH AMERICA

South America has its own unique deer fauna including marsh deer, pampas deer, guemal, and two species each of brocket deer and pudu. Nevertheless, fallow deer have been imported from Germany, Poland and Spain and are established in Argentina, Chile and Peru.

Argentina. Early this century fallow were introduced to the Peryra Iraola Park near La Plata in Argentina and, about the same time, don Ernesto Tornquist imported some to the Sierra de la Ventana. About 1930, his sons liberated the deer in mountainous country around Cura-Malal, Ventana and the Three Peaks of the Province of Buenos Aires where there are now estimated to be about 6,000. Fallow from this area were taken to other places in the Province, namely Bolivar and the Huetal Ranch at Halle. The latter population is enclosed and at one time was said to number 20,000. Fallow from the Tornquist estate also were taken to the opposite, western, side of the country where they were liberated on Victoria Island in the National Park of Lake Nahuel Huapi. A smaller herd of about 40 fallow lives in Park Diana in San Martin de Los Andes, some 80 kilometres to the north.

Chile. About 1925 some fallow were imported, from Hamburg Zoo, to estates between Temuco and Puerto Moutt in the Valparaiso Province of central Chile. About 30 still live there in semi-confinement. From this stock some animals were introduced to two southerly provinces, Bió-Bió and Osorno. More recently some privately-owned farm herds have been established, again in semi-confinement.

Peru. The Huocraruco Ranch in the province of Cajamarco was the site of the introduction, in 1948, of fallow deer to northern Peru. Initially the deer were in reserves but were later released in the valley of the River Chicama, 600 kilometres north of Lima, but their numbers have been much reduced by poaching in recent years.

AUSTRALASIA

Unlike Africa, the Americas and Asia, Australasia has no large native game mammals. Consequently many exotic animals, including deer, were introduced, mainly during the nineteenth century. According to Bentley in *An Introduction to the Deer of Australia,* probably the first liberations of fallow were in Victoria, before 1840. Altogether about 15 species of deer have been introduced to Australia and New Zealand, not all of them successfully. The introductions were arranged both by wealthy settlers and by acclimatisation societies which were established with the ideal of exchanging wildlife to attain a more equal distribution of the world's most beautiful and useful species. These societies were formed and flourished in the second half of the nineteenth century and the early part of the present century, particularly in Australia and New Zealand although they existed also in Europe. Their formation accelerated the importation of foreign species, especially when the P and O Steamship Co. undertook free carriage of livestock for the societies. In their enthusiasm the Victoria Acclimatisation Society presented Manning Thatcher with a medal, engraved by Thomas Landseer with a fallow buck and many other animals, to commemorate his transporting some animals including deer and rabbits. The State Department of Agriculture must find this honour ironical, for the rabbit became a serious pest, causing damage on a vast scale.

At least 25 liberations of fallow in New Zealand were made from 1864 onwards when the first three animals, from Richmond Park, were released near Nelson on South Island. Several Acts were passed in New Zealand during this period to encourage the liberation and protection of foreign animals. The changes in the fauna, with the extinction of some species and the rapid spread of others, has been described by Wodzicki in *Introduced Mammals of New Zealand.* All but one of the introductions were successful and now fallow are the second, after red deer, most numerous deer. The mean rate of dispersal of fallow, over a period exceeding 50 years, has been calculated by Caughley as 0.8 kilometre per year. In general, introduced deer appear to have succeeded better in New Zealand than in Australia.

By 1930, red deer in New Zealand had increased to such an extent that they were regarded as important economic pests.

Fallow deer occur now in five of the eight states and territories of Australia, and in both North and South Islands of New Zealand. Although Bentley stated that fallow were introduced to New Guinea he subsequently showed that there was no evidence for this: rusa and axis are now believed to be the only species of deer on the island.

Australia. One of the earliest introductions of fallow to New South Wales was in 1886 when a pair was released north-east of Canberra, near Lake George. Here they increased to about 200 over the next 30 years and some still survive. On the southern border of the state, fallow have lived in the Albury district for about 90 years and some cross the Murray River into Victoria. In the north-east of the state they occur on the New England Range.

Fallow were among the four species of deer introduced to the Coburg Peninsula, Northern Territory in 1912. How long they survived is unknown but none remains now. They also met with little success in Western Australia where several releases were made from 1899 onwards in the Cape Leeuwin area, but there have been no reports since 1956; another introduction, at Gingin, also failed.

In Queensland fallow occur in the south-east of the state. Their main localities are the Upper Freestone Valley, south of Maryvale where the Queensland Acclimatisation Society released some on the Darling Downs in 1870, and around Pikedale, west of Stanthorpe, where some were liberated 20 years later.

Most introductions of fallow to South Australia were in the south-east. Much of their habitat has been cleared in recent years and they lack legal protection, being regarded as vermin. Wild fallow still surviving in the Millicent area, near the state's eastern boundary, probably originated from Yallum Park where they were introduced in 1895. Descendants of escapees from the former park at Rosebank Station near Mount Pleasant now live in the Mount Crawford and Springton area where they find refuge in the state plantations in which, generally speaking, hunting is not permitted. In the Two Wells district animals descended from stock released in Buckland Park about 1912 frequent the tidal-flats and salt marshes of the Gawler estuary. In the 1940s, 1,500 were estimated to be in the vicinity of the Park but over-shooting for commercial interests greatly reduced them in the 1960s.

In Victoria too, the clearance of scrub for farmland and an increase in hunting have caused a decline in the number of fallow and only a few small herds survive, mainly in an area north-east of Melbourne and south of Mansfield, and near Bendigo. Some are held in captivity by conservationists and farming enterprises.

Only in Tasmania are fallow numerous, the population being estimated at 8,000. Since their introduction, they have extended their range over 400,000 hectares of the island's farmland and eucalyptus forest.

New Zealand. In New Zealand, fallow occur in about 15 widely separated areas. Two of the largest populations are in the Blue Mountains, Otago, where about 1,500 are now shot each year, and the Caples Valley, south-west of Lake Wakatipu. The other main South Island localities are North-west Westland between the Paparoa Range and the River Grey; in the Fairlie area some 56 kilometres west of Timaru in south Canterbury; and both sides of the northern limbs of Lake Wakatipu. On North Island the main fallow country is east and west of the River Wanganui. They also live on the southern peninsula of Kaipara Harbour in North Auckland; in South Auckland there are small scattered herds in the vicinities of Cambridge, Thames and Manukau Head.

SUMMARY

The transporting of fallow around the world has resulted in their being established in many countries. Where their hold is tenuous or their range restricted, this is often the result of man's activities rather than the animal's inability to adapt to natural conditions. Uncontrolled hunting, competition with domestic stock, and the encroachment of urban development obviously have a limiting influence on the spread of fallow. Despite the adaptability of the species to live in a variety of habitats in latitudes which range from about 65 degrees north to about 47 degrees south, there are natural factors which limit the fallow's survival.

Although fallow in England appear to drink seldom, usually obtaining enough water with their food, on Sidney Island in Canada the animals which swam there before ponds were made did not survive long. Since fresh water has been available the population has flourished. Hard weather, accompanied by snow, also seems an important factor. When deep snow covers the ground fallow cannot graze and the amount of browse they can reach is limited. Even in parks were supplementary winter feed, such as hay, roots and cereals, are provided, many fallow died in the very severe English winter of 1946-47 when snow persisted for weeks. Although fallow have lived in the most northerly counties of Scotland, their range was the more sheltered lowland areas, not the exposed highlands, and even so, many losses occurred in hard winters and large populations were not established. On Hankö in Norway the fallow need supplementary feed in winter and attempts to introduce them elsewhere in that country have failed. The fallow reaches its most northerly range in Sweden: it lives in the lowland southern provinces but not the more mountainous colder parts.

Given a habitat which can provide sufficient food and shelter and is free from excessive snow or intense cold, the European fallow is able to flourish. Its wide distribution seems assured even though the numbers in its original or former range in Turkey and the Mediterranean countries are low.

CHAPTER FIVE

Structure, Function and Growth

Structure

THE MAJOR roles of the skeleton in any mammal are to give shape and support, to provide anchorage points for the muscles which bring about movement, and to protect delicate organs. The latter function is well illustrated in the fallow deer's wedge-shaped skull (Page 72). In addition to the skull and lower jaws, the skeleton of a fallow deer consists of 208 bones (Figure 1). When cleaned, boiled and dried the entire skeleton weighs between six and eight per cent of the adult deer's body weight. In the living animal, the bones with their blood, cells and fat will account for a higher proportion of the animal's weight. Forty-one vertebrae form the backbone: seven are in the neck, thirteen are thoracic, six are lumbar, four are sacral and fused to form a sacrum, and eleven are tail vertebrae. Thirteen pairs of ribs are connected, by costal cartilages, to the breastbone. Each shoulder blade lies embedded in muscle adjacent to the fore ribs. In fallow deer the blade's curved upper end remains cartilagenous, not becoming bony, even in mature animals. As there is no collar bone to link it to the breast bone, the shoulder blade can be moved forward and backward within the limits of the muscle slings which hang it from the trunk. The system is analogous to the moving seat of a racing skiff: it lengthens the stride and also efficiently positions the limb for the power stroke.

The sequence of the limb bones follows the same basic pattern in the fore and the hind legs. To appreciate the significance of this pattern in fallow deer and why, for example, the ankle is half way up the leg, one needs to recall the arrangement, shown in Figure 2, which existed millions of years ago in primitive, unspecialised mammals which walked on five toes on each foot. The upper bones in each fore leg of the fallow depart only slightly from the basic mammalian pattern. The wrist, often called the "knee" of the front leg, is composed of seven small bones which are closely packed but allow considerable bending for, according to Yalden, the wrist can be flexed through about 150 degrees. Below the wrist the leg bones depart widely from the basic ancestoral pattern because, during the evolution of the deer, elongation, fusion and loss of bones have all occurred. The metacarpals are represented by a single, long, straight bone known as the cannon bone which is formed by the fusing together, during gestation, of the metacarpals of digits three and four: their fusion gives a reduction in width and weight but an increase in strength. The metacarpal bones belonging to digits two and five exist only in a

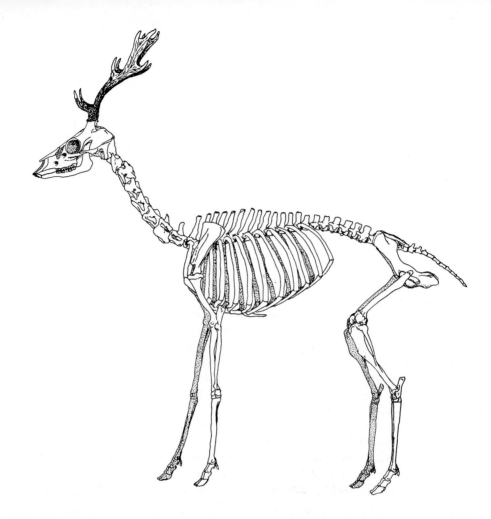

Skeleton of a fallow buck.   Figure 1.

much reduced state, as small splint bones, one on each side of the upper end of the cannon bone. This is the plesiometacarpalian condition, seen also in red deer but not in the roe whose splint bones are at the base of the cannon bone, the teleometacarpalian condition. The two functional digits, which are fingers three and four, each have three phalanges: the first is the longest and the middle bone the shortest, the third is triangular. The hoof consist of the terminal phalange with a covering sheath of hard-wearing horn. The dew claws, which lie at the back of the leg just above the hooves, represent the vestiges of digits two and five. Each is a miniature of a functional digit, having three tiny phalanges capped in horn.

The arrangement of the bones of the hind leg is similar except that there are no splint bones. The cannon bone, the fused metatarsals of toes three and four, is slightly longer than that of the front leg and is grooved down the front for the passage of blood vessels. This groove is closed to form a tube at the extreme lower end, a characteristic which distinguishes deer metatarsals from those of similar sized animals, such as goats and sheep, which may be found with them at archaeological sites.

Associated with the elongation of the skeletal elements of the limbs is the modification of the muscle arrangement. The muscles are concentrated in the upper parts of the limbs, thus lightening the lower part of the leg, so when a deer moves it does not have to swing forward a great weight. In the fore leg, about 80 per cent of the weight lies above the wrist. The foot is meat-less since the muscles which move it are higher up the leg and have long tendons extending as far as the toes. A small contraction of muscles in the upper leg results in the leg describing a wide arc.

The loss of some bones, the elongation of others and the change to walking on toes only, rather than the whole foot, are adaptions which have occurred to varying degrees in all hooved animals, undoubtedly contributing to the success of the group. An athlete runs not on the flat of his foot but on his toes, bringing the bones of the sole, the metatarsals, temporarily into line with the rest of the leg. Thus he apes the condition which has evolved as the normal arrangement in the deer and their fleet-footed relations which can attain and maintain high speeds over long distances. The maximum speed attainable by fallow does not seem to have been

Arrangement of the bones in the lower fore limb (a) primitive mammal; (b) fallow deer, showing fusion and reduction in number.   Figure 2.

A
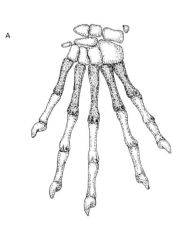

B
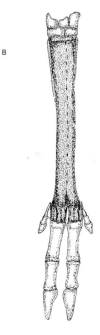

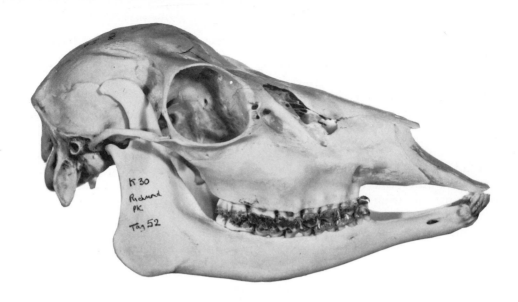

Skull and jaws of a doe. The wedge shape, large eye sockets and absence of incisiform teeth in the upper jaws are characteristic. *J. R. Mercer.*

recorded but Conquest informs us that they reached 65 kilometres per hour when being caught from a vehicle in South Australia. The ability to leap fences six feet high further indicates the agility of the fallow.

Beneath the skin and above the backbone a massive ligament extends from the back of the skull to the sacrum. Its important function is to assist the neck muscles to support the head which is heavy, particularly in an antlered buck. Prior to the rut a buck's neck becomes much thicker as a result of an increase in size of the muscles. Several activities in which the bucks indulge during the rut involve strenuous movements of the neck and head, so the increase in neck musculature seems to be associated with the need to bring about rapid movements of these parts of the body and generally add to his size and powerful appearance. The flesh of deer is very lean, not being marbled by fat, but some is usually present and the amount varies seasonally. When present, it lies mainly over the very muscular rump, around the kidneys and in the caul of tissue which overlies the gut, but fat may also be deposited around the heart, against the breast-bone and over the back. The pre-winter deposition of fat is usual in many mammals, fat being a convenient and efficient form in which to store reserve energy and water for a period during which the animal does not feed or cannot obtain enough food of sufficient nutritive value.

Digestive System

The outstanding feature of ruminants is the specialisation of the digestive system. In the fallow deer, as in the other cud-chewing mammals, the stomach has four compartments. The rumen is the first and, in adults, by far the largest of these chambers. Abutting against the diaphragm and occupying most of the left side of the abdomen, it serves as a storage bag. The second and smallest compartment is the reticulum. The third chamber is the omasum which leads into the fourth, the elongated abomasum or true stomach, analogous to the single stomach of non-ruminants. The linings of the four stomach chambers are different, as connoisseurs of tripe will know. The rumen is densely lined with small finger-like villi and the reticulum has a network pattern of raised polygonal shapes: both these linings are tough enough to protect the underlying soft tissues from abrasion by the fibrous plant food. The omasum has folds resembling the pages of a book. All these devices increase the surface area over which absorption of nutrients can take place. The abomasum has slight folding, giving way to an almost smooth lining at the duodenal end. Fallow deer consume large quantities of food which pass down the gullet into the capacious rumen. When the animal is at rest, this food is regurgitated, a bolus at a time. In the mouth the process of chewing the cud takes place. The vegetation is ground between the cheek teeth as the jaws move from side to side. When well-chewed, the bolus of food passes down the gullet but this time it is diverted to the omasum.

The functioning of a ruminant's specialised stomach depends upon the presence, principally in the rumen, of its microscopic flora and fauna. The vital role of these micro-organisms, which are bacteria and ciliated protozoa, lies in their ability to break down cellulose, the carbohydrate which forms the cell walls of

Faeces of fallow doe.

plants, into glucose which is fermented in the rumen, producing enormous quantities of gases, principally methane and carbon dioxide. Obviously the gases cannot remain in the stomach: a complex and efficient mechanism of eructation ensures their removal. The gases pass up the gullet, into the back of the throat, some being forced down the windpipe into the lungs and absorbed into the blood. This re-cycling of some gas to the lungs and expulsion of the rest through the mouth is achieved almost silently, without any audible belch of appreciation for a good graze! If for any reason the gas is not released from the stomach chambers the animal suffers from bloat. A dead fallow deer soon becomes severely bloated, the reason being that fermentation and the production of gas continues in the rumen for a while after death but the eructation mechanism no longer operates. The gases therefore build up rapidly, causing great distension of the abdomen and making the skin taut, like a drum.

The density of the stomach's population of micro-organisms varies with the availability and type of food, and consequently with the time of year and with the physiological condition of the deer. A rutting red deer stag, which eats little, has only half the number of protozoa of a non-rutting stag whereas lactating hinds have a far higher number of micro-organisms than a non-lactating female. Similar changes probably occur in fallow deer. Prins and his colleagues examined the rumina of 16 fallow deer shot in the Netherlands in the winter and calculated that the number of ciliate protozoa ranged from about 106 thousand to more than 2 million per millilitre of rumen contents. Over 80 per cent, and in some cases 100 per cent, of the protozoa were species of *Entodinium*. A few thousand million bacteria are also usually present in each millilitre of fallow rumen contents. These are digested and their proteins utilised by the deer. Thus a mighty fallow buck depends for his survival upon millions of single-celled organisms without which the vegetation he eats would be useless to him.

The relative sizes of the four stomach compartments vary with age in young deer. In a newly-born fallow fawn receiving milk, the first three chambers are unimportant in digestion and therefore very small but the abomasum is comparatively large since it deals with the digestion of milk prior to its passage to the intestines. The changes in the proportions of the stomach chambers have been studied in a subspecies of white-tailed deer, similar in size to fallow. At birth, the rumen plus reticulum account for only ten per cent of the total stomach volume. Two weeks later this volume has increased fourfold and some microbial activity has begun. Fallow fawns of this age usually have some vegetation in the stomach as well as 'cheesy' milk. Between the ages of one and two months the rumen and reticulum of white-tailed deer increase tremendously, to account for 70 per cent of the total volume. By this time the fawns are mainly dependent on rumen activity with milk forming only a small proportion of the total stomach contents. By four months the fawn's stomach chambers attain the same proportions as in the adult, when the rumen and reticulum together account for 85 per cent of the total volume. Although no precise measurements are available for fallow deer, the pattern of change and the relative proportions are similar to those that occur in white-tailed deer.

In the fifteenth century the liver, kidney and entrails, collectively known as numbles, were made into a pie and served at the hunt feast to the lesser mortals whilst the nobility supped on haunch and saddle. The word numbles has evolved through umbles and humbles and survives to-day with the metaphorical eating of humble pie. The pancreas, testes and tongue were regarded as dainty morsels for the noblemen. The fallow has a large liver but there is no gall bladder, a feature shared by deer with a few other species of mammal including horses, rats and giraffes.

In the rectum the faeces are formed. These fewmets, as they are sometimes called, are cylindrical, firm, black, glossy and striated pellets which, when voided at the anus, may adhere to each other or form a string but usually fall in loose heaps or crotties of perhaps a hundred. Occasionally the faeces are soft and amorphous: Jackson found this type in the New Forest in May and June. On the ground, they frequently become covered with fungi and may look like a ball of fluff. Larsen studied fallow deer faeces in a park near Copenhagen and found that 55 species of fungi could occur on these droppings. The spores of at least 37 species were able to withstand passage through the gut and for some species this was essential before they could germinate.

In medieval times the condition of a deer was sometimes judged by its faeces, then called fumes, fewmishings or cotyings. It was customary for the huntsman to show the monarch a dish of fewmets, genteely arranged amid a garnish of leaves, before he or she signified approval that the beast in question was a worthy quarry, in prime condition. This quaint ceremony may have been restricted to red deer stags for, in the fourteenth century, Gaston de Foix wrote about the fallow bucks "nor are his fumes put in judgement as those of the hart". Deer droppings still serve a useful purpose to the deer-watcher, for they are often the first signs of the presence of deer. The fewmets from an adult fallow doe are about 15 mm long and 8 mm wide but the size varies; one end is pointed, the other rounded. Bucks have larger droppings which are also pointed at one end but often concave at the other. The droppings of many deer species are similar in shape and extreme caution must be exercised before trying to identify the species of a deer from its droppings. The fewmets of a fawn of one species may resemble, in size as well as shape, those of an adult of smaller species.

Coat and Moulting

The attractive appearance of a fallow deer depends partly upon the coat, which

A fallow's cloven footprint, measuring 5 cm wide by 6 cm long, within that of a horse.

is made up of coarse guard or primary hairs amongst which finer, closely grouped secondary hairs are dispersed. Jenkinson found the ratio of secondary to primary hairs to be seven to one at the eight body sites that he examined, but on the legs the secondary hairs were fewer and the primary hairs thinner.

The colours of the hairs vary according to the colour variety of the deer, the position on the body and the season. The pigment is more concentrated towards the free ends of the hairs, the ends close to the body being paler so that, when the hairs are parted, white or a colour paler than the external coat is seen. Sandy coloured hairs with black tips are frequent in common-coloured fallow. The hairs are very slightly waved and each has three concentic zones with the pigment in the second zone. The cuticle, the outermost layer, consists of slightly overlapping scales and the innermost core, or medulla, has a lattice-like appearance, being composed of cells of irregular sizes and various rounded shapes. The hairs of the trunk slope backwards from head to tail, giving the deer a sleek appearance and providing a thatch-like covering. The skin was prized for leather, particularly for buckskin hunting breeches. In John Gay's poem "The Squabble", published in 1745, a tobacco pouch "made of the skin of sleekest fallow deer" was the prize in a wager.

Most of the primary hairs are about 4 cm long but some longer ones, about 13 cm, are scattered over the body. These are about as long as the primary hairs on the long-haired variety of fallow deer found in Mortimer Forest: perhaps the Mortimer variant represents a more exaggerated stage. The hairs of the tail are coarse and about 11 cm long, but over the perianal area the hairs are short, fine and sparse. Fallow does have hairs forming a tuft, equivalent to the brush on the male's penis sheath, hanging just below the vulva: in an adult the tuft is about 12 cm long.

The hooves are deeply cleft, the two halves of each foot being united only at the "heel". As their edges are razor-sharp, it is not surprising that a well-developed foetus has a waxy-looking, polythene-textured covering over the tips and edges of the hooves to prevent damage to the mother's tissues. Soon after birth this covering shrivels and is worn away.

Apart from the hooves, the nose is the only part of the body not covered by hairs. The head is covered by short hairs but on each side of the face are five groups of longer, thicker and stiffer hairs serving a tactile function. The longest of these vibrissae form the eye brows and a smaller, shorter clump lies below the eye. The other tufts are on the upper lip, above the nostril and below the mouth. Many closely-set lashes border the upper eyelid but the lower lid has far fewer (see below). The ear flaps, about 15 cm long, are densely covered by short hairs on the outer surface. The inner surface is almost bare at the centre but haired towards the pointed tip, the edges and the base.

Moulting in fallow deer takes place twice a year, in spring and autumn. During the spring moult the fallow loses its well-groomed appearance and becomes tatty,

Fallow doe. Note the eyelashes, closed suborbital glands and position of ears.

the neck and face often showing the shabbiness first as the old hairs fall out and the new ones push through the skin. The rump may be the next area to show signs of moulting, patches of the still growing, glossy summer hairs appearing like holes in the longer, duller and dead winter coat. There is, however, much individual variation in the sequence of the moult: in many fallow it begins over the shoulders and progresses to the base of the neck and along the back towards the rump and downwards to the belly and legs. Other individuals show the first signs of moulting in the flanks. The back of the neck and top of the head are often the last areas of the neck and head to attain the full summer coat, the old hairs on the head sometimes remaining like a skull-cap or wig when the rest has new hairs. Loose hairs come out in clumps and also are scattered when the deer shakes itself. Small birds, such as chaffinches, sometimes collect them as nesting material whereas jackdaws, magpies and starlings will stand on the back of fallow deer and pluck the loose hairs.

In southern England, the spring moult usually begins in April but the times of onset and completion vary even among healthy individuals within one population; any sick or under-nourished animal is likely to be late in moulting. Usually by the third week in April most fallow in Richmond Park look tatty over the shoulders, neck or flanks and in some animals distinct patches of new coat can be seen. Some Park fallow complete their moult by the end of May: by the time the fawns are born in mid-June most are in full summer coat. In some years, at least, the wild fallow at South Weald are ahead of these dates, being in almost complete summer pelage by mid-May. In Germany, Ueckermann and Hansen state that generally young animals begin their moult about 5th May whereas older ones do not begin until 15th to 20th May. Despite the late start, most fallow there are in summer pelage by the end of June since the moult lasts about forty days.

In England, fallow retain the summer coat throughout July and August but usually by the fourth week in September the autumn moult has begun. The progress of this moult is insidious as the glossy summer pelage is gradually replaced by a duller, thicker coat. The woollier texture of the coat is most noticeable in the neck region. The "moth-eaten" appearance seen during the spring moult is not a marked feature of the autumn moult. Again there is much individual variation in the time of moulting. Some wild Essex does complete their winter coat by the fourth week in October whereas in others the winter pelage is still coming through in mid-November. In Germany, does usually have completed their winter pelage by mid-October but the bucks take longer, perhaps two weeks more, possibly because at the same time they are contending with the rut.

Scent Glands and Senses

The importance and significance of scent glands must be hard for man, with his relatively poor sense of smell, to appreciate although for generations he has exploited commercially the scents of some animals such as musk deer and civets.

The fallow deer has several scent glands, which are areas of specialised skin rich in secretory cells, and these were studied at the turn of the century by Tempel and by Zeitzschmann. These glands, the interdigital, the metatarsal and the suborbital, are all paired and occur in both sexes. In addition, bucks may have a scent gland in the penis sheath. Whilst the specific functions of these glands have not yet been demonstrated in fallow, they are probably a very important means of communication among members of the species.

The presence of interdigital or pedal glands has long been recognised: in medieval times the fallow buck and doe were described as beasts of sweet foot. At the base of each leg, in the mid-line immediately above the two cleaves of the hoof, is a fissure or narrow pocket in the skin. On the hind feet a pale yellow, soft waxy secretion, with a not unpleasant fatty-acid odour reminiscent of rancid butter, can be seen adhering to the hairs lining the pocket. The strength of the smell, as judged by the human nose, remains about the same throughout the year in both sexes. Our noses have not detected any smell from these glands in newly-born fawns but by the time a deer is two or three weeks old the glands are active. Interdigital glands are present also in antelope such as the sable, in which the gland opens to the outside by a central pore or duct. In fallow deer there is no central collecting duct, the secretion exuding from the skin. Microscopical examination shows that, below the thin epidermis, the upper part of the dermis has a regular pattern of areas of muscle interspersed with hair follicles with large sebaceous glands; the lower half of the dermis is composed of a mass of very large and much coiled sweat glands. The front foot also has a pocket but the skin is thinner and has less extensive glands, lacking the large zone of sweat glands present on the hind foot. The stain and odour associated with the hind feet are absent.

The position of the metatarsal scent gland is clearly marked externally by a raised oval cushion of paler hairs just below the hock, on the outer side of each hind leg. The cushion, about 40 mm long and 35 mm wide in an adult fallow, feels firm and has numerous very densely packed hairs which at their lower end are more or less embedded in a creamy coloured waxy secretion which has a faint fatty acid smell. A section through the gland shows that there is a deep zone of massive, sebaceous glands in the dermis, below which is a layer, of similar depth, of large, much coiled sweat glands. The glandular cushion is well defined in a newly-born fawn but appears to lack the scent of the adult.

Below the corner of each eye is a pocket in the skin which forms the scent gland known by a variety of terms which all indicate its position, namely, suborbital, preorbital, infraorbital or antorbital. Sebaceous and sweat glands are present in the skin lining the pocket, which is frequently filled with a brown wax.

During the rut a buck has a very pungent and distinctive odour. A similar smell can be detected in the scrapes in the ground into which a rutting buck has urinated.

Rutting buck with suborbital gland, next to the eye, wide open.

Urine withdrawn from the bladder of a freshly dead rutting buck does not have this smell but the brush on the penis sheath reeks and becomes heavily stained during the rut. It seems that the characteristic smell is imparted to the urine either as it passes down the urethra or on contact with the air. The surface of the last 15 to 20 mm of the penis sheath is usually cream in colour and has numerous short, finger-like dermal papillae on the inner wall. Just before the rut the tip of the sheath becomes everted, so the papillae are on the outside and they become enlarged and black: the whole area becomes flattened and looks like cracked earth, as shown on page 81. Examination of an organ in this state, which looks as though it may be decomposing, must have prompted a comment which was the subject of a letter by Wherry in *The British Medical Journal* for September 1902, which said: Sir Thomas Browne corrects the vulgar error that the stag also sheds his 'pizzle' after the yearly rut . . . . it does not annually rot away. Fallow bucks are often called "stags", even now. The tip of the sheath reverts to its normal shape and colour soon after the rut. Adjacent to the blackened area, the skin of the penis sheath has large multilobular sebaceous glands and large sweat glands and the area appears similar to other skin regions specialised for scent production. It is thought that the substance responsible for the rutty odour of a billy goat is produced by the sebaceous glands and their secretion causes discolouration of the skin. It is known that in at least some mammals, androgens, the male hormones, cause an increase in size and activity of sebaceous glands. Since the testes of fallow deer are at their maximum activity at the time of the rut, the androgen level is almost certainly at or near its highest. The large size of the sebaceous glands in the penis sheath suggest that they may be associated with the production of the buck's rutty odour.

80

As would be expected in a species well-endowed with scent-glands, fallow deer have an acute sense of smell. The eyes are set on the sides of the head, the pupils are horizontal and the face slopes downwards, all of which contribute to giving the fallow deer a wide field of vision, seeing from straight ahead to far behind, although not immediately behind it. The ears are situated high on the head in a more or less vertical position. They are nearly twice as long as they are broad and can be swivelled, in unison or separately, through about 180 degrees in a forward-backward direction while the rest of the head remains still. This enables the animal to pick up sounds from any direction without drawing attention to itself by turning the whole head. As well as communicating by non-vocal means such as scent glands, fallow deer can utter a variety of sounds from the mewing of a fawn to the groaning of a buck.

Growth and Development

During their growth and development bucks become considerably larger than does, although the weights of newly born fawns in Richmond Park are the same for both sexes. Three fawns, weighed within hours of birth and again seven or eight days later, showed increases ranging from 2.7 to 3.2 kg on birth weights of about 4.5 kg, or increases of about nine per cent of the birth weight per day. It is difficult to determine the exact age of very young fawns so those which meet with fatal accidents in July and August cannot be used to assess the rate of growth unless their dates of birth are known. An error of a week or two at this age substantially alters the calculation. The ideal way to calculate rates of growth would be to reweigh the same animals at frequent intervals but repeated disturbance or frequent handling may affect their rate of growth. Most fallow fawns seem to quadruple their birth

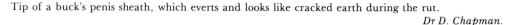

Tip of a buck's penis sheath, which everts and looks like cracked earth during the rut.

Dr D. Chapman.

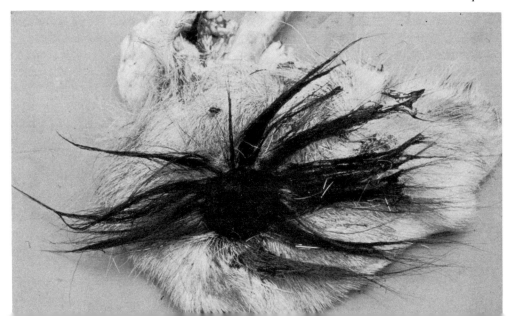

The waxy-looking covering on the tips of a fawn's hooves soon shrivels after birth and is worn away.

weight by three to four months. By seven months, sixteen culled doe fawns from Richmond Park weighed an average of 24 kg, ranging from 18 to 28 kg; thirteen male fawns, average 27 kg, ranging from 23 to 32 kg. Culled animals are likely to include some in below average condition, deliberately selected as "poor doers" which may not survive the winter: this may account for the wide range of weights. Alternatively, the fawns of low weight may have been born late and were therefore younger, although their tooth development was similar to that of the heavier fawns. Most female fallow in the Park attain a maximum weight when about three years old. In contrast, bucks continue to increase in weight, not reaching their maximum until at least six years. Similar ages for maximum clean weights were obtained by Mehlitz and Siefke after examining 984 fallow deer culled in the game research areas of Nedlitz and Serrahn in East Germany. Clean weight was undefined. In the New Forest, Jackson claims that both bucks and does reach a maximum weight at about eight to nine years of age; this is surprisingly late, particularly for does.

Superimposed on the male's overall increase in weight there is an annual cyclical fluctuation associated with the rut. The weights of twelve bucks, aged three years upwards, killed in August, September and the first half of October, were compared with nine bucks, of similar ages, killed in the second half of October, November and December. The average weight of the pre-rut bucks was much higher, 80 kg (range 68 to 92), than that of the post-rut animals, 63 kg (range 43 to 72). The weights suggest that a buck is in his finest condition before the rut and loses weight during the rut when he probably eats less and is undertaking considerable physical exertions. Baker found that bucks in New Zealand also lost weight during the rut and in East Germany, according to Mehlitz and Siefke, yearling bucks lost from five to nine per cent of their pre-rut clean weight whereas bucks of five years and older lost from 13 to 22 per cent. Most of this loss in weight occurred in the second half of October, during the rut, and the loss was still apparent in January. The milder conditions and more plentiful supply of food in spring permits a steady increase in weight which reaches its peak in summer. Studies of a few captive mule deer have shown cyclical fluctuations of this pattern too, marked in bucks but also detectable in the does.

Whilst a fawn's weight is increasing, so too is its height and length. A detailed study by Mehlitz and Siefke showed that the length, from head to rump, increased rapidly from about 110 cm in four month old fawns to about 150 cm for bucks and about 130 cm for does at three years. The greatest length, bucks about 155 cm and does about 135 cm, however, was not reached until seven to eight years. Shoulder height followed a similar pattern and was about 85 cm for bucks and 75 cm for does. The lower jaws, usually discarded when deer are culled, can be used conveniently as one indicator of growth. During the first year of life, growth is very rapid but then slows down until, at about thirty months, growth of the jaws has almost ceased. The jaws of the males become significantly larger than those of the female during the first twelve months and from eighteen months there is a distinct sexual dimorphism, particularly in their length (Figure 3) and in that of the diastema but, to a smaller extent, in height also. The variation with age of the length of the jaw and skull of male fallow from Nedlitz and Serrahn is similar to that for bucks in Britain.

There is a considerable range in the size of adult jaws. Table 4 compiled from jaws from about 50 female and 70 male adult fallow from eight localities, wild and parks, in Britain shows the variation. Figures such as these may be useful in

Rising, hind legs first.

identifying and comparing fossil and archaeological specimens with present-day fallow.

The other bones of the skeleton are elongating at the same time but not necessarily at the same rate as the jaws. By about two and a quarter years the lower epiphyses, the growing ends, of the cannon bones become fused to the shaft of the bone. The fontanelle of the skull closes between three and four months.

Table 4. Lower jaw measurements of adult fallow deer

Lower jaw	Sex	Mean, mm	Range, mm
Length	Male	200	185 - 216
	Female	191	175 - 203
Height	Male	106.9	99.5 - 115.5
	Female	102.7	99.5 - 109.0
Length of diastema	Male	53.3	46.2 - 62.0
	Female	48.8	43.7 - 54.5
Length of molariform tooth row	Male	85.6	80.5 - 93.8
	Female	84.2	76.1 - 89.3

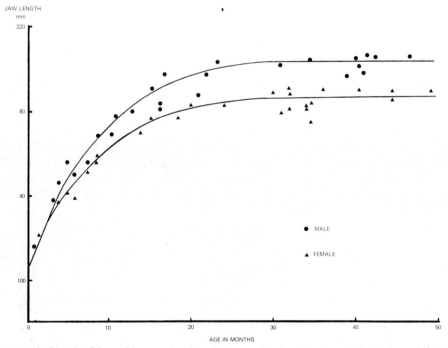

Increase in length of jaw with age; showing difference in size between adult bucks and does.

Figure 3.

CHAPTER SIX

Age Estimation and Teeth

A T FIRST sight it may seem strange to place teeth and age estimation together in the same chapter but the two subjects are closely related. The teeth of deer, like those of children, erupt at certain chronological ages and, once fully developed, wear sets in. Again, as in children, the age at which each tooth erupts varies to some extent among individuals. Examination of the teeth of fallow deer does, in fact, provide one of the best indications of age. One needs to know the age of deer in order to answer such questions as: At what age do fallow deer first give birth? Are young or old deer more likely to be road casualties? How long do fallow deer live? Answers to questions such as these are necessary to understand fully their natural history and are prerequisites to the successful management of deer herds. There are two aspects of this particularly difficult problem: estimation of the age of living deer in the field and of the age of deer either found dead or culled.

Age Estimation

Let us consider living deer first of all. Fawns of the year can be recognised by their smaller size but, by the time they are about seven to nine months of age, their height, particularly that of a buck fawn, is approaching that of its dam. If the deer are standing still, then careful observation should enable fawns to be distinguished from adults. However, if several deer are bounding across a ploughed field then it may be very difficult to distinguish, with reasonable certainty, the fawns from the adults. A fawn on its own may also be more difficult to identify because there will not be any adults for comparison. Fawns appear to have a proportionally shorter face than adults and, when seen in profile, this is often a useful characteristic by which to identify them (Page 86). The older the fawn, the more difficult the problem of recognition becomes, particularly in the case of doe fawns. With buck fawns the problem disappears once their antler pedicles become visible. Even before, it is sometimes possible to distinguish does from male offspring of similar size by the presence of the brush of hairs around the penis, which is visible in male fawns in the field from about two months of age.

We can all recognise the babies, the adults and the really aged in our towns and villages but how many of us would claim to be able to tell the exact age of these people? Some of us, no doubt, are better than others at guessing the ages of people but, nonetheless, they are guesses. The same problem arises when we try to estimate

Fawns have proportionally shorter faces than adults. The pedicles of the nine month old fawn are just developing. *Diane Hughes.*

the ages of fallow deer, particularly does. People who claim to be able to recognise a fallow deer as being, say, five years old are deluding themselves in thinking that they can estimate the age of a deer so accurately. They would probably never dream of saying that a stranger in the street is 48 years old. They might say "he is around 50" or "he is probably in his late forties". Unfortunately this claim to be able to tell accurately the age of a deer arises time and time again, particularly in hunting circles. De Nahlik, for example, tells us in his book, *Wild Deer,* to cull so many fallow does of age one, two, three etc. right up to nine to ten years, which implies that all these age groups can be recognised readily. Such, unfortunately, is not the case unless of course the deer have been marked, as they have in a few deer parks.

Various characteristics such as posture and appearance may be a guide to whether a doe is young or old, but they are no more than that. Appearance may change during the moult and posture may be affected by injury or disease. An experienced deer keeper once shot a "tatty old doe" in our presence but, when the animal was examined, it was found to be just under two and a half years old, having been ear-tagged as a newly-born fawn. The doe was moulting and had a ruffled coat, which had led the keeper to misjudge her age badly. It is probably best not to attempt to classify fallow does beyond young of the year, that is fawns, and adults. With experience, and particularly if one is culling deer regularly, it may be possible to recognise aged does in a particular population. If these supposedly aged deer are culled and the teeth are found to be very worn, then this is further evidence that the animal was of mature years. If this process is repeated several times and in each case the aged does are found to have very worn teeth, then one can start to become reasonably confident that these old animals can be identified in the field in that particular locality.

Bucks, because they have antlers, present a slightly easier problem as regards age estimation. The antler development of bucks in relation to age is dealt with in the next chapter. Fallow with spike antlers in velvet will be around one year old. In late spring, however, care should be taken to distinguish these fawns from young bucks with hard spike antlers which may not be cast until their owners are almost two years old. Although the precise age of a buck cannot be told from its antlers, they may often provide a rough indication of a deer's age. In Richmond Park, fallow deer with slightly forked antlers, such as those shown on page 111 are usually between two and three years old. However, a few two to three year old deer in this Park have much better developed antlers (page 90). Therefore, although we are fairly safe in assuming the age of deer with the first type of antlers are between two and three years, we are not sure whether deer with the second type of antlers are two to three years or older. Yearling red deer also usually grow spike antlers in the south of England but animals living under particularly favourable conditions have been known to grow branched antlers in their second year. The same thing could occur in fallow deer and so animals with slightly forked antlers could, on occasions, be only yearlings. However, none of the deer of this age has been found to have antlers with well-developed palms: the deer are usually several years old before they begin to develop this type of antler. Therefore we can start to classify bucks into age classes depending on the size and shape of their antlers provided that we have studied the antler development of animals of known age in that locality first. It

Thirty-three month old buck with second head of antlers typical for Richmond Park deer, without any palmation.

Seven years old. Would you have guessed correctly?

must be stressed that this does not enable us to determine the age of the bucks but merely to classify them into a few arbitrary groups. These criteria are applicable only to the deer population where they have been developed. Even then, deer may be wrongly classified because they have antlers greatly different from expectation for their age. We have encountered these problems in an enclosed herd of fallow deer, many of which have been ear-tagged at birth; how much greater they must be with unmarked deer or in wild herds. The variation in fallow deer antlers in Germany is well illustrated by Hansen in his book *Damwildhege mit der Büchse*. The only way to be absolutely certain of the age of a deer is to have marked it at birth, or within a few months, so that it can be identified unequivocally at a later date. Although this requires much work it has been done in parts of Europe for many years and it is becoming increasingly recognised in Britain that any serious study of either wild or park deer requires them to be marked in this way.

There are many methods of estimating the age of dead mammals and these have been well reviewed by Morris. It should be remembered that all methods of age estimation require a source of known-age animals if accurate results are to be obtained and with deer this means catching and marking them at birth or soon afterwards. Eruption and wear of the teeth, growth rings in the dental cement and in the antler pedicles, fusion of the epiphyses of the bones, suture lines in the skull, and weight of the animal have all been used to estimate the age of culled deer.

The dental cement of Scottish red deer shows layers reminiscent of the growth rings in the cross-section of a tree trunk. The layers, which appear to be laid down annually, can be used to estimate the age of the deer, but there are many problems in interpreting the layers in tooth sections; a layer may be missing or indistinct in some individuals. However, many studies by Mitchell with specimens of known age have shown that there is a close relationship between the number of layers and the actual age in years, and the method has been applied to a wide range of mammals. Similar growth rings occur in the antler pedicles of some reindeer. These growth rings have been seen both in the cement between the roots of the teeth and in the antler pedicles of fallow deer but we found that they were indistinct and very difficult to interpret. The cause of these rings is unknown but it may be that the more uniform climatic conditions in the south of England, compared with those in the north-east of Scotland, preclude the formation of distinct layers in fallow deer. Growth rings occur in the cement of the first permanent incisor and of the first molar of New Zealand fallow. Baker found that counting the layers in the incisor teeth was easier than counting those in the molars, but lack of sufficient deer of

Yearling buck, 206, with a good first head of antlers. The birth of this animal is described in Chapter Nine.

Buck 206 with his second head of antlers, showing some palmation.

known age precluded an accurate method of age estimation to be devised. The weight of fallow deer does not provide an accurate indication of age because it is so variable: thus the weight of fawns may be lower in the spring than in early winter.

The only method of age estimation which has been widely applied to fallow deer is that based on the eruption and wear of the teeth. This technique has been used for a long time to estimate the age of domestic mammals. The saying "Never look a gift horse in the mouth" is attributed to Saint Jerome of the fifth century. The age at which tooth eruption occurs in fallow deer (Table 5) is given merely as a guide and applies strictly only to the fallow deer in Richmond Park. However, as the teeth of fallow deer in Germany and New Zealand also erupt at very similar ages according to Rieck and Baker respectively, use of the Table probably provides a reasonable indication of age in fallow deer in general. This method of age estimation is not very precise because the interval between different teeth erupting may be either several months or only a few days. The first molar, for example, erupts at three to four months but the next tooth to erupt, the first incisor, does not do so until seven to eight months whereas the second and third permanent premolars both erupt at about the same time. Of course, the degree of eruption can be taken into consideration but then the individual variation between one deer and the next needs to be known. The reason for wanting to know the age of the deer and how precise it needs to be must also be borne in mind. In many cases it is often sufficient to know that the animal is, for example, "about six months" or "about one year" without defining the age more precisely.

Table 5. The percentage of fallow deer in each age group with each tooth in the lower jaw erupted

Age, months	n	M_1	I_1	M_2	I_2	I_3	C	M_3	P_4	P_3	P_2
0-2	16	0	—	—	—	—	—	—	—	—	—
3-4	4	50	0	—	—	—	—	—	—	—	—
5-6	23	100	0	0	—	—	—	—	—	—	—
7-8	17	100	24	0	—	—	—	—	—	—	—
9-10	22	—	100	18	0	0	0	0	—	—	—
11-14	8	—	100	75	10	0	0	0	0	—	—
15-18	25	—	—	100	100	100	100	16	0	0	0
19-22	23	—	—	100	100	100	100	52	100	10	0
23-26	4	—	—	—	—	—	—	100	100	100	75
27-30	38	—	—	—	—	—	—	100	100	100	100

n = number of animals

Once all the teeth have erupted, the degree of wear can be used to provide an estimate of the age of older animals. This, combined with a knowledge of the date of death, will enable one to say, for example, that the animal was probably about four and a quarter years of age. A description and photographs of the diagnostic features exhibited by the molariform teeth of fallow deer of various ages are given in Appendix II. This information is based on known-age fallow deer from Richmond Park. At present the features characteristic of the teeth of deer older than seven

Buck 206 now three and a half years old, with his third head of antlers.

years are unknown. The characteristics of the teeth are different from those given in *Das Damwild* for fallow deer in Germany, which are different again from those given by Rieck for fallow deer in that country. The use of the information provided about German fallow deer would give a very wrong impression of age if applied to fallow deer in Richmond Park.

Much as one would like to be able to provide definite criteria applicable to all populations of fallow deer, this is not possible with the present state of our knowledge, but accumulation of data from different populations will help us to assess the overall validity of the technique. Eruption and wear of the teeth in man are very variable and give no more than a crude indication of age. Why should the eruption and wear of the teeth of fallow deer be any more uniform? At present there is no substitute for really getting to know the deer, for knowing over what period fawns are born and then applying intelligently the methods of tooth eruption and wear to estimate their approximate age.

The maximum age to which wild fallow deer live is unknown and there is very little precise information on their longevity in captivity. Fallow deer in zoos have lived for over 20 years but such ages are probably uncommon and, in deer parks, most animals, particularly bucks, are probably culled before they reach old age.

Dentition

Because teeth provide such an important means of estimating the age of fallow deer let us look at the eruption and wear of their teeth in more detail. Fallow deer have two successive sets of teeth, a deciduous or milk dentition normally comprising 20 teeth, and a permanent dentition normally comprising 32 teeth, although variations in the number of teeth have been observed. The 12 molar teeth are not represented in the deciduous dentition and develop only later in life. The teeth of a mammal are customarily described by means of a dental formula which in the case of adult fallow deer is:

$$\text{Incisors } \frac{0}{3} \quad \text{Canines } \frac{0}{1} \quad \text{Premolars } \frac{3}{3} \quad \text{Molars } \frac{3}{3} \times 2 = 32$$

There are 20 teeth in the lower jaw and 12 in the upper, which are arranged symmetrically about the mid-line. The eight front teeth in the lower jaw are the incisors and canines but, because they all have a similar spatulate shape and the same function, they are often referred to as incisiform teeth. This similarity of shape is usual in ruminants whereas in other groups of mammals, such as carnivores, the canine teeth are quite different in shape from the incisors. In fallow deer, the middle two teeth, the first incisors (I_1), are the largest of the incisiform teeth and are almost twice as wide as either the second (I_2) or third (I_3) incisors or the canines (C). Instead of upper incisors and canines, there is a thick pad of fibrous connective tissue against which the lower incisors and canines bite. The incisiform teeth are used for plucking grasses and herbs and biting off leaves and the tips of shoots. There is a large gap or diastema between the incisiform teeth and the premolars. The original dentition of placental mammals is believed to have included four premolars in each half jaw. In some ungulates, such as the pig, the first premolar has taken on the form and function of a canine, whereas in deer this tooth is missing and only premolars two, three and four remain. This means that the first cheek-tooth in the jaw is referred to as the second premolar (P_2) and the second and third teeth as (P_3) and (P_4) respectively. The fourth, fifth and sixth cheek teeth, the molars, are called M_1, M_2, and M_3 respectively. The shapes of the cusps of the molariform teeth fall into two groups. The deciduous second and third premolars and all the permanent premolars are said to be lophodont, which means that all the cusps connect to form ridges across the teeth. The cusps of the deciduous fourth premolar and all the molars are crescent shaped and so the teeth are said to be selenodont. With the exception of the deciduous fourth premolar and the third molar, the molariform teeth each have two pairs of cusps (quadritubercular) and each has two roots. The deciduous fourth premolar and the third molar have an additional pair of cusps (sexitubercular) and three roots. The molariform teeth, which are used for grinding the food when the deer ruminates, have developed to cope with the problem of chewing grass and leaves, which are hard, gritty foods. These high-crowned teeth, which have tall cusps, are said to be hypsodont and they continue to erupt throughout the life of the animal. They are composed largely of dentine, which is covered by a layer of very hard enamel in turn covered by a layer of cement. This arrangement means that the relatively soft dentine is protected to some extent by the enamel. As these teeth wear, it can be seen that nine layers of contrasting materials are exposed at the surface (Figure 4). The dentine wears away quicker than the harder enamel and so the tooth develops a characteristic pattern of ridges. It is the changes in the proportion of cement, dentine and enamel exposed and the pattern of ridges that enable teeth to be used to estimate the age of deer.

The two sets, right and left, of molariform teeth in the lower jaws are closer together than they are in the upper jaws and they diverge from the front in the form of a slightly curved 'V'. The crests of the lower molariform teeth nearest the tongue stand higher than the crests nearest the cheek so that the teeth of the lower jaws tilt slightly in the direction of the cheeks. The reverse is true of the maxillary teeth of the upper jaws which tilt towards the roof of the mouth. When chewing, the deer's lower jaws move laterally in relation to the upper jaws. Therefore, when the cusps nearest the cheek on one side of the lower jaws are in contact with the teeth of the upper jaws, it is the cusps nearest the tongue on the other side which are in contact and *vice versa*.

Eruption and Wear

Fallow deer fawns are born with six deciduous incisors, two deciduous canines and twelve deciduous premolars only; these may be covered by a membrane for the first day or two of life. As the fawn grows, and the jaws lengthen, the first molars

(M_1), which are the first permanent teeth, start to erupt. The socket or alveolus in the jaw into which the tooth fits makes its appearance for M_1 when the fawn is about three months of age. As the fawn grows, the molars erupt and the deciduous teeth are gradually replaced by permanent ones. The permanent teeth erupt in a regular sequence. A tooth has been considered to have erupted if any part of it is visible above the bone of the jaw, even though it may not be functional. By comparing each tooth with every other tooth the order of eruption of the permanent teeth in the lower jaws of fallow deer was found to be:

M_1, I_1, M_2, I_2, (I_3, C,) M_3, P_4, P_3, P_2.

The order of eruption of the permanent teeth in the upper jaws of fallow deer is:

M_1, M_2, M_3, P_4, P_3, P_2.

A similar order of tooth eruption occurs in many other species of deer and is probably usual for the deer family. However, in the family Bovidae, which includes cattle and antelopes, the first molar is the first permanent tooth to erupt and this is usually followed by the second molar and first incisor, as in deer. The third molar, the second incisor and the premolars erupt next, followed by the third incisor and the canine, this order being the reverse of that in deer.

Tooth eruption occurs in a definite sequence but the age at which this happens varies somewhat from animal to animal. The permanent molariform teeth start eruption at three to four months of age and the third molar has erupted by 23 to 26 months although it does not become completely functional until the deer is almost three years old. The permanent incisiform teeth start erupting at seven to eight months, the third incisor and canine being fully erupted by 15 to 18 months; so their development is much more rapid than in the molars. This is because the permanent incisiform teeth merely replace a decidous dentition whereas the molars cannot erupt until the jaw has grown sufficiently to accommodate them. The time taken for the teeth to erupt is similar to that for red deer and sika deer but is much shorter than the four years usually taken by sheep to acquire a full set of teeth.

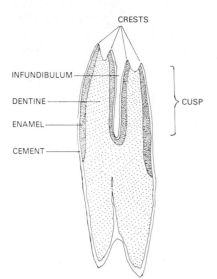

Vertical cross-section of molariform teeth of a fallow deer. There are nine successive layers of different material; the two layers of cement lining the infundibulum counting as one.

Figure 4.

Because the four different incisiform teeth take almost four years to erupt in sheep, the age of young animals can be estimated by inspection of the mouth and this has led to sheep being called two tooth, three tooth, etc. Unfortunately, the age of fallow deer cannot be estimated so readily.

Once the tooth becomes functional and starts to grind food, it begins to wear but, although the teeth continue to erupt, this does not compensate completely for the attrition. This can be seen from the difference in height of the teeth above the bone in young and old animals and the much greater amount of root exposed in the older deer. The number of years required for the teeth to wear down to the roots will depend not only on the environment but also upon the chewing habits of individual animals. Some deer, for example, show practically no wear on the second premolars in their lower jaws whereas in others the teeth become well worn. At the time of writing, the oldest animals of precisely known age from Richmond Park are only eight years and these deer still have full sets of good teeth. It is probable, therefore, that they will still have functional teeth for several years to come. In Germany, Rieck has found that fallow deer even 12 to 14 years of age still have full sets of teeth although they are well worn and rather smooth. The amount of wear may not be uniform and poor occlusion can lead to excessive wear in certain areas and very little wear in other areas even in a single tooth (see App. II). This uneven wear may be caused by fibres of food or even pieces of string getting wedged between the teeth and causing abscesses which, presumably, are painful; so the deer, as we would, avoids chewing with these teeth. However, whereas we can get the infection treated, deer cannot and permanent damage to the jaw and the teeth may result.

Abnormal Dentition

Mammals may have either fewer or more teeth than usual and deer are no exception. Adult fallow deer do not usually have canine teeth in the upper jaws but about a quarter of the fawns born in Richmond Park have these teeth (Table 6). Upper canines were found more frequently in female than in male fawns but the difference was probably due to chance because of the small number of animals examined. These teeth, which are only 7 to 9 mm long and have an open root, are situated at the junction of the maxillary and premaxillary bones although the socket is lacking. The teeth evidently are lost at an early age because of 389 bucks, does and six-month fawns examined from this Park, only one animal had an upper canine tooth and this was an eighteen month old doe. At present it is not known whether this herd of deer is unusual or whether the occurrence of these teeth in newly-born fallow fawns is widespread but has been overlooked in the past. An adult fallow deer with an upper canine tooth has been recorded occasionally from other areas of England and Germany and sometimes a tooth socket was present. The presence of upper canine teeth in deer is the most frequently reported dental abnormality in species usually lacking them, but the incidence is usually lower than in fallow fawns.

Table 6. Frequency of upper canine teeth in fallow deer fawns from Richmond Park, 1970-1972

	Number	Per cent
Fawns examined	68	100
Fawns with left upper canine	4	6
Fawns with right upper canine	7	10
Fawns with both upper canines	6	9
Total with upper canine(s)	17	25

Another congenital dental abnormality in fallow deer in Richmond Park is the absence of either the third or fourth incisiform tooth, together with its socket, from one or both sides of the lower jaws. Because these two teeth are so similar, particularly when worn, it is not possible to say which tooth is missing. Nineteen per cent of bucks and does examined had missing teeth and this abnormality occurred in both the deciduous and permanent dentition (Table 7). The incidence of missing teeth in 95 newly-born fallow fawns caught from 1969 to 1973 was 16 per cent, which is very similar to that in the adult deer. However, the frequency varied widely from year to year and ranged from zero when 20 fawns were examined in 1972 to 31 per cent when 16 fawns were examined in 1970, although fawns of both sexes were equally affected. Several of these newly-born fawns have been examined again when adult and it appears that, if one or two teeth were missing at birth, then the equivalent teeth were missing from the permanent dentition. This dental abnormality has been found in fallow deer from other localities in England and Scotland but the incidence, approximately five per cent, was much lower than that in the Richmond Park fallow. Absence of some incisiform teeth appears to be a rare abnormality in deer. Other dental abnormalities, such as extra molariform teeth and teeth in the wrong position in the jaws, have been found very occasionally in fallow deer.

Table 7. Frequency of missing incisiform teeth in 202 fallow deer from Richmond Park, 1967-1973

| | MALES | | FEMALES | |
	Fawns	Adults	Fawns	Adults
Deer examined	58	64	37	43
Deer with tooth missing from each side	3	4	4	5
Deer with tooth missing from left side only	2	4	1	3
Deer with tooth missing from right side only	4	2	1	1
Total with missing teeth	9	10	9	9

A magnificent park buck. Menil variety in summer coat and velvet antlers.

CHAPTER SEVEN

Antlers

A NTLERS are sometimes incorrectly described as horns but the distinction is not just one of terminology: they differ in both structure and their mode of growth. Antlers are paired, often branched, bony protruberances and in most species of deer, including fallow, are restricted to the males. Horns are usually unbranched, permanent structures which are often carried by the females as well as the males. They are composed of a living core of bone covered by true horn, which is similar in composition to human finger nails. This covering grows from the base and, in the fully grown horn, makes good the wear which occurs at the tip. Unlike antlers, both the bony core and the horny covering of horns are retained throughout the life of the animal, except in the pronghorn antelope of America which casts its horn covering annually.

Antlers grow from permanent bony pedicles arising from the frontal bones of the skull. Whilst growing, they are covered with soft, hairy skin which has the very descriptive name of "velvet". Once growth has been completed, this skin dies and is shed, leaving the bare antler, which is simply dead bone. Later the antlers, but not the pedicles, are cast and the process is repeated with the growth of a new pair of antlers. This fascinating cycle of casting and regrowth occurs annually in fallow and most other species of deer.

The antlers of fallow deer vary greatly in size during the buck's life, ranging from small knobs or spikes in yearlings (pages 89 and 99) to large palmate structures in mature animals (page 101). Antlers are the *raison d'être* of deer hunters and consequently their trophies frequently adorn the walls of baronial halls or country cottages; fallow deer antlers with broad, gently curved palms have even been made into comfortable chairs.

Not surprisingly, a specialised and complex terminology was developed and, to some extent, is still in use at the present time although the more obscure terms have largely fallen into disuse. A sketch of a typical mature fallow deer antler is shown in Figure 5 with some of the terms still in use.

The palmate antlers of a mature buck are characteristic of fallow and, unlike the antlers of most species of deer, are much wider at the top than at the bottom. A well-developed, forward-pointing brow tine leaves the beam, just above the coronet, at an angle of about 110 degrees to the pedicle and curves upwards at its

98

Yearling buck, or "pricket", with poor first head of antlers.

tip. The beam curves outwards and backwards at about 60 degrees to the pedicle. A smaller, outward-pointing trez tine leaves the beam just below the palm. The large broad palm usually curves inwards at the top and often has many small rear-pointing projections or spellers, the lowest of which may be quite a well-developed rear tine. The total length of the antler, measured along its outer surface, may reach about 70cm, the length of the palm about 40cm and its width about 18cm. A pair of fallow deer antlers may attain a weight of about four kilograms. These are figures given in *Das Damwild* for the largest German fallow but many never grow so large. The size of the antlers varies considerably and depends upon the animal's environment, age and condition, and hereditary factors. The world record head for length, 95cm, from a Turkish animal killed near Karaboga, on the south-west side of the Sea of Marmara, was pictured in *The Field* on 13th January, 1955.

The newly grown antler, stripped of its velvet, is rough and pale but it soon becomes smoother and acquires its characteristic brown colour as its owner uses his newly acquired adornment. There is disagreement about the cause of this darkening, which has been attributed to blood and to juices from the vegetation against which the antlers are rubbed. The beam often has a ribbed appearance which may be particularly pronounced on the under surface. The valleys between the ribs, which contained blood vessels in the growing antler, become shallower and more widely spaced on the palm.

Menil fawn a few days old.

Structure

Pedicles and antlers are both formed of bone but, before the structure of these organs is discussed, it is necessary to consider the various types of bone and the ways in which they are formed.

In general, there are three kinds of bone, each of which can be formed by either of two processes, intracartilaginous ossification and intramembranous ossification. In the former process, the bones-to-be are preformed in cartilage which is then replaced by bone: this occurs, for example, in the formation of the bones of arms and legs. In the latter process, the membranous layer is replaced directly by bone without going through the cartilage stage: this happens in the bones of the skull.

The three types of bone are:

(i) Immature or woven bone, which occurs in embryos and in the repair of fractures. Most of the bone which occurs in embryonic development is replaced by mature bone.

(ii) Mature bone can be divided into two readily recognisable types, as anybody who has cut through the leg bone of a mammal will know. The two types are:

    (a) Hard, compact cortical bone such as occurs in the *shaft* of the bones of arms and legs.

    (b) Spongy or trabecular bone which occurs in the *ends* of arm and leg bones and in the bones of the skull.

A pair of antlers to be proud of.

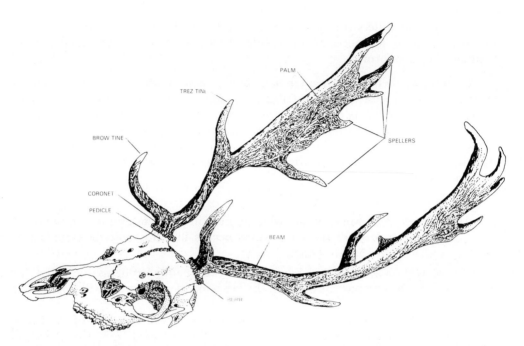

Antlers of a fallow buck.   Figure 5.

Antler pedicles are extensions of the frontal bones of the skull, both being composed of spongy bone and having a common blood supply. Macewen in *The Growth and Shedding of the Antler of the Deer* suggested that the growing pedicles of fallow were covered with cartilage which ossified from the base up. However, later studies on the antlers of other species of deer by Wislocki and his colleagues have thrown some doubt on this view. The mode of formation of the pedicle is now thought to be intermediate between the two types of ossification, but it is still undecided whether the pedicle is composed initially of immature bone. As the animal gets older the pedicle becomes thicker and shorter. This change is probably an annual event associated with antler casting and regrowth.

The structure of the antler-pedicle union varies at different stages of the antler cycle. In the fully developed, dead antler there is a very strong union to support its weight and to resist the forces of impact when the animals fight. It is not uncommon to see fallow bucks with broken antlers but it is very rare to see one with an antler broken from the pedicle.

The growing antlers are covered with velvet whereas the pedicles are covered with longer, coarser hairs similar to those on other parts of the body. The skin over the antlers differs from that covering the animal's body in that the epidermis, or outer layer, is much thicker. Hair follicles and sebaceous glands are present in the velvet of fallow deer antlers and sweat glands are also reputed to occur, but their presence requires confirmation as they are apparently absent from the velvet of other species of deer whose antlers have been studied.

Although the precise type of bone present in the growing antler and its mode of formation have been in dispute for well over a century, the problem is still not completely resolved. One school of thought considered that the antler-to-be was preformed in cartilage whereas the other view proposed its formation by intra-membranous ossification. These differences of opinion have probably arisen because the structure of the growing antler varies with the stage of development. Antlers grow from the tips so that these areas are composed of the youngest tissue and those at the base the oldest. It seems likely that the ossification of fallow deer antlers is probably intermediate between the two types mentioned above. When the growing antler has almost attained its final shape, it undergoes internal recon-struction and further calcification and its rounded, fleshy appearance changes to a firmer, more angular shape.

Half cast. 20 April.

New antlers soon begin to grow. Those of the buck on the right are the further advanced. 24 May.

In the early stages of antler growth there is an appreciable internal supply of blood to and from the antler through the pedicle. As the antler matures and the base ossifies, the importance of the internal blood vessels diminishes and the antler depends more and more on the blood vessels in the velvet. The flow of blood to the antler is probably both copious and rapid, judging from the warmth of the growing tips, although damage to the tips results in little loss of blood. It seems likely that the arteries are able to constrict instantly in response to injury, a valuable asset when bucks with large velvet-covered antlers move through dense woodland. Growing antlers are abundantly supplied with nerves which arise from the trigeminal nerve. These nerves and the blood vessels die when the antler matures and have to be renewed annually as a new antler grows. This regrowth of nerves is surprising because, in general, it is thought that cell division in the mammalian nervous system is complete before birth, so no new nerve tissue can be formed afterwards. Antlers clearly provide an exception to the rule.

Antlers have a composition similar to that of ordinary bone and are made up of salts, organic matter and water. The cast antlers of six fallow deer from Quebec Zoo were analysed by Bernard who found them to consist of eight per cent water, 48 per cent salts and 44 per cent organic matter. Calcium accounted for 18 per cent and phosphorus for nine per cent of the antlers. These values are very similar to those for skeletal bone. When antlers from seven species of deer were analysed, the lowest concentrations of salts were found in those from fallow deer. This suggests that, in these fallow at least, the degree of calcification of the antlers was less than in the other species, a view supported by the specific gravity measurements of 1.51 which were also the lowest.

Growth

Fallow deer are born without pedicles and the skulls of newly born male and female fawns are indistinguishable. Pedicles usually start to develop in winter when the fawn is about six to seven months old but at this stage the slight bumps on the head are difficult to distinguish on the living animal. They appear to be formed from the membrane (periosteum) covering the frontal bones and not from the skin covering this area. In Europe, the hairy pedicles are generally well-developed and easily visible by March, as can be seen on page 86. In precocious animals, the antler itself may be well-developed by this time of year. The pedicles continue to grow during the spring and by May-June, when the fawns are almost a year old, the

Buck 015. Brow tines start to appear. 2 June.

Buck 015. Brow and trez tines are well developed. Note the two bumps on the animal's right brow tine. 6 July.

antlers are well grown. Growth continues throughout the summer until the antler is fully formed from about the end of July to mid-August when it dies and the velvet is shed. In poorly developed fawns, both pedicle and antler growth may be delayed and in some deer parks it is not uncommon to see them with virtually no pedicle development even by their first birthday. These deer, however, still develop antlers which are cleaned of velvet at about the same time as their better endowed brethren.

The first pair of antlers of fallow deer are simple, unbranched spikes which range in length from about 1cm to about 20cm in a well-developed head, as shown on pages 89 and 99. These antlers may have a club-shaped thickening at the base which may form a very irregular pearled coronet up to about 5cm in diameter or which may continue up the antler. Pedicles and antlers require a certain period of time to complete their growth and it seems likely that poorly developed antlers may result because insufficient time is available due to late pedicle development, but this has yet to be proved. These simple, spike antlers, which have given rise to yearling bucks being called "prickets", are retained until the following summer. The antlers are cast about June when the young bucks are about two years old. Resorption of the bone occurs locally both internally and around the circumference of the pedicle and these areas expand rapidly until they merge. When the antler is cast, the bare surface of the pedicle bleeds but skin from around the pedicle soon grows over and heals the wound. A scab forms and, between this and the bony pedicle, a layer of tissue forms which is the first stage in the growth of the new antlers. It appears to be the dermal layer of the skin which gives rise to the new antler. On the whole, adult mammals cannot regenerate normal skin in areas where the entire thickness has been destroyed. Healing of such wounds results in the formation of scar tissue that is covered by epithelium migrating from the margins of the wound. The original skin from the wound margins is drawn inwards and so the size of the scar is reduced. It has been suggested by Lojda that antler velvet originates in this way but Billingham and his colleagues have made an alternative suggestion that the velvet arises anew from cellular elements in the pedicle. If this second view proves to be correct, then the growth of antlers will provide a good example that, exceptionally, regeneration of hair and skin can take place in adult mammals.

There appears to be little precise information on the duration of each phase of the antler cycle in fallow deer and how this is affected by age and environmental conditions. In Richmond Park, adult fallow bucks cast their antlers in late April and May and the velvet is usually shed at the end of August, so growth lasts for three to four months. Most older animals cast before the younger ones although they all shed the velvet from their antlers at about the same time.

The average time taken for antlers to grow can be calculated from the date of casting of one head and the date of velvet shedding for the next head because, in

Buck 015. Still growing! Note the flies where the antler has rubbed. 21 July.

Buck 015. Growth completed, antlers clean. The two bumps on the right brow tine are still present. 31 August.

fallow deer, the new antlers start to grow immediately the old ones are cast. For example, the first head of antlers is cast about 6th June and the second head of antlers is free of velvet about 28th August, so the period of growth of the second head is approximately 12 to 13 weeks. The time taken for the first head of antlers to grow is unknown because, in the field, it is impossible to decide when pedicle growth ceases and antler growth commences. Typical average dates recorded by John Fawcett for the fallow deer in Richmond Park are given in Table 8.

Table 8. Periods of antler growth for fallow deer in Richmond Park

	Growth started (Casting of previous head of antlers)	Velvet shed	Growing period (weeks)
1st head	—	31st August	—
2nd head	6th June	28th August	12-13
3rd head	21st May	27th August	c.14
4th head	10th May	26th August	15-16
Later heads	1st May	26th August	16-17

In Richmond Park, fallow, unlike red deer, are not usually attracted by water.

Bucks in other parts of southern England may cast their antlers at the end of March but this is probably unusually early. Shedding of the velvet commonly occurs at the end of August in other deer parks also. These periods of antler growth are about the same as those recorded by Gilbert in 1964 for captive fallow deer in the United States. The twelfth Duke of Bedford recalls that in Woburn Park in Bedfordshire the first fallow deer to lose the velvet from their antlers are the forward yearlings. Removal of the velvet then proceeds in order of youth and not of seniority; adult bucks with particularly fine antlers usually are the last to shed their velvet, with the exception of the backward yearlings. A similar order apparently occurs in fallow deer in Germany where the yearlings' antlers may be clean by late July. This order is the reverse of that which occurs in Richmond Park. Observations over 20 years on antler growth in a small herd of captive fallow deer in New Zealand have been recorded by Riney. Most of the bucks started to shed the velvet from their antlers between 15th and 28th February. The period over which bucks cleaned velvet from their antlers in any one year varied from nine to 32 days; the earliest and latest dates recorded were 23rd January and 4th March although the former date appears to be exceptional. On most occasions only 24 hours were required for the velvet to be lost, only small pieces near the base of the antler remaining after this time. The bucks cast their antlers between 11th October and 20th November although in most cases the antlers had been lost by early November. The time between antler-casting of the first and last bucks in any one year was

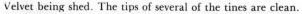

Velvet being shed. The tips of several of the tines are clean.

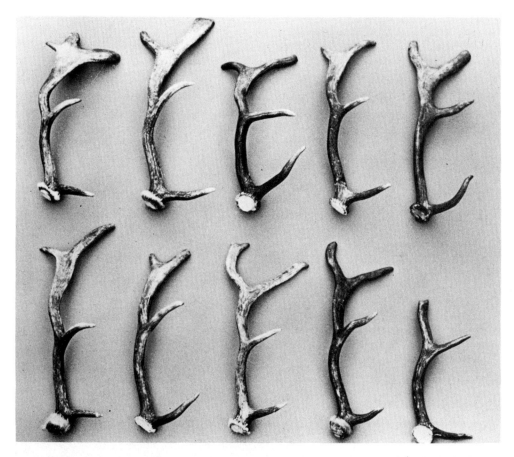

Right antlers of 10 bucks showing variations in the second head of deer born in 1971 in Richmond Park. *Dr D. Chapman.*

reputed to range from zero to 29 days; the number in the herd when they all cast their antlers on the same day is n ot given. About two-thirds of the animals cast both their antlers on the same days although in some cases the second antler was not cast until four days later. The older bucks usually cast their antlers two to three weeks earlier than the younger ones. These observations show how fallow deer adapt their antler cycle when moved across the equator, the deer in both England and New Zealand casting their antlers in the spring as the days lengthen and shedding the velvet in the autumn when daylight is decreasing.

Antler growth is slowest at the beginning and end of the process. The rate of growth of the antlers of a mature buck shown in Figure 6 was measured by Goss

Menil fawn a few days old.

who found that the maximum rate was almost 7mm a day and even the average was about 5mm a day. Growth was most rapid about four weeks after the old antlers had been cast and when the brow tine and the beam had started to differentiate. In southern England, up to three weeks elapse between the casting of the old antlers and loss of the scabs on the new antlers. At this time the brow tine and main beam have started to separate and by about six weeks, growth of the brow tine is almost complete. After eight weeks the trez tine has been formed and the full length of the antler has been attained after about 14 weeks. During the following two weeks, final hardening and calcification occurs prior to the velvet being shed.

The majority of the second heads of fallow antlers from Richmond Park have rounded, porous, soft tips at the top although the brow and trez tines are hard and polished. The proportion of third heads of antlers with porous tips is less and they

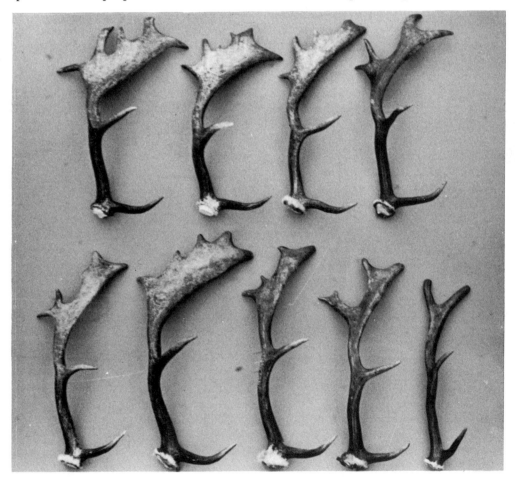

Right antlers of 9 bucks showing variations in the third head of deer born in 1970 in Richmond Park.
Dr D. Chapman.

occur only occasionally in subsequent heads. The period of antler growth increases, on average, from about 12 to 13 weeks for second heads to about 14 weeks for third heads and to about 15 to 17 weeks for older heads. It appears that calcification is not completed in the younger animals before the antler loses its velvet. In contrast, the second heads of antlers of red deer from the same park are hard, pointed and polished but then they take an average of 14 to 15 weeks to grow. Antlers from young fallow deer from other localities in England have also been found to have some porous tips. In addition, it is not uncommon to see a buck with a broken antler beam or tine whereas it is rare to see a red deer stag with a broken antler in the Park.

Just as the first pair of antlers varies widely in size among individuals, so do the second and subsequent pairs. The second head of antlers may or may not be palmated, as shown on pages 19 and 111. The same type of variation occurs in wild deer in England and in other countries, although in *Das Damwild* it is claimed that it is rare for the second head of German fallow antlers not to display a distinct palmation. In general, a buck's antlers become larger and more palmated with increasing age until he reaches his prime. Once he is past his prime it is reputed that his antlers start to deteriorate or "go back". However, most bucks never attain their prime, let alone pass it, and, because it is difficult to estimate accurately the age of a living buck, it is virtually impossible to define this prime age unless the animal has been marked since birth. A buck with exceptionally well-developed antlers is usually referred to as being in his prime, whatever his age. In parts of Germany, the game control authorities consider that a fallow buck's antlers generally reach their maximum development with the eighth or ninth head. It is admitted that there are bucks which develop more quickly, reaching their maximum antler development with their sixth head. The variation with age of antler size and weight of a large number of fallow from the game research areas of Nedlitz and Serrahn in East Germany has been studied recently by Mehlitz and Siefke. The maximum *average* antler size and weight occurred at nine to ten years of age but thereafter, apart from the length of the beam, size and weight decreased. The pedicle reached a maximum diameter at about nine to ten years and maintained this size thereafter. Antler weight varied from 1.6 per cent of the clean body weight for two year old bucks to 4.3 per cent for nine to ten year old animals.

Many guesses have been made about antler development by people who thought they could tell the age of a buck. Unfortunately, as a result, a number of stylised sketches of fallow deer antlers at specified ages have been published. Some such sketches were clearly not based on deer of known ages, because the antlers develop earlier with successive editions of the book! Although the caveat is added that variation of antlers can be very extensive, these sketches give a very misleading impression and still lead people to estimate the age of bucks from the shape and size of their antlers. For this reason no such sketches are reproduced in this book;

instead a series of photographs of the antlers of deer of known age, having been marked at birth, are reproduced to try to show the great variation that can and does occur even in one park (pages 111 and 113). Antler development in fallow deer in this park is very variable, even among deer born in the same year and subjected to more or less the same environmental conditions. Hereditary factors and social stress, such as the loss of the dam, may be important, although as yet unknown, factors in antler development.

Antlers and Hormones

Let us now consider some of the physiological changes that cause a buck's antlers to be cast and regrown annually. That a relationship exists between a deer's antlers and his reproductive organs has been known for over 2,000 years since the Greek philosopher, Aristotle, wrote:

"If stags are castrated before they are old enough to have horns, these never appear; but if castrated after they have horns, their size never varies, nor are they subject to their annual change".

Subsequent investigations have amply confirmed this relationship in fallow deer. Castration of fallow soon after birth prevents both pedicle and antler development. This suggests that pedicle development is initiated by the male hormones, or androgens, and in red deer there is certainly an increase in hormone secretion at the time of pedicle development. The hormone level then declines rapidly before antler growth commences but increases again in time for the rut. It seems more than likely that initiation of pedicle growth in fallow deer is controlled in a similar way. In 1955, Rehn postulated that both pedicle and antler growth were controlled by nerve centres and this idea has been developed by Bubenik and his colleagues, from their experiments on fallow and other species of deer, into their theory of "Centres of Antler Growth" ("Zentren der Geweihtrophik" or ZGT). They have suggested that each pedicle, with the corresponding frontal bone, has its own independent centre located in the central nervous system and that the centres are activated initially by the male hormones before puberty. However, exactly what factor stimulates pedicle development is unknown. Experiments have been carried out by Pavlansky and Bubenik on fallow bucks and on other species of deer to try to define precisely from which tissues the antlers develop and from what areas they are capable of developing. It appears that, if an antler has never grown, removal of the pedicle prevents future antler development whereas if an antler has once grown, removal of the pedicle does not necessarily prevent subsequent antler growth. Although the pedicles seem to originate from the membrane covering the frontal bones, the antlers appear to originate from the dermal portion of the skin of the pedicles. However, the results are difficult to interpret because the degree of surgical interference affects subsequent growth of the antlers, even the one that has not been operated upon. Furthermore it is difficult to be sure that all the tissue that it was intended to remove, or to transplant, was in fact taken.

Fallow cast their antlers and start growing new ones in the spring and early summer when spermatogenesis has virtually ceased and the deer's organs are sexually quiescent. Unfortunately, levels of male hormones have not been measured in fallow deer but histological changes in the testes suggest that the levels are at their lowest in the spring. Re-activation of the reproductive organs occurs in late summer when spermatogenesis recommences, hormone levels start to rise and antler growth nears completion. Final ossification of the antler and shedding of the velvet depend on an adequate level of hormone; without this these changes do not occur. This dependence of fallow antlers on male hormones has been confirmed by an interesting series of experiments by Zawadowsky at the Zoopak of Moscow in the early 1920s and by Jaczewski in Poland: their observations can be summarised as follows. If fallow fawns are castrated soon after birth, then neither pedicles nor antlers grow. If a fallow deer has already grown antlers, the effect of castration will depend on the time of year when the operation is performed. If the buck is castrated when it has hard antlers these will be cast prematurely, usually within a week or so, and a new pair will start to develop immediately. These new antlers will continue to grow but tines and palmation will probably be lacking, ossification will not be completed and the velvet will not be shed. Furthermore, the antlers will be retained and not cast. Castration of a buck with antlers in velvet will prevent them from completing their growth and from being cast. Fallow deer which retain their antlers in velvet as a result of either castration or damage to the reproductive organs are said to have perruque heads, like that depicted on page 120. Perruque heads do not seem to occur naturally in fallow deer nearly as frequently as they do in other species; the roe buck appears to be particularly prone to this abnormality.

Early experiments on the unilateral castration of fallow deer were reported to affect the growth of antlers on the opposite side. However, surgical shock rather than castration itself appears to be the more likely cause, particularly when it is remembered that these operations were performed many years ago before the advent of modern anaesthetics. More recent experiments by Zawadowsky and Jaczewski have shown that unilateral castration does not affect the antlers. Occasionally bucks are found with only one testis in the scrotum, the other either being in the abdominal cavity or reputed to be missing. The animal is known as a unilateral cryptorchid or, in the words of the horse-dealer, a rig. These animals are, in effect, unilaterally castrated and the antlers of one such buck, killed in a road accident in Richmond Park, are shown on page 120; it can be seen that the antlers are perfectly normal. Other unilaterally cryptorchid bucks may not have such uniform antlers but that does not prove a cause and effect relationship.

Almost nothing is known about the effect of other hormones on antler growth in fallow deer. Antler casting was reported to be delayed in bucks which had been given injections of human chorionic gonadotrophin, a hormone produced by pregnant women and which affects the ovaries. Injections of thyroxin, a hormone from the thyroid gland, have been claimed to produce enhanced antler growth in yearling fallow bucks.

Size and Shape

The size and shape of adult fallow antlers vary enormously, even from the same locality. The differences in antler shape and size have led hunters to devise a scheme for measuring and assessing them, so that points can be awarded in competitions held for the "best" antlers. An international formula was agreed in 1937 under the auspices of the Conseil International de la Chasse and details are given by Nüsslein. This formula is based partly on measurements and partly on subjective impressions of appearance. Points can be added for colour, number of spellers and uniformity of shape, and deducted for "faulty" shape if the antler does not match up to the "ideal". The formula is useful in providing a uniform method of measuring antlers but, for biological purposes, the points system is best ignored. A hunter's idea of "faulty" may be different from the biologist's and such antlers may not be detrimental to the deer. One of the limitations of comparing antlers is that animals of different ages are being compared and, unless deer are allowed to mature, large much-palmated antlers will not be obtained. Nevertheless, some generalisations are justified and the antlers of fallow deer from some parts of Denmark, Germany and Hungary consistently grow bigger than those of wild deer in Britain. The sizes of some "trophy" antlers from various countries are given in Table 9. These antlers were measured at the international hunting exhibition at Budapest in 1971 and so the figures are comparable. Unfortunately, no British fallow deer antlers appear to have been measured. The weights given are for both antlers and include part of the frontal bones. The best "trophy" antlers from many European countries are described and beautifully illustrated by Sartorius in *Stärkste Damschaufler der Welt*.

Table 9. Average sizes of fallow deer antlers exhibited at Budapest in 1971

	Czechoslovakia	German Democratic Republic	German Federal Republic	Hungary	Spain
Number of animals	6	19	10	44	8
Length of antlers, cm	69.6	68.7	68.5	72.7	71.0
Length of palms, cm	42.6	40.3	40.9	44.2	44.9
Breadth of palms, cm	16.6	17.0	16.0	18.6	17.2
Length of brow tines, cm	20.4	18.9	20.0	22.6	19.1
Weight of antlers, kg	3.37	3.06	3.27	3.74	2.91

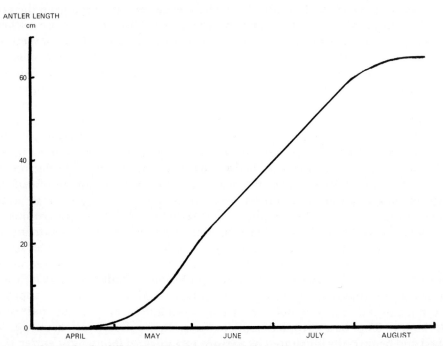

The rate of growth of a fallow deer's antler (adapted from Goss).　　　　　　Figure 6.

However, what is really wanted is not the sizes of a few "trophy" antlers but the sizes of large numbers of representative antlers from different countries and various localities within those countries. A start has been made by Mehlitz and Siefke who have published average dimensions for the antlers from large numbers of bucks of different ages from Nedlitz and Serrahn. Unfortunately, the range of sizes for any given age has not been included. The dimensions of the antlers of 14 adult bucks which were killed in accidents in Epping Forest are given in Table 10. The animals have been split into three groups depending on the amount of wear shown by the molariform teeth. Group A had only slightly worn teeth, group B had well-worn teeth and group C had very well-worn teeth. The ages of the deer are unknown but had they been Richmond Park bucks, these groups would have corresponded approximately to three to four years, four to seven years and over seven years respectively. The sizes of some British park and wild fallow deer antlers have been given by Whitehead in *The Deer of Great Britain and Ireland.*

Table 10. Sizes of antlers and pedicles of adult fallow bucks killed in accidents in Epping Forest, 1963-1967

	Group		
	A	B	C
Number of animals	4	6	4
Length of antlers, cm	36 (22-50)	45 (36-59)	55 (47-60)
Length of palms, cm	16 (8-30)	19 (7-31)	28 (20-34)
Breadth of palms, cm	5 (3-9)	6 (3-11)	8 (5-12)
Length of brow tines, cm	10 (6-14)	13 (10-17)	13 (9-18)
Inside span (max.), cm	46 (45-48)	46 (38-59)	59 (57-62)
Circumference of beams, cm	7.6 (6.3-8.4)	8.1 (7.0-9.8)	9.6 (8.0-10.0)
Diameter of coronets, cm	4.3 (3.7-4.7)	4.6 (3.5-5.3)	5.3 (4.8-5.6)
Diameter of pedicles, cm	2.8 (2.4-3.2)	3.0 (2.4-3.4)	3.5 (3.0-3.8)

The shape of the palm may be basically rectangular or triangular, with or without large indentations, and some of the many shapes that occur are depicted by Hansen, Bülow and Lotze in *Das Ansprechen des Damschauflers.* Sometimes a certain shape is claimed to be associated with one locality, but much more information, especially in relation to age, is required before definite assertions of this kind can be accepted.

Abnormal variations in antler size and shape occur but the causes of these are rarely known. Cadman claims that lungworm and particularly liverfluke cause antler deformities but, as Dunn has pointed out, a careful distinction must be made between the presence of parasites and the presence of disease or abnormality due to that infection. It is very easy to blame the parasites simply because they happened to be present in the animal. Injuries to the pedicles and the growing antlers cause abnormal development, as shown by the experimental work of Pavlansky and Bubenik.

Normal antlers although from a uni-laterally cryptorchid buck; the right testis was abdominal. Two tines of the left antler were broken in an accident.

A perruque fallow buck shot by Mr L. Preston in October 1970 near Roberts-bridge in Sussex.

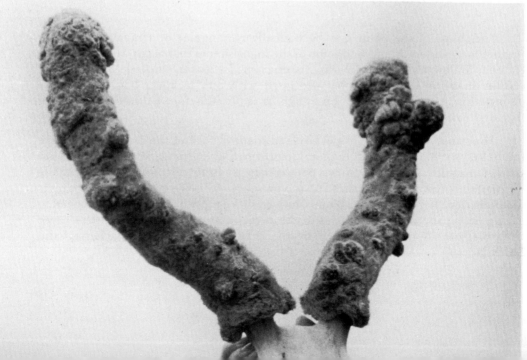

Adult male deer which do not grow antlers are called hummels. This condition, although not uncommon in red deer, appears to be very rare in fallow deer and the only recent record we have been able to find is that of a buck shot by Ratky at Bramfield in Hampshire in October 1968. This animal had flat-topped pedicles without any trace of antler growth and its age was estimated at six to seven years.

In Germany, the most common antler malformation in fallow is reputed to be the so-called "double-head". It occurs when a yearling fails to cast his spike antlers and the second head of antlers grows beside them. This leads to the strange sight of a buck with velvet antlers and hard, clean antlers, both at the same time. The first head of antlers is usually cast with the second but the condition is apparently rarely found in deer over three years old. We have never encountered this condition in British bucks. It has been suggested that the first head of antlers is not cast because of the "lack of leverage" due to their small weight. This explanation seems unlikely. Why should fallow yearlings cast their antlers in Britain, yet apparently not infrequently fail to cast them in Germany? The proportion of fallow yearlings failing to cast their antlers, however, and their distribution throughout Germany do not appear to have been reported.

Function

Many views have been expressed as to the function of antlers but very few quantitative observations have been made on the use to which they are put by fallow deer. Consequently the following comment has to be speculative. The antlers of fallow deer develop at puberty as a secondary sexual characteristic and are cast and regrown annually in time for the rut. This suggests that one of their main roles is related to sexual behaviour and the antlers of fallow deer are certainly used frequently at rutting time in fighting, thrashing vegetation, scoring trees and preparing scrapes in the ground. However, fallow deer carry their antlers for about five to six months after the main period of the rut, which suggests that antlers also have functions not related directly to sexual behaviour.

Traditionally, antlers are regarded as weapons, used by bucks in the rutting season to defend their harems, but this is only part of the story. Fighting between bucks, with the infliction of severe or even fatal injuries, as well as shoving matches, occur in fallow deer. On one such occasion during the rut we heard, in the still of the night, tremendous clashings of antlers. Driving across the field towards the sound, we suddenly saw in the car's headlights two large bucks violently fighting, while a smaller buck looked on. So engrossed were the animals that they took no notice when we approached within about 15 metres. Suddenly one of the bucks decided that he had had enough, turned and walked away, limping badly. The intensity of the fighting can be judged by the fact that the clashing of antlers against antlers had been heard over 400 metres away.

It is not unusual to see yearlings and fallow bucks with non-palmate antlers standing around or even amongst the does accompanying large rutting buck, the large buck, as page 134 shows, making no attempt to chase away or fight these lesser deer. Large antlers, therefore, probably also have a visual role and function as status symbols, determining the social hierarchy or peck order of the bucks without actual conflict, a suggestion first proposed, for red deer, by Beninde in 1937. Antlers are not the only means of displaying threatening behaviour in the rut; the buck's swollen neck, strong odour and groaning may also have a similar function.

A buck's antlers have other functions in relation to sexual behaviour in addition to their roles as weapons and status symbols. A rutting fallow buck has a very pungent odour, partly because he uses his antlers to transfer mud from the ground on which he has urinated, to his body and vegetation. The antlers may also be used to transfer urine directly to his body. Before and during the rut, bucks fray and thrash the vegetation and also rub their antlers against the boles of trees. These activities are discussed more fully in the context of rutting behaviour. It has been suggested that, in other species of deer, the thrashing of vegetation may be practice for real fights. Bubenik has proposed that it may also enable the buck to get the measure of his new antlers, to make sure that he is familiar with their spatial arrangement.

Even less is known about the function of fallow deer antlers outside the rutting season than within it. Bruhin has suggested that the antlers continue to act as status symbols and dictate the social hierarchy in the bachelor groups, loss of antlers resulting in a fall in the animal's position in the hierarchy; the higher ranking animals have priority for food and shelter. In many parks in winter, the deer are fed corn and beans. If a large antlered buck and a yearling put their heads down for the same pile of food, it is the yearling that jumps away. Shoving matches between bucks certainly take place outside the rutting season and these are probably means of establishing dominance. Geist has suggested that in deer such hierarchies allow individual males to live in a predictable social environment, as each can anticipate specific actions from dominant and subdominant animals.

To summarise the functions of antlers, perhaps we can tentatively conclude that, as the dimensions of antlers generally increase with the animal's size and age, fallow bucks learn to associate antler size with agonistic potential, particularly in the rut. Outside the rutting period, the adult bucks usually live in bachelor groups in which a stable hierarchy is probably developed, at least as long as they carry their hard antlers.

CHAPTER EIGHT

The Rut and Male Reproduction

FALLOW bucks are seasonally breeding animals although the breeding season is much longer than is implied by the short duration of the rut. It is necessary to distinguish between the rut and the breeding season. The latter can be defined as the period of the year during which the bucks are fertile and copulate, whereas the rut is a more restricted period of the breeding season when the bucks show especially intense sexual behaviour which has been described by Lincoln as a kind of sexual extravaganza. The great majority of conceptions usually occur during the rut although some may be delayed until later in the breeding season. A short period of rutting behaviour is characteristic of many species of deer. Before describing this behaviour for fallow let us consider the physiological changes that cause bucks to rut. A fallow buck's appearance, antlers and behaviour are influenced profoundly by the condition of his reproductive organs. Consequently a knowledge of the function of these and their seasonal changes helps us to understand these aspects of fallow deer biology better.

Reproductive Organs

The organs consist of a pair of testes and a pair of epididymides in a pendulous scrotum. A narrow canal known as the vas deferens connects each to the rest of the reproductive tract which includes the accessory glands: the ampulla, urethra, prostate and seminal vesicles, all lying within the pelvis. The penis is enclosed in a sheath which is united to the wall of the abdomen for most of its length and opens behind the umbilicus, a tuft or brush of long hairs marking the position.

A detailed description of the reproductive organs of the buck was first provided by Weiss and by Hinz about 45 years ago but these writers did not describe the conspicuous seasonal changes which occur in the organs.

Each testis consists of two main components, the seminiferous tubules, which produce spermatozoa, and the interstitial tissue lying between the tubules, which produces the male hormones or androgens, of which the principal one in mammals is testosterone. It is these hormones which have a stimulating effect on spermatogenesis and on the accessory glands, affect the animal's odour and rutting behaviour and play such an important part in regulating the antler cycle. Both parts of the testis are under the control of the anterior pituitary gland which is

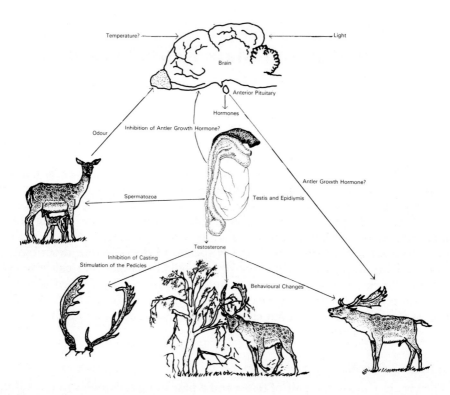

Temperature? ⟶   ⟵ Light

Brain

Anterior Pituitary

Hormones

Odour

Inhibition of Antler Growth Hormone?

Antler Growth Hormone?

Spermatozoa   Testis and Epidiymis

Testosterone

Inhibition of Casting
Stimulation of the Pedicles

Behavioural Changes

The buck's reproductive organs are controlled by external factors and affect his antlers, appearance and behaviour.   Figure 7.

situated at the base of the brain. In mammals, the secretion of hormones by the anterior pituitary gland is controlled by the hypothalamus, a part of the brain which is itself influenced by external factors such as light, temperature and odour. Light certainly influences the reproductive cycle and associated behaviour of fallow bucks, as is shown by their rutting six months out of phase when transferred from the northern to the southern hemisphere. The function and control of the buck's reproductive organs is shown schematically in Figure 7.

The role of the epididymis, which is closely attached to the testis, is to act both as a storage organ for the spermatozoa and as a place in which they complete their maturation. The function of the accessory glands is to produce various secretions comprising the seminal plasma which, together with spermatozoa, forms semen. Although the growth, development and annual cycle of the testes and epididymides of fallow deer have been studied, little is known of the changes that occur in the accessory glands.

Puberty

The reproductive organs of newly born fallow buck fawns are small and sexually inactive. The testes and epididymides remain inactive until about seven months of age when there is a gradual increase in their weight and the first stages of spermatogenesis occur. The antler pedicles also start to develop at about this age. Lincoln has shown that in red deer stags these changes are related to increased levels of testosterone and the same is probably true for fallow bucks although hormone levels have not been measured. By the time the fawns are about one year old, there has been a large increase in the weights of the testes and epididymides and, in yearlings, both organs are about ten times as heavy as those of young fawns; spermatozoa are now present. The organs attain their maximum weight in the cycle just before the rut in October and November but, as Figure 8 shows, the weights

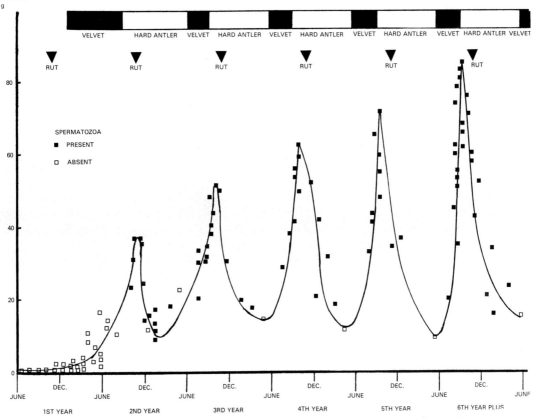

The annual reproductive cycle of fallow bucks. The weight of the testes reach a maximum about the time of the rut, then decline to a minimum in the spring when the antlers are cast.   Figure 8.

gradually decrease during the winter although the organs do not return to their size at birth. Spermatogenesis gradually declines and the young buck becomes sexually quiescent in the late spring and early summer, when his spike antlers are cast and new ones start to grow. These changes in spermatogenesis are paralleled by changes in the size of the seminiferous tubules of the testes, so measurement of tubule diameter affords a good quantitative indication of sexual function.

Puberty in bucks is probably best defined as the period between the commencement of male hormone production and the formation of spermatozoa by the testes, rather than as one point in time. Thus puberty in fallow bucks occurs from about seven months, when pedicle growth usually commences, to about 14 months when spermatozoa first appear in the testes. A distinction should be drawn, perhaps, between puberty and maturity of sexual behaviour, the latter being defined as the time when the animal plays an effective role in reproduction within the herd. Whereas most yearling does become pregnant at about 16 months of age, showing that they reached maturity at the time of their second breeding season, it seems likely that male fallow reach maturity later in life as they do not rut fully as yearlings. A captive fallow doe has been mated successfully by a yearling male, the only buck present, and in due course gave birth to a fawn. Although such youngsters are fertile and capable of breeding, the social hierarchy among bucks probably prevents many matings by them. Lincoln has shown that whereas red deer stags on the Isle of Rhum in Scotland reach puberty between nine and 15 months of age, they are not behaviourally mature until at least seven years old.

Annual Cycle

In the adult full spermatogenesis recommences in the summer and the activity of the testes reaches a peak by the autumn. At this time the bucks show full rutting behaviour. Following the rut the sexual functions gradually decline through the winter until by late spring the bucks become infertile. During the sexually quiescent period, the antlers are growing rapidly and so small amounts of testosterone are probably still being secreted by the testes because antlers do not develop normally in castrated bucks. In effect, fallow bucks undergo a kind of annual puberty similar to the initial puberty undergone by yearlings. The changes in the sizes of the testes are shown in relation to antler growth and the rut in Figure 8 which depicts their annual nature. These changes in size of the organs have two components. There is the cyclical change in the weight of the testis itself which is accentuated by changes in the body weight of the animal; the heavier the buck, the heavier its testes. We have seen already that there is a cyclical change in the weight of bucks and that also they generally increase in weight with increasing age. Although the size of the testes still rises in the autumn and falls in winter and spring, the peak weight of the testes at the time of the rut is fairly constant in relation to the body weight of animals in their third year and later. There is a wide variation in the weights of bucks of the same age and hence of their reproductive organs. Furthermore, not all animals will be at the same stage of rutting at the same time. There is also an appreciable spread in the weights of the testes of fawns approaching a year old, reflecting the wide variation in the age at which the onset of puberty occurs. The development of pedicles and antlers also varies greatly in animals of this age group.

Fallow bucks appear to be in breeding condition from September to February or March in the northern hemisphere, a period of about six months. The occasional birth of fallow fawns in late autumn suggests that bucks actually mate and are fertile as late as February or March. This demonstrates that the spermatozoa in the testes and epididymides towards the end of the breeding season are viable and able to achieve normal fertilization. The reproductive physiology of fallow deer in the Blue Mountains of New Zealand has been studied by Baker. He found that the occurrence of puberty, the initiation of pedicle and antler growth, and the buck's reproductive cycle were the same as for bucks in England except that they were six months out of phase. In both South America and New Zealand, the peak of rutting activity occurs in the latter half of April.

Besides the antlers, other secondary sexual characteristics develop in time for the rut, namely the voice, a strong rutting-odour, a large increase in the girth of the neck and eversion and staining of the end of the penis sheath. These characteristics are associated with the rut rather than the entire breeding season. In the rut, the bucks develop a deep belching groan which, once heard, is unlikely to be mistaken. Groaning may start in September but in southern England usually it is heard in October and early November and occasionally into the New Year. The end of the penis sheath everts at this time of year and becomes a rough black swelling with a pungent odour; the hairs surrounding the sheath also become darkly stained, as page 81 shows. The buck also develops a pungent odour, reminiscent of a rutting billy goat. Fawns do not develop these conspicuous features associated with rutting. They first become apparent in yearling bucks, although less so than in mature animals.

In several deer parks, some of the males were castrated, often as fawns, so that they were incapable of rutting. These animals, known as haviers, were used to provide a supply of venison between the fat buck season and the time when the does were considered fit for eating. This practice appears to have died out although three haviers were present in Houghton Park in Norfolk as late as 1961.

The Rut

The rut is the climax of events in the buck's year. Preparations start when they begin to migrate to the areas occupied by the does, which in England occurs in late August and September. At South Weald, young bucks just over two years old with clean antlers have been seen on the estate from the last week of August but the

During the rut, bucks may be dangerous.

earliest that mature bucks have been seen is the last few days of September. This suggests that the younger animals may have the rutting urge before the older ones. Alternatively, the mature bucks may get the urge at the same time, but remain in their summer ranges until the urge to rut overcomes their caution; perhaps a case of fools rush in where angels fear to tread! Bucks exhibit territorial behaviour at rutting time and defend territories or rutting "stands". One of the characteristics of the rut is that mature bucks, normally so secretive and wary, become bold and lose much of their fear of man (see above). One morning in late October, after having watched a fight between two bucks, we had just climbed down from a high seat and were talking at the bottom of the ladder when a mature buck came trotting down the field and passed quite unperturbed only 20 metres from us, before entering the adjacent wood. On another occasion, we were examining the area where a buck had been rutting, when we heard movement through the vegetation. On looking up, we saw a buck crossing a ride and entering the wood; it eventually walked past only ten metres away.

Many rutting areas are traditional in the sense that bucks, although not necessarily the same animals, return to them each year. Clues announcing the presence of bucks are scrapes in the ground and thrashed and frayed bushes and trees. Scrapes are made in the soil by the buck pawing the ground with his fore feet and scraping with his antlers. They may be made in a wood, in a ride between two blocks of woodland or in fields. If made in fields, they usually appear to be alongside a hedge or an adjacent wood rather than in the middle. Scrapes may be as small as 30cm in diameter or as much as ten times that area. Their size depends partly upon the nature of the surface and hardness of the ground; those in damp situations are often larger and deeper than those on dry, hard soil. The bucks sometimes adds his pungent-smelling urine to the scrape which then acquires the characteristic "rutty buck" odour. Some of the soil from these scrapes may be transferred to his body by his antlers. The tassel of hairs on the penis sheath may facilitate the dispersal of urine. He may also urinate upon himself or his antlers by turning and lowering his head towards his hind quarters. Unlike red deer and wapiti, fallow do not appear to wallow in their scrapes.

Fallow bucks indulge in two distinct types of behaviour, each of which causes a characteristic type of damage to trees and shrubs, namely fraying and thrashing. These activities make deer unpopular with the forester, particularly when many trees in a plantation may be attacked. Unfortunately, a clear distinction is not always made between these two types of behaviour. Although many people must have been enthralled by a performance of bucks thrashing or fraying, we have been unable to find any precise descriptions of the animal's activities. In fact, it was not until writing this book that we realised that we were as remiss as others! Thrashing of bushes and saplings (page 130) results from the buck's attacking them repeatedly with his antlers, whole branches often being completely broken off and scattered about. Young elder bushes and willow trees are popular targets but the lower

A scrape in soil adjacent to frayed hornbeam saplings.

Making a scrape.

Th·ashed elder bush.

branches of other trees such as hawthorn or hornbeam may also be attacked. A rutting buck sometimes puts his head amongst the beaten foliage and, according to Cadman, then deposits scent from his suborbital glands. Fraying is caused by the buck rubbing his antlers on saplings; hawthorn, birch, hornbeam, ash, willow and conifers are all chosen. The fraying, which removes the bark and exposes the wood, often on one side of the tree only, may extend for just a few centimetres but often reaches 50 to 100cm or more up the trunk (page 132). Gilbert, who studied certain aspects of the social behaviour of fallow in a 22 hectare enclosure at the Duke University Field Station for Animal Behaviour Studies in North Carolina, noted that, associated with fraying, stereotyped movements of the head were made in which the suborbital gland was drawn against the trees. Mature trees may be seen to beat scars from attacks in previous years when they were saplings. Larger trees are not necessarily safe from attack as they too may be frayed or scored by the tines of the antlers, quite a deep groove sometimes being made. Occasionally other trees are used as anointing posts: the bark is worn and the trunk appears stained and oily, and smells more strongly than the frayed trees. The odour is very similar to that emanating from the buck's suborbital glands and is quite distinct from the "rutty buck" odour of the scrapes. A buck anoints by rubbing his head on the trunk of the tree and depositing scent from his suborbital glands.

Often fraying is first noticed at the time bucks shed the velvet from their antlers which, in England, is about the end of August. At South Weald the earliest date on which we have found fraying and thrashing has been 27th August; a young buck, with hard antlers, had been seen for the first time the previous day. All bucks, apart from yearlings, have always had hard, clean antlers when seen on the estate, so here fraying is not associated with the shedding of velvet. Once fraying and thrashing have started, they occur with increasing frequency, reaching a peak at the time of the rut, in the second half of October. Schloeth has observed that red deer in the Swiss National Park fray and thrash trees from the time the velvet is shed to the time the antlers are cast, the highest incidence occurring at the time of the rut. Fallow deer also carry out these same activities to a limited extent after the rut and we have seen fallow bucks thrashing bushes as late as the middle of April. Figure 9 shows the incidence of these activities in a three hectare block of woodland at South Weald in mid-October: 28 scrapes, 96 frayed saplings and 38 thrashed bushes were found. There was no obvious correlation between the distribution of these signs and where the bucks rutted. It must be remembered, though, that this type of activity may be carried out over a month or two and a false impression may be gained by considering the damage as if it had occurred at one time. Ideally, one would like to know how the incidence and distribution of these activities change during the period leading up to, during, and after the rut. Unfortunately, attempts to measure and record these activities would certainly affect the behaviour of the bucks and consequently invalidate the results obtained.

Frayed trunk of elder tree. Bark has
been removed by a buck during the
rut. Adjacent trunk has been scored
by antlers.   *Dr D. Chapman.*

The incidence of frayings, scrapes and
thrashings in three hectares of woodland at South Weald in which at least
two bucks were rutting.   Figure 9.

Cadman believes that bucks begin to mark out their territories by thrashing trees and bushes which are situated approximately around the perimeter of the rutting "stand" they intend to occupy, which at that time may extend to several hectares. He considers that by mid-October each "master" buck will have decided on his rutting "stand" which is confined to an area about 65 metres by 35 metres or about one fifth of a hectare. If this is what happens and the bucks delineate a smaller and smaller territory as the rut approaches, it could explain the distribution of scrapes and damaged trees in the area. On the other hand, our impression is that even very fresh signs of activity are widely spread. It is not only the territorial bucks that thrash and fray but the younger ones do it as well, perhaps either relieving their frustration at not being allowed to rut or just trying their luck. Courtier has informed us that if one can enter a rutting territory unobserved and thrash a bush, the rutting buck may, if suitably impressed, run in at high speed to investigate the noise: an experiment not to be undertaken lightly. If the thrashing is solely territorial it remains to be explained why this habit occurs long after the rut is over. More bucks may be seen in an area nearer the peak of the rut, perhaps causing each animal to reduce the size of his territory.

Large, mature bucks are not seen at South Weald much before the end of September. During the next two or three weeks they establish their territories and it is not until the latter half of October that the rut proper gets under way. Some bucks make a brief appearance on the estate and are not seen again that season, presumably moving on to rut elsewhere. The size and composition of groups of fallow change as the rut progresses to its climax. Espmark and Brunner have described the rutting behaviour of fallow on the Baltic island of Öland. They found that there was a decrease in the number of single does seen but an increase in the number of single fawns. With mixed groups, the proportion of males that were young or yearlings fell from about one third to one fifth, whereas the proportion of males that were territorial bucks increased from about one fifth to a half. Only large, mature bucks seem capable of establishing and holding territories and these may be quite close to one another. The nearest that we have found two wild bucks rutting in woodland was between 100 and 150 metres.

The rut proper is a period of tremendous activity. A rutting buck parades up and down his territory, groaning frequently and chivying the does and their fawns which have been attracted to him. With fallow, it is the does that congregate around the rutting buck, he does not appear to round up and hold a harem as intensively as a red deer stag does. However, a buck will often follow and attempt to herd does that stray from this area. A few bucks, which appear incapable of establishing a territory, at least in the peak of the rut, hang about on the edge of the herd (page 134). They may even be tolerated, to a surprising extent, in the herd itself. If disturbed, bucks may move to an alternative rutting territory and return later to the original one.

The climax of the rut. Suborbital glands of both mating animals are open. Another buck and the does show little interest.

When groaning, the buck opens his mouth and lifts his head so that the forehead is almost horizontal, the larynx dropping about 15cm. The suborbital glands open (page 80) and the tail may be curled sharply over his back and the under hairs flared out, a position sometimes adopted by fawns when being suckled. Gilbert noted that each groan lasted about one second and that one buck gave a series of 134 groans in four minutes and seventeen seconds. The interval between any two groans was not greater than four or five seconds and usually less than one second. The does show varying degrees of interest in the proceedings, presumably depending upon whether they are in season. Many will just ignore the buck and continue resting or grazing; others will skip out of the way as he approaches, whereas some stand their ground. Frequently mewing and whickering may be heard and the suborbital gland may be wiped on the doe's flank. A buck may nudge a doe lying down, apparently to make her stand before he sniffs and licks the anal area and the tuft of hairs just below the vulva, and he may then exhibit the activity known as flehmen (page 135). This consists of raising the head, curling back the upper lip and dropping the lower one, and is exhibited by many ungulates after savouring the female's urine. The function of sniffing the anal area and tasting the the urine seems to be to test whether the doe is in oestrus. Many mammals are said to derive their body odour from sweat which does not smell, at least to the human nose, until it has been acted upon by bacteria. Research in Czechoslovakia showed that in female fallow the area richest in sweat glands was around the margins of the vulva and around the anus. The most marked increase in activity of the glands occurred when the does were in oestrus.

Little appears to be known about the courting and mating behaviour of fallow, few writers mentioning the subject. Courtship may involve the buck chasing the doe, which sometimes runs well away from the rutting area, with head and neck stretched forward. The doe may also lie with head and neck stretched along the ground, sometimes pointing her head vertically in response to his caress (page 137). When the doe is ready to be mated, she stands and allows the buck to mount and copulate. The buck stands on his rear legs, placing his fore legs on either side of the doe's hindquarters and his neck on her back. Mating may occur away from the rutting territory.

One late October morning, just as dawn was breaking, we were lying in a ditch at the edge of a wood and watching a rutting buck groaning only 20 metres away. Suddenly, he chased a white doe out of the wood and across the adjacent field. At the same time we realised that groaning was coming from the area where the buck had been rutting, another buck having come in and taken over the territory and the does immediately the other buck had left. The first buck soon returned across the field, without the doe, and as he entered the wood the second buck stopped groaning and walked off in the opposite direction. Although we had not seen him, the second buck must have been standing on the sideline awaiting his opportunity. Two years later, we were watching, from the comfort of a high seat, a buck rutting in exactly the same area. Another buck was rutting only a couple of hundred metres away in another corner of the same wood. This time, the first buck followed a doe going in the direction of the second buck. As they crossed a narrow ride, he was met by the second buck, a clash of antlers echoed through the wood and the fight was on. Fights between bucks are largely shoving matches, with antlers locked. The noise of clashing antlers usually results from tine striking tine as the adversaries twist and manoeuvre for position rather than repeated head-on clashes. The tremendous power exerted by the deer as they try to force each other backwards is clearly shown on page 192. The head is lowered so that the crown and antlers are presented to the

Flehmen, after savouring a doe's urine.

The Adam's apple drops during groaning.

opponent, the animal's nose pointing to the ground or even slightly back in the direction of the fore legs. Sometimes the head and antlers are turned through 90 degrees as the buck tries to gain an advantage over his opponent. When the weaker buck turns away from a fight, he may be raked or even gashed along the side by the brow tines of the winner. A rutting buck appears to tolerate the presence of yearlings and young bucks and even mature bucks if they stay in the background, presumably because they are outside the limits of his territory. However, if a mature buck oversteps the mark and enters the rutting animal's territory, a fight may ensue.

The thickness of the fallow's skin varies on different parts of the body and in adult males it reaches a considerable depth on the forehead, especially between the pedicles. The increase is mainly in the lower part of the dermis, the inner layer of the skin. Comparison of samples from males of different ages and at various times of the year showed that this dermal shield was thickest during the autumn, particularly in the older bucks. The skin depth ranged from about 2mm in a four month old male fawn to about 9mm in a buck over seven years old, both killed in October. Adult does have skin about 2mm thick in this region of the head. Scrapes and scabs are not unusual on the forehead of bucks. The thick dermis, which includes much collagen and elastin fibres, giving the skin resilience against knocks, no doubt prevents more serious injury to the underlying skull. Similar protective areas occur in the same region of the billy goat, which fights with head-on blows, but in mountain goats, which aim at their opponent's haunches, the skin is thickest on their rumps. In male impala, which have long, pointed horns, a dermal shield covers the neck and upper shoulders.

Finally, let us consider why the buck groans, scrapes the ground, frays and thrashes vegetation, uses his scent glands and becomes aggressive to other bucks, behaviour which is so common among many species of deer. The popular concept that a fallow buck carries out these activities just to define his territory is, without doubt, an over-simplification, the real reason being complex and still imperfectly known. There is no doubt that a fallow buck defends a rutting territory, but why does he need all these behavioural traits?

When the buck starts to fray, when his velvet is being shed, it is generally implied that he does this specifically to remove the velvet from his newly grown antlers. However, removal of the velvet may be incidental, the buck primarily satisfying an urge to wield his antlers against the vegetation irrespective of their condition. Bucks sometimes gently rub their antlers against thistles some days before the velvet starts to be shed. Roe bucks may start making scrapes whilst their antlers are still in velvet, which suggests that their territorial urge is well-developed by the time the velvet is ready to be shed. Do roe, therefore, fray trees as part of the urge to establish or further define a territory or do they do it to remove the velvet from their antlers? Fallow bucks also prepare scrapes well before the rut, the earliest

Courting.

we have found them being 5th September. This suggests that fallow may also develop a territorial urge soon after the antlers are free of velvet. Another aspect of fraying to consider is how the fallow bucks damage the plants. If they fray to remove the velvet from their antlers, then it is logical to conclude that all or most parts of the antlers will be involved. Bucks fraying in the rut, however, are said to rub their heads and the basal parts of their antlers against a tree trunk. Yearling bucks as well as adults fray vegetation. It has been suggested that fraying and thrashing may be a deviation of the combative instinct or that, by doing this, the bucks get a measure of the size of their newly grown weapons. If the antlers are cleaned of velvet by fraying before the bucks move to their rutting areas, one might expect to find certain places with frayed trees only around the end of August and early September. Does this in fact occur? If fraying to remove velvet and fraying associated with the rut are all part of the same pattern of behaviour, does the buck fray whilst moving from one area to another? Certainly at South Weald, occasional trees bordering a stream and a golf course, some way from the bucks usual rutting territories, have been frayed and thrashed. What of the later aspects of fraying and thrashing? If these activities are solely to delineate a buck's territory, why are they widespread in a wood? Perhaps the buck uses the frayed and scented trees to announce his presence in the area not only to other bucks but to the does that he wishes to attract to his rutting territory. The more trees he marks, the greater their chance of coming across one.

Groaning and a strong rutting odour may enable the does and other bucks to pinpoint a buck's position whilst he is actually rutting. If a rutting buck leaves his territory or is disturbed, groaning ceases. We have seen already how other bucks may be standing in the wings waiting to acquire a territory. The eversion and blackening of the end of the penis sheath and the possibility of the presence of a scent gland associated with the buck's pungent rutting odour, have been mentioned already. This scent is deposited in some fresh scrapes but not others, the strongly smelling ones usually having a small moist area, where a little fluid has fallen. Several species of deer impregnate themselves with their own urine when rutting and presumably this has the greatest effect on those nearest to them, namely the does. Fallow bucks come into season before the does. Their rutting odour may be a pheromone and help to bring the does into breeding condition, so helping to synchronise the oestrous cycle of the females; the majority of conceptions do, indeed, occur in the rut. The presence of the billy goat and the ram has a stimulating effect upon the initiation of the oestrous cycle and ovulation in goats and sheep. The effect of a fallow buck on the does may be similar. A doe in season also has an effect on the buck, the odour of her anal region probably stimulating him to mate.

Much of what has been said in the last few paragraphs is speculative, being based on few hard facts. Clearly a great deal still remains to be learnt about the rutting behaviour of fallow deer.

CHAPTER NINE

Female Reproduction and Maternal Behaviour

THE BREEDING season of does, like that of bucks, is more extensive than is generally realised. After the rut in the autumn, fawns are born in the early summer. In this respect, fallow deer are similar to sheep and goats, which are also seasonal breeders and mate in the autumn as the days shorten. The amount of daylight, or photoperiod, is an important factor, although not necessarily the only one, in causing the does to come into oestrus or "season". Donne records in *The Game Animals of New Zealand* that the breeding season of fallow deer transported across the equator to New Zealand changed: the animals mated in April and gave birth in December, six months later than in the northern hemisphere. Gillian Puttick also observed that fallow deer mated in late April in South Africa and fallow deer at about the same latitude in Argentina also start rutting at this time of year. These observations at various latitudes provide further evidence of the importance of light in determining the breeding season of fallow deer.

The reproductive organs of a fallow doe consist of a vagina and a bicornuate uterus divided into two horns from each of which a sinuous oviduct or Fallopian tube leads to an ovary. An egg or ovum is shed by the ovary and, after fertilisation, the embryo develops in the uterus. The size of the reproductive organs depends upon the age and stage of pregnancy of the doe. In a six month old fawn the length of the vagina plus uterus is about 8 cm. As the fawn develops, so do the organs, until in a virgin doe the length of the vagina plus uterus is about 15 cm although they are pencil thin. If the doe becomes pregnant, the uterus gradually enlarges and becomes distended until, just before parturition, it is a large-filled sac about 30 cm in diameter. After parturition, the uterus regresses and within about a month returns to its usual compact form, although not quite to its virgin size. The blood vessels of the suspending membranes attached to the uterus are quite distinct in a doe that has been pregnant and given birth, whereas they are indistinct in a virgin doe. This feature is a useful guide for distinguishing between the organs of virgin and parturient does. Examining and recording the condition of the reproductive organs is always worthwhile so that a picture can be built up of the reproductive potential of a deer population and the proportion of does that have bred.

Pregnancy and Foetal Development

The ovaries of a fawn are inactive, small and little bigger than grains of rice, but increase in size gradually as the animal grows and reaches puberty, when they become the size of large peas. At this age, large fluid-filled follicles occur in each ovary; fallow does usually shed only a single ovum following the rupture of a follicle; this may come from either ovary as they are equally active. The ruptured follicle develops into a solid, pale yellow body known as a corpus luteum, the presence of which indicates that the doe has reached puberty and has ovulated. Small, accessory corpora lutea are very rarely found in the ovaries of fallow deer although they occur commonly in those of some other species such as red and sika deer. If the doe conceives, the corpus luteum persists for the duration of pregnancy and regresses only after parturition. Hormones secreted by the corpus luteum seem essential for the maintenance of pregnancy. If the doe fails to conceive, the corpus luteum regresses quite quickly and the animal returns to oestrus and ovulation occurs again. The doe will continue coming into oestrus periodically and this may continue until early spring when the day length is increasing rapidly. Although most fallow fawns in southern England are born in June, occasionally a fawn will be born as late as October or November, which suggests that the does are still capable of conceiving until March. The length of the oestrous cycle in fallow deer is not known precisely but Cowan claimed it was 24 to 26 days for does in Victoria Park in British Columbia and Baker believed it was 26 days in New Zealand.

The age at which puberty occurs markedly affects the rate of increase of the population. Table 11 shows the incidence of ovulation in fallow does of various ages from the New Forest in Hampshire and from Richmond Park. None of the fawns had ovulated whereas 88 per cent of the yearling park deer and all the yearling wild deer had ovulated. Most of the fallow does, therefore, had reached puberty at about 16 months of age. The percentage of park deer which had ovulated increased from 80 in November to 85 in December and to 94 in January—March. Many of the yearling park deer would probably have ovulated later in the season had they not been culled. Examination of small numbers of culled park and wild deer from ten localities in England and Scotland indicated that most female fallow deer attain puberty and breed for the first time at about 16 months of age; the same appears to be true of fallow does in Germany and New Zealand. Harrison and Hyett came to the same conclusion after examining the reproductive tracts of fallow does killed in parks in southern England. Cadman's view that it is usual for does not to breed until they are about 28 months is probably wrong.

Even if a doe ovulates and is mated, pregnancy does not necessarily follow. Table 11 suggests that the proportion of does conceiving may be lower than the proportion that ovulate. Nevertheless the true incidence of conception is probably higher than that indicated by the figures, which record only the presence of embryos. Fertilised eggs are difficult to find and may have been overlooked.

Table 11. Incidence of ovulation and pregnancy in fallow deer from Richmond Park and the New Forest

Age, years	Richmond Park			New Forest*		
	Number of Animals	Per cent Ovulated	Per cent Pregnant	Number of Animals	Per cent Ovulated	Per cent Pregnant
0-1	39	0	0	14	0	0
1-2	34	88	85	4	100	100
2-3	20	100	100	10	100	100
3-4	13	100	92	14	100	93
4-5	8	88	88	3	100	100
5-6	12	100	83	6	100	83
6-7	3	100	100	4	100	100
7+	23	100	83	6	100	92

*The ages quoted for the does over 2 years old from the New Forest are only very approximate but this does not matter as there was no significant change with age.

Furthermore, late conceptions almost certainly would have occurred had the deer not been killed. This is suggested by the following data from various localities in England and Scotland which show that the percentage of culled fallow does carrying embryos increased in the months following the rut in October.

	Number of Does	Per cent with Embryos
November	32	72
December	121	86
January	107	96

For several species of mammal it has been shown that the cube root of the weight and the crown-rump length of the foetus are each proportional to its age. There is, at present, no method of determining the precise age of fallow deer foetuses and so the date of death is used instead. Figure 10 shows this relationship for the cube root of the weight of foetuses from 275 fallow. Most foetuses were conceived in a fairly restricted period because the weights of most of them fall on or close to a straight line. The date of conception can be *estimated* from three variables, the total gestation period, the weight and the date of death of the foetus. The estimated dates of conception of foetuses from fallow deer culled in Richmond Park and the New Forest are shown in Figure 11. The estimated conception dates of fallow fawns caught within a few days of birth in Richmond Park, which have been calculated by subtracting a mean gestation period of 229 days from the date of catching, have also been included in Figure 11. Conception appears to occur from about 1st October to about 2nd December with a peak from 21st October to 3rd

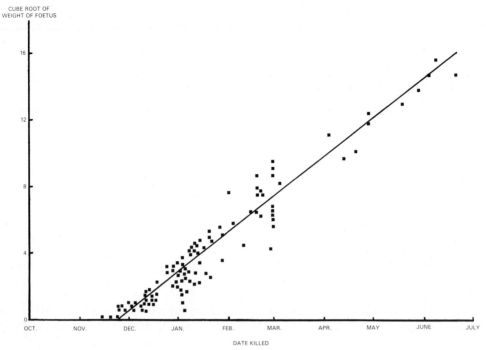

Growth of the fallow deer foetus, based on 275 animals.   Figure 10.

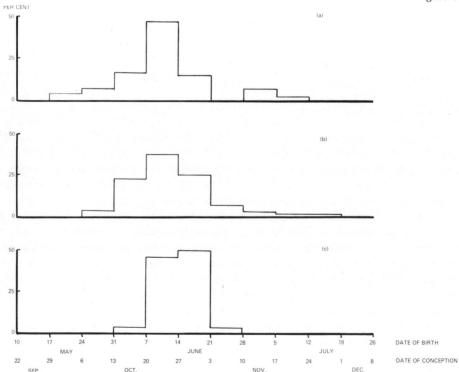

Estimated dates of conception and predicted dates of birth: (a) 45 New Forest foetuses; (b) 101 Richmond Park foetuses; (c) Estimated dates of conception and actual dates of birth of 149 Richmond Park fawns.
                                                                          Figure 11.

November. The late Professor Hamilton and his colleagues occasionally observed recently ruptured follicles in the ovaries of does killed in December and early January, which is further evidence of late conceptions.

After conception, development takes place slowly for the first few weeks until the embryo establishes a placental circulation. Harrison and Hyett have made detailed investigations of the formation of the fallow deer placenta, which is composed of several egg-shaped placentomes which vary greatly in size. Each placentome develops by the interlocking of a foetal component, the villi, with a maternal component, the crypts. Their function is to provide a route whereby nutrients can be transferred from the doe to the developing foetus and waste products passed in the opposite direction. The number of placentomes ranges from 6 to 12; the largest are often nearest the foetus, the others being distributed throughout both horns of the uterus. This type of placenta occurs in sheep and goats but these animals usually have many more placentomes. Growth of the foetus is rapid once it becomes established in a stable environment, which usually occurs about a month after conception in southern England.

The most marked changes in appearance in gestation occur early, as the fertilised egg passes through the embryonic stages to the foetal stages. Approximately five weeks after conception the foetus is about 2 cm long; the head, legs, cloven hoofs and tail can be distinguished. The following descriptions give some idea of the stages of foetal development. There is some individual variation; so the lengths of gestation, weights and the crown-rump lengths, listed in sequence, are only approximate.

6 weeks, 2g, 3cm.	The ribs and liver are clearly visible through the translucent skin and the eyes are without lids.
7 weeks, 3.5g, 5cm.	The hairless foetus is now recognisable as a potential deer and its sex can be determined from the external genitalia. Eyelids are present.
18 weeks, 465g, 26cm.	The skin is no longer translucent and short hairs are present above and below the eyes, around the muzzle and around the umbilicus.
23 weeks, 1250g, 36cm.	Hairs are appearing on the shoulder, the lower part of the neck and the rump. The skin is pigmented and spots may be visible. Incipient pedicles are present as small bumps above the eyes in males.
25 weeks, 1850g, 31cm.	The foetus is sparsely covered with fine, short hairs and it may be well-spotted.
27 weeks, 2400g, 45cm.	The foetus is well-covered with hair and looks like a small fawn. Pedicles are no longer visible.
33 weeks, 4500g, 55cm.	The foetus is fully developed and ready to be born.

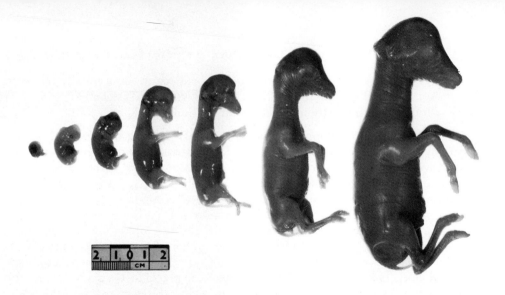

Foetuses at an estimated 40, 46, 49, 56, 60, 71 and 85 days after conception.

The gestation period of fallow deer is about seven and a half months. The only precise values we have been able to find are the dates of mating and parturition recorded by Prell for 11 deer in Hamburg Zoo and by Baker for two deer in New Zealand. The gestation period of the German deer ranged from 225 to 234 days with a mean of 229 days whereas that of the New Zealand deer was 237 days. A gestation period of 229 days has been used to estimate the dates of conception and parturition for deer in England. Although it is not ideal to compare zoo animals in one country to wild and park deer in another, this is the only information available. Some indirect support for this is that Prell's average value for the gestation period of nine red deer, 234 days, agrees well with the average period of 231 days recorded by the Hon. Fiona Guinness and her colleagues for 13 red deer on the Isle of Rhum in Scotland. Fallow fawns are born from mid-May onwards and the *predicted* dates of birth for deer in Richmond Park and the New Forest are given in Figure 11. Also included are the dates of birth, within a day, of newly born fawns from the Park. The data for the dates of birth is biased because searching for fawns was carried out only from the last week of May to the last week of June, so late births would have been missed. Searching was discontinued at this time because so few newly born fawns were found, which supports the idea of a restricted fawning period. The very close agreement between these two sets of observations is yet further justification for using the gestation period given by Prell. In the New Forest, Jackson observed newly born fawns from late May to the end of September although the majority were seen in June. According to Rieck, the peak period of birth for wild fawns in Germany was mid-June; of 107 births, 12 per cent occurred in May, 72 per cent in June and 16 per cent in July.

The sex ratio of 154 fawns caught within a few days of birth in Richmond Park from 1965 to 1973 was 130 males to 100 females. In most years the sex ratio was about one to one but in three years about two to three times as many male as female fawns were caught. The sex ratio of 78 foetuses collected from does culled in this park from 1964 to 1973 was 73 males to 100 females. The ratio was variable and ranged from 88 males to 100 females for 30 foetuses in 1964-65 to 58 males to 100 females for 27 foetuses in 1972-73. The sex ratio of 40 foetuses from does killed in the New Forest in 1965-66 was 111 males to 100 females. The overall sex ratio of 145 foetuses from several localities in England and Scotland was 110 males to 100 females. Baker found that the sex ratio of 44 foetuses from fallow in New Zealand was 76 males to 100 females.

The following figures, based upon the presence of apparently viable foetuses at various stages of gestation show the percentage of 266 adult fallow deer found to be pregnant, when culled, killed in accidents or dead from other causes.

	Number of Does	Per cent Pregnant
December	116	88
January-March	130	97
April-June	20	90

Many of the deer killed in December had ovulated and so the true proportion of does pregnant then is likely to be greater than 88 per cent. The two does not pregnant in April-June had not necessarily lost a foetus; they might not have become pregnant that season. These figures suggest that there is some pre-natal mortality in these deer and that it could be as high as ten per cent. The same is true

Mating, watched by a sheep.

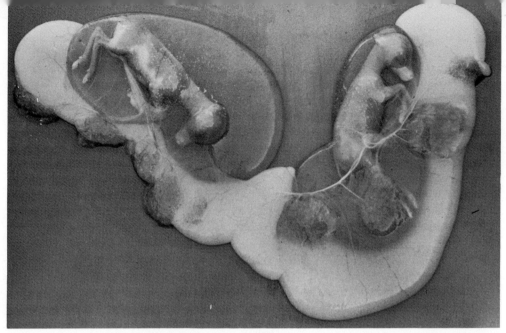

Twin foetuses, of opposite sex, from an aged doe killed in Richmond Park, March 1970. The dark patches are parts of the placentomes. *Dr L. B. Jeffcott.*

of New Zealand fallow, Baker finding that only nine per cent of 70 does shot between May and December were not pregnant.

The sex ratio of foetuses from a sample of does killed is readily determined and it is difficult to believe that the sex of the foetus affects the chances of the dam being killed. According to Jensen, female red deer in their prime produce more female than male calves. Consequently the sex of the offspring may be influenced by the age of the mother and therefore the sex ratio of fawns born by the age structure of the population. Whether the sex ratio of the newly born fallow fawns caught is representative of those in the population depends upon whether the chances of the animals being seen or caught is the same for both sexes. It is difficult to reconcile the differences between sex ratio of foetuses and of fawns for the Richmond Park deer but, as pre-natal mortality appears to be low, it would appear that buck fawns may be more easily found and caught than doe fawns.

Fallow deer usually give birth to a single fawn; the only example we have been able to find of twins being born, is that given by Baker for a twelve year old captive doe. Reports of twins are not infrequent but invariably appear to be cases of does being followed by two fawns: this is not evidence of twins having been born. The only way to be sure that a doe produces twins is to observe their birth. Harrison and Hyett examined the reproductive tracts of 240 pregnant does and found only one example of twin foetuses. The reproductive organs of 270 pregnant does from ten localities in England and Scotland have been examined by us but only two examples of twins were found, an incidence of less than one per cent. An aged, lactating doe shot in Richmond Park on 8th March 1970 was carrying apparently viable twin foetuses of opposite sex which are shown on page 146. The other exception, a doe carrying twin female foetuses, was killed in a road accident in Epping Forest on 29th May 1969. One foetus weighed 2.7 kg and appeared to have been living at the time of the accident but the other weighed only 1.5 kg and had been dead for some time. Therefore, even if a doe carries twins, there is no guarantee that they will survive to term.

The average weight of 93 fawns, within one day of birth, in Richmond Park was 4.6 kg for males and 4.4 kg for females. The weights ranged from 1.8 kg for both sexes to 5.9 kg for male to 5.5 kg for female fawns. Only a few fawns had a birth weight near the lower limit of 1.8 kg: these are discussed in relation to fawn mortality in Chapter Twelve. The weights of 12 newly born wild fawns found in Essex were similar.

Lactation

The mammary glands undergo an annual cycle of growth and regression; lactation may last up to about nine months. Some days before parturition occurs, the glands get much bigger as lactation commences and the udder becomes very obvious in does seen from the rear. The weight of the mammary glands at the time of parturition is about 400 to 800g. The precise time before parturition that these changes take place appears to be unknown, probably because of the difficulty of being sure that the same animal is being observed until she gives birth. A prominent

Just born. This was a rare occasion when the doe had left the still damp fawn without eating the afterbirth.

udder in a doe indicates that either she is shortly to give birth or she has already done so. The doe's shape usually enables one to decide whether the fawn has been born.

The udder remains large during the period in which the fawn is completely dependent on milk for its nourishment, the size decreasing gradually as solid food starts to become a major part of the fawn's diet. Examination of the mammary glands from 90 wild and park does older than two years showed that the length of lactation varies greatly, some does becoming dry by October-November whereas many are still lactating in December-January. Unfortunately only seven adult does were available for examination in February-March and, although four were still lactating, the figures are too small to be considered representative. Flerov, however, considers that nursing of fallow fawns continues until the spring after their birth. Although the number of animals examined from June to September was also small, observations on behaviour in the field indicate that most does, yearlings excepted, are lactating during this period.

Hybridisation

The only genuine example of hybridisation in fallow deer appears to be that between the two subspecies, the European and the Persian. Eight hybrids between a Persian fallow buck and European fallow does were born in the London Zoo between 1878 and 1885, according to Zuckerman, and some of the hybrid does produced fawns when mated with a Persian fallow buck. These two subspecies have also hybridised in other zoos, notably Munich where there were nine hybrids in 1972.

There does not appear to be any firm evidence of hybridisation of fallow deer with other species. Attempts to produce hybrids by the artificial insemination of European fallow does with semen from red deer stags proved unsuccessful, as did repeated matings between a male mule deer and two European fallow does. Claims that an animal is a hybrid have often rested solely on appearance. Fallow deer may occasionally have antlers similar to those of a red deer stag, page 153 shows such an animal in Richmond Park that was known as "Staghead". Red deer may also, on occasion, have palmate antlers: a photograph of such an animal from Exmoor was published in *Country Life* on 28th November 1952. These deer are probably mutant types, not hybrids. The chromosome number of European fallow deer is 68.

Annie Gray in *Mammalian Hydrids* records the following claims for European fallow deer hybrids:
1. A male hog deer x female fallow in Bloemfontein Zoo.
2. A supposedly red deer x fallow hybrid doe and her calf were shot but the same doe was identified by other people as either pure sika or a sika x red deer hybrid!

Parturition

The fascinating relationship between a fallow doe and her fawn, and the behavioural changes which occur as the fawn grows up have been studied in small groups of captive deer by Meier-Mühlemann in Zurich and by Gilbert in America.

A day or two before birth takes place, the vulva of the doe become swollen and appears rather loose. Captive does have been seen to pace about their enclosure more than usual and, according to Gilbert, give short high-pitched bleats, repeated about once a second, one continuous series containing 110 bleats. The behaviour of the fallow does just before the birth of their fawns is little known. In Richmond Park, we watched a doe give birth in the midst of 17 other does and followers and seven red deer. After a while the other deer got up and gradually moved away grazing, leaving the dam and her 27 minute old fawn alone. Several instances of does giving birth close to a herd have been recorded but on other occasions does have given birth in a dense patch of bracken with few, if any, other deer in sight. Although does that have given birth recently are often found on their own, it may be that many just drop out of the group as parturition begins, the herd moving away from the doe rather than the doe seeking isolation. Heidemann believes that fallow does exhibit a certain degree of territorial behaviour at this time of year. This implies that they are defending a territory or an area of ground but, whereas does may exhibit aggressive behaviour towards other fallow at this time, they may simply be defending their fawns. The pattern of behaviour seems to vary greatly between individuals. Some does allow other deer to sniff their young fawns and on several occasions we have been led to a fawn by seeing several other fallow peering at something in the grass, close to a doe. Aggression usually takes the form of the doe, with neck extended and lowered, ears flattened back, running as if to butt the intruder with the top of her head; the attacked animal running away before contact is made. The doe may also strike out with a fore leg or attempt to bite the back of the other animal. In our experience, aggressive behaviour of this kind is infrequent.

A solitary yearling may be only 20 to 30 metres away from a doe giving birth and a doe running to answer the distress call of her fawn may be followed closely by a yearling. The yearling, usually female, is presumably the previous year's fawn, so it seems likely that the bond between mother and female fawn is retained until after the next fawn is born. Yearling bucks are seen less frequently with does and the bond between them is probably broken at this time if not beforehand. A somewhat similar situation appears to exist in white-tailed deer in America. Hawkins and Klimstra found that the bond between mother and daughter, although temporarily interrupted at the time of parturition, is usually reformed whereas that between mother and son is broken but rarely reformed. It must be remembered, however, that frequently white-tailed deer give birth as yearlings whereas this is not the case with fallow.

Menil new-born fawn.

Fawns may be dropped amongst grass, bracken, rushes, stinging nettles or even on bare leaf litter. In the wild, hay or corn fields are popular fawning areas, the does finding both cover and food close at hand. The doe is restless in labour, alternately lying and standing. The fore legs are usually the first part of the fawn to appear, followed by the head. In most of the few births which have been recorded, the doe is lying on her side during the last stage of birth, the umbilical cord being severed close to the fawn's body as the doe moves. The birth is usually over quite quickly, Lau recording times of 100, 125 and 195 minutes in Berlin Zoo and Meier-Mühlemann times from 134 to 201 minutes for four fawns. The rapidity with which a fawn may be born is confirmed by the following observations on a doe in Richmond Park:

1714 hours	Doe standing and licking a bag of hazy fluid about the size of a grapefruit hanging from her vulva. Well-developed udder and prominent nipples.
1728 hours	Doe still standing and licking bag and her legs. No sign of the fawn.
1730 hours	Bag burst.
1736 hours	Doe standing and straining; tips of fawn's feet appeared.
1737 hours	One front foot and part of fawn's head visible. Doe straining.
1738 hours	Doe lying on her right side and straining, standing after 30 seconds and licking her legs and udder.
1739 hours	Doe lying on her left side and straining, stands after 30 seconds.
1740 hours	Doe lies down on her right side, stands after 30 seconds.
1741 hours	Doe on her left side and straining, head stretched out.

1742 hours	Doe standing; then down and up again. Eating and pulling part of the bag. Feet and part of fawn's head just visible.
1744 hours	Fawn's head suddenly appearing and then the body dropping to the ground from the doe, which is still standing, followed by a lot of blood-stained fluid. Cord severed as the fawn falls.
1745 hours	Doe licking fawn.
1749 hours	Doe lies down and continues to lick fawn.
1757 hours	Fawn tries to stand, its hind legs are straight but it cannot straighten its fore legs.
1803 hours	Fawn standing for the first time (19 minutes old). Fore legs give way and it collapses.
1807 hours	Fawn standing and taking a few steps (23 minutes old). Doe eating afterbirth.

The birth of 17 fawns in Berlin Zoo occurred from 0730 hours to 2115 hours, eight of them between 1100 hours and 1330 hours. In Richmond Park, eight fawns that had just been born were all found between 0900 hours and 1744 hours and of these, four were found between 1100 hours and 1300 hours. Newly born fawns, which had been licked dry but were very shaky on their feet, were found throughout the day from dawn onwards. Birth therefore probably takes place throughout the day and night but more information is required before we can say whether there is a peak around mid-day.

Maternal Behaviour

Immediately after the fawn has been born, it is given a very thorough licking

Young black fawn rests while the sun highlights the glossy coat.

A watchful doe suckles her fawn.

by the dam. This serves not only to clean and dry the fawn but is the initial step in establishing a bond between them and helps the doe to learn the characteristic smell of her fawn and so to be able to recognise it in the future. Experiments have shown that domestic sheep learn to recognise their offspring in this way within two hours of birth. Fawns are active within minutes of birth, being able to stand, albeit rather unsteadily, soon after. Suckling first occurs within an hour or so of birth; the time taken depends upon how readily the fawn finds the teats of the doe. Often it will try to suck at the fore legs or some other part of her body. When a nipple is found, the udder is butted vigorously before the fawn begins sucking. When feeding, the fawn stands with its body pointing in the opposite direction to that of the dam but with its body at angle to hers (as above). While the young fawn is being suckled, it is licked repeatedly by the doe, particularly around the anal region. This action stimulates the fawn not only to suck but to curl its tail over its back and to urinate and defecate, the doe probably consuming the waste products. Anybody who has successfully reared a young fawn will know how important it is to massage its rear with a damp flannel. The doe may nurse while lying or standing but the latter is more usual. She will also lick and groom other parts of the fawn's body, the head and neck, the ears, the back and so on. As well as cleaning the fawn, the doe eats the afterbirth.

Fawns generally rest near where they were born for several hours after birth. If they do move away, it is usually not far although they have been known to follow the doe for more than 50 metres. Most of the fawn's early life is spent resting, usually trying to conceal itself next to a clump of grass, in a bed of nettles or in other dense vegetation such as bracken. Its dappled coat provides excellent camouflage and it is surprising what little vegetation is required to hide it; two or three stalks of young bracken may successfully conceal a fawn lying on the mat of dead stalks from last year, as anybody who has searched for newly born fawns can testify. Even a fawn lying in short but rough grass can be very difficult to find although, once seen, it is very obvious. The doe remains separate from her hidden fawn for much of the day and carries on her regular activities of feeding and resting. She may rejoin the herd although frequently she seems to remain on her own or with a yearling. Often she grazes for a while and then stands, perhaps under a tree, just gazing over the landscape, but obviously watchful. The maximum distance she wanders from her

"Staghead". A fallow buck with antlers reminiscent of those of a red deer stag.

fawn is not known, perhaps 200 to 300 metres, but she appears to be within hearing distance of a fawn's distress call, sight and sound appearing to be more important than smell. A dog or human wandering too close to her concealed fawn may cause her to trot towards the disturbance, stand a little way off and bark several times. A dog may be followed, the doe using a stiff-legged walk until she considers the danger is past.

A fawn when handled often lets out a long, piercing cry, although fawns only a day or two old generally remain silent. This distress call, which may be repeated several times but stops when the animal is released, usually brings the return of the doe, even if she was not in sight when the fawn was disturbed. Several does may respond to the call but, in contrast to red deer, most of the herd ignore the plea for help. If a dog disturbs the fawn or gets too close, the doe may attack, striking out with her fore feet and trying to trample the animal, sometimes killing it in the process. The doe visits the fawn periodically to feed it and our impression is that in Richmond Park this is more frequent in the early morning, around mid-day and at dusk. Until they are at least four months of age, fawns are suckled, on average, once every four hours although Meier-Mühlemann concluded that suckling occurred more frequently around mid-day and between 1700 hours and 2100 hours. When ready to visit her fawn, the doe starts moving in the direction that she thinks it is hidden. She may either walk fairly purposefully in that direction or gradually graze there, giving the impression that she is not very concerned where she is going. Unless disturbed, the fawn generally remains in hiding until roused by the doe and does not call when hungry. An apparently lost fawn, wandering aimlessly and mewing, also described as "peeping" and "pheeping", is sometimes seen. The doe may bleat as she approaches her fawn or, if it is not where she expected to find it, she may wander around bleating and "looking" for it. A bleat is similar to the fawn's pheep but deeper. Groups of does and fawns can be heard bleating to each other even in late winter and the call appears to be for making contact.

The doe usually initiates contact with the young fawn and it seems that at least for the first few days after birth, it is she who recognises her fawn and not vice versa, this apparently being done by smell. Later on it seems likely that recognition is by the fawn as well as by the doe, the former recognising its mother's bleat. When a fawn is disturbed and runs away, it may be followed by several does who, when they catch up with it, stretch out their necks and smell it in turn until one of them accepts it; then the fawn is licked and groomed. The ears, head and neck are licked most frequently, followed by the rump; other areas are rarely licked. A newly born fawn is often said to have no smell and so cannot be detected by predators. However, because a doe is capable of recognising her own fawn, presumably from its smell, it must have some odour. The anal region is 'nosed' most frequently. The interdigital glands of a newly born fawn lack the smell of those of older fawns and adults, at least as judged by the human nose, and this may have given rise to the belief that such fawns have no smell. When the doe finds her own fawn she licks it, causing it to rise if it has not already responded to her approach, and to start to suck. After the fawn has fed, it often gambols around before going back to rest, either to the same place or to one very close. Sometimes the doe rests for a while with her fawn. The doe may also paw the fawn with her fore leg or nudge it with her head, actions often used when a very young fawn tries to follow its dam rather than conceal itself. After a fawn has been handled briefly by a human the doe accepts it but usually gives it a very thorough licking. On two occasions known to us, however, the doe has attacked the fawn, striking at it with her fore feet, before leading it away. Much handling by a human may cause the doe to abandon her offspring, particularly if it has not yet been licked dry or if it is moved far from where it was found. A strange fawn may be tolerated or it may be bitten or kicked.

The young fawn may stay in the same area for at least a week, the period probably depending on the amount of disturbance. The young fawn rests either in a curled-up position, with head tucked against a flank, or it lies with chin and neck stretched along the ground. Both these positions are adopted by older deer when resting and at ease. For a variable period after birth, often about an hour, the fawn is unsteady on its feet. If disturbed it "freezes", a behaviour pattern which is probably very effective in avoiding detection by the casual passer-by. Although fawns can be found when searched for, we often wonder how many fawns have seen us without our seeing them because they "froze". As their running ability develops, they tend to take flight rather than "freeze". Meier-Mühlemann found the fawn's flight distance to be about six metres at ten days old. When disturbed, it may either follow its mother or other does or go to another patch of cover. We have watched fawns pause and stand, with head lowered, under a few bracken fronds, after disturbance. If not alarmed again, they turn round once or twice before lying down but with head raised and alert.

Gilbert considered that fawns changed from a "freezing" to a fleeing attitude from 12 to 48 hours after birth. Our experience suggests that the change is more gradual and prolonged and varies widely with the individual. A fawn disturbed when alert and in the presence of its dam will follow her. A very young fawn will not follow her far before lying down, particularly if someone gets between them, but slightly older fawns may follow their dams for several hundred metres. If the doe is absent and the fawn is resting, it may "freeze" rather than flee. Some fawns appear to be of a quieter disposition than others, for some marked soon after birth were catchable a week later because they "froze" when found whereas others fled. The degree of disturbance also affects the animal's behaviour. A person talking and rushing through the vegetation will often cause a fawn to flee whereas a stealthy approach may cause it to "freeze".

The effects of the doe's behaviour on the development of reaction by the fawn to danger signals has also been studied by Gilbert. By comparing the behaviour of fawns reared by their dams to that of hand-reared fawns isolated from other deer within 24 hours of birth, he found that the isolated fawns reacted to danger by using the same visual and vocal signals as the others. After eight to nine months, the fawns were re-introduced to the herd from which they had been removed. They did not, however, rejoin the herd but remained as a separate group. Even though the hand-reared deer were accustomed to humans, they reacted in the same way as the other deer when they were alarmed by a person, all rushing from one end of the paddock to the other. The important implication resulting from Gilbert's experiments is that hand-reared deer, if released into the wild, may never become completely integrated with wild deer. This reinforces our view that it is unwise to remove and attempt to rear so-called "lost" fawns. Anyone doing so, should be prepared to keep an animal that may live for a dozen years, weigh up to 100kg, jump a two metre fence and become aggressive and dangerous.

As the fawn grows up it follows its dam more and more and becomes increasingly active. Does and fawns form small groups of about half a dozen by mid-July although frequently does may still be seen alone. By mid-August, when fawns are about two months old, they may be seen playing together in the fields and the does and young form larger groups. A large group of fawns may be left in the care of a few adults whilst the other does go off to feed. On one occasion, a party of 15 fawns and six does was observed at South Weald; they were resting under an oak whilst the main herd of 21 does grazed in another field a few hundred metres away. From about the this age, the fawns appear to become integrated fully with the herd. The most extensive changes in behaviour occur during the first few months of life. In this period the fawn changes from being an almost helpless creature, staying alone in one place and depending on its mother for food and protection, to a more independent animal, having to find much of its own food, associating with other deer, but following its dam almost everywhere she goes. Like many young mammals, fawns are extremely playful. They chase around at high speed either on their own or with other fawns, stop, change direction and rush off again. They may leap into the air, backs arched, heads shaking and legs kicking rather like a bucking bronco, the adult does sometimes joining in. These activities may go on for half an hour or more and, at South Weald, we have noticed that play frequently occurs just before dusk.

CHAPTER TEN

Social Organisation and Behaviour

THE BEHAVIOUR of fallow deer varies from one locality to another and depends on the amount of disturbance, particularly by man, as well as the type of habitat and the weather. For example, Taylor Page in his booklet *Fallow Deer* stated that large herds of wild deer are rarely found and cites the small groups found in Epping Forest as an example. However, at South Weald, only 15 kilometres away, a large herd of does and followers comprising up to 30 animals is a common sight throughout the year. The most comprehensive study of the social behaviour of wild fallow is that carried out by Heidemann at Salzau in Germany. He studied a herd of about 60 deer in an area of small woods and agricultural land; his observations are referred to extensively in this chapter.

Some preliminary observations on the behaviour of fallow were carried out by Gillian Puttick on the Groote Schuur estate near Cape Town in South Africa. Numerous articles contain information on various aspects of fallow behaviour but many are merely anecdotal. Factual information is sparse and the problem of studying fallow behaviour is aggravated by the two factors already mentioned: difficulties in estimating age and recognition of individual deer in the field. Whereas information on disease, reproduction, and growth can be obtained from culled deer, this is obviously impossible on the case of behaviour. Another important point: watching deer often leads to disturbance and so one's observations may not reflect accurately the true behaviour of the wild animal.

Fallow deer are gregarious and form herds. In this respect, they are similar to red and sika deer, but differ from roe deer whose social organisation is based on small family groups. The size and composition of the herds vary with the time of year. For an appreciable part of the year, the adult bucks form bachelor groups and live apart from the doe herds, which comprise adult females, yearlings and fawns; the two herds combining for the rut. This arrangement means that the bucks and does are separate when the former are renewing their antlers and the latter are giving birth. Apart from the rut and possibly at parturition, fallow do not exhibit territorial behaviour.

Population Density

The density of wild fallow deer depends on the type of herd and the time of year. In considering density, a distinction should be made between the number of deer in the area that is regularly used by the animals and the number of deer in the area surveyed. At South Weald, in 11 counts from January to March over six years, the deer have been found repeatedly in an area of about 125 hectares, the density varying from 18 to 43 per 100 hectares. The deer are very rarely seen on certain other parts of the estate but, had these areas been included, the density would have been much lower. A similar density, 22 per 100 hectares, was estimated by Collier in March 1965 for a herd near Peterborough. Heidemann estimated that, in April, the density of fallow at Salzau was eight per 100 hectares. However, in January and February, the deer frequented only about one third of the area, giving a density of 24 per 100 hectares. A similar density, 19 per 100 hectares, was estimated by Bencze to occur in 8,000 hectares of woodland near Balaton in Hungary. These high densities are surprisingly similar and indicate the gregarious nature of fallow deer, particularly in winter and spring when most of the counts were taken. Estimates of deer density are made usually at this time of year because ground cover is sparse. At other times, the density may be lower as the deer may range more widely. Heidemann, however, considered that the deer remained within 730 hectares throughout the year and the density in summer was about 12 per 100 hectares.

Our studies at South Weald have shown that, whereas the does remain in the area, the bucks leave around the turn of the year and do not rejoin the does until the following August or September. This does not mean that individual does or fawns do not leave the area; they do, but there are always some does and young present. This segregation of bucks and does for a portion of the year appears to be general, having been observed in many other areas of Britain, in Alsace, in northern Germany and in South Africa. The separation of the sexes can be seen to some extent even in the larger deer parks. The period during which the bucks stay apart from the does is at least five months but may be longer. In some areas, the bucks leave immediately after the rut whereas in others they remain until early spring. The degree of disturbance may influence the bucks' departure. One gets the impression that the younger bucks are the last to leave and the first to return, but this may be because the older animals are not so easily seen. A few does may be found with the buck herd.

The sizes of the herds vary with the time of year. The highest number of deer seen at South Weald in a compact group was in September and October just before the rut, when about 40 deer, predominantly does, yearlings and fawns were grazing in one small field of about 3 hectares. At the other extreme, in July, by which time most does had given birth, the maximum number of deer seen in any one group was ten and the does were widely dispersed in small groups. The general trend of large groups just before the rut and small groups soon after the birth of fawns is supported by observations from other areas. Heidemann found that there were more groups of two or three does in July than at other times and that groups of more than seven does occurred from December to April. Larger groups of does sometimes reformed in late July and August when the fawns started to feed regularly with their dams. In California, Jurek recorded that fallow congregated into larger groups from late autumn to early spring. After the rut, large numbers of bucks, sometimes up to 30 or 40, may form one group. Once they have cast their antlers, however, bachelor herds of wild deer rarely comprise more than about six animals. Larger herds of bucks with growing antlers may be seen in deer parks, probably as a result of the unnatural conditions imposed by man. Heidemann found most buck groups comprised only two or three animals from May to December, this being particularly true in October and November, at the time of the rut. Mature bucks are largely nocturnal at this time although as summer progresses they may be found during the day in cornfields.

Sex Ratio

The sex ratio varies at different times of the year and will depend both on management and on the type of herd that is being studied. At South Weald we cannot distinguish with certainty adult does from yearling does in the field, so we recognise only bucks, yearling males, does and fawns. Furthermore our population counts are held in January and in March when the bucks have left the area. During the rut, however, attempts are made to identify all the bucks and an approximate estimate of the size of the herd can then be made because does, fawns and male yearlings often congregate in the fields at dusk and can be counted. From these rather approximate figures, we have calculated that the proportion of adult bucks is between 24 and 40 per 100 adult and yearling does. As no distinction is made between adult and yearling females, it is better to combine the figures for adult and yearling bucks, the sex ratio then being between 44 and 60 males per 100 females. Gillian Puttick found 24 adult males to 100 adult females but considered this ratio somewhat low because of the difficulty of counting the adult bucks. The total strength of the herd was estimated to be 270 plus or minus 20, but the time of year when the count was undertaken was not stated. The fallow population at Salzau in April 1969 comprised 15 bucks, 13 yearling bucks or prickets, 11 does, 5 yearling does and 15 fawns. There is a very high proportion of males in this area compared with elsewhere. The proportions of yearlings and fawns to does are also very high, which suggests that either many young deer had moved into the area or many does had emigrated. Jurek believes that of an estimated population of 200 to 400 fallow in Mendocino County, California, less than ten per cent are bucks over two years of age; this figure is similar to that given by Gillian Puttick and our results at South Weald if allowance is made for fawns and yearlings.

Social Organisation

The basic unit of the doe herd is the doe and her fawn. There seems to be very little overt aggressive behaviour between does and, except at fawning time, it is rare to see does threaten one another. The organisation of the herd appears to be one of passive leadership rather than a hierarchy arising out of dominance-subordination relations. Gilbert studied the order of flight amongst six marked does and found that the same doe led the group on 99 occasions out of 100. Another particular doe took second place on 91 per cent of the occasions whilst another was third for 75 per cent of the time. There was no definite order amongst the other three does which never led the herd and were very rarely in second or third place. This suggests that in wild fallow there may be a definite order of precedence in the leading animals but not in the majority of followers. It is tempting to speculate that if the leader leaves the herd or is removed, the doe in second place takes over. There is no evidence to support this idea and removal of the leader could result in a complete reshuffle with the emergence of a new leader from the ranks. Having an exclusive leader means that this animal initiates flight activity in the herd and also that other deer follow her example. Ungulates that live in herds, however, often adopt the activities of other members of the herd: each animal is very aware of the movements of its companions. This type of behaviour is seen frequently when a herd of wild fallow does is disturbed; when one takes flight the rest follow. Not all members of a herd react in exactly the same way at the same time; it is a gradual process, almost as if their behaviour was contagious. First a few does will run off, then others follow until eventually the entire herd is running away. The deer run off in single file although they may bunch at a hedge or fence. Leadership does not extend to adult bucks when they are with the doe herd because they often flee in the opposite direction. The age of the leading doe relative to that of the other members of the herd is unknown although it is frequently claimed that she is an old animal. The leader in Gilbert's group of does was especially active and was less easily excited or had a "low level of nervousness" as judged from the frequency of her "tail-up" alarm signals compared with the other does. Leadership must not be confused with dominance. In a group of rutting fallow, the mature buck is the dominant animal even though the herd when disturbed is still led by a doe. The social hierarchy amongst the members of the bachelor groups of bucks is unknown. Herds of red deer stags develop a peck order based on threats and submission, which is related to age and size of antlers; the older deer, which usually have the larger antlers, are dominant to the younger ones. Probably a peck order is established amongst the fallow bucks in much the same way as it is for red deer.

Home Range

A home range is not an area defined by rigid boundaries but rather the result of man's attempt to measure the area used by the animals. The methods used and different definitions have led to ambiguities in the use of the term. Calhoun has described home range as the area to which an animal confines itself in its day-to-day activities. Home range has a temporal quality as well as a spacial one. Therefore in accepting this definition for fallow deer, it must be realised that adult bucks have at least two seasonal home ranges; one in the spring and summer whilst they are in bachelor groups and another whilst they are with the doe herds for the rut. Home range does not include the migratory route of bucks in moving from one area to another. The total area used by a fallow deer is probably best described as its lifetime range which has been defined by Jewell as "the total area with which an animal has become familiar, including seasonal home ranges, excursions for mating, and routes of movement". This is a difficult parameter to measure in the case of fallow because of their longevity. Furthermore a buck may be born and grow up in one area, and yet may never visit that area again after leaving it as a yearling. A common method of determining home range is to observe the animal over a given period of time, plot the sightings on a map and join the outermost points. The enclosed area is regarded as a measure of the animal's home range. This is a rather crude method because it assumes that the animal is being observed over the whole of its range and that its habits are not affected by the observer. Recent improvements involve attaching a radio transmitter to the deer in order to monitor its movements but this has not yet been used for fallow. Heidemann believes that, as individual fallow move in the same way as the herd, the home range of the herd can be regarded as the same as that of the individual. This takes no account of emigration from and immigration to the herd and, furthermore, individual deer may restrict their movements to only part of the area covered by the herd. Consequently, an attempt also should be made to determine the home ranges of individual animals.

Observations of marked fallow at South Weald have shown that does apparently leave the herd for periods which may be as long as two to three years. One such doe was caught as an adult in November 1968, was seen in May 1969, but was not seen again until June 1972. During her long absence, numerous observations on other marked deer were made in the area and it is most unlikely that, had she been present for any length of time, she would not have been seen. Although immigration and emigration of females occur, as yet no seasonal pattern appears to be emerging and the reason for their movement is not clear. More observations on marked deer are required.

Movements of this type lead to problems in determining home range. If there is no well-defined seasonal migratory pattern, and the deer may well be on an adjoining, less frequently observed estate only a couple of kilometres away, should one define home range as the entire area used by the animals or just the separate areas? It is probably best to consider the entire area as the home range and to define those particular parts used most frequently as core areas.

Dahlberg and Guettinger have suggested that some white-tailed deer develop an affinity for a small area with which they become familiar and remain there until conditions force them to leave. Each core area supplied all the animal's requirements at the time it was used. Over a period of one month, Sparrowe and Springer found that a yearling white-tailed buck, fitted with a radio transmitter, stayed in each of four core areas for between four and 11 days. In each area the daily movements of the buck were so small as to be immeasurable by triangulation.

A similar situation seems to exist amongst the fallow does and followers at South Weald. Some of the does have been seen over a period of up to four and a quarter years. For example, one doe, number 158, was caught in December 1969 as a six month old fawn and was seen on the estate on 37 different occasions in 17 of the following 41 months, in 35 of which observations were made. The longest consecutive period for which the doe was not seen was four months in mid-winter even though the area was visited ten times in that period. The areas in which she was seen each year overlapped substantially; the area encompassing all the observations totalled 45 hectares. Another doe, number 108, was tagged as a newly born fawn in June 1968. She was seen on the estate on 31 different occasions in 15 of the following 40 months, observations being made in all but five of them. She was not seen for ten consecutive months in this period although observations were made about twice a month, when other tagged deer were seen regularly. Again the areas in which she was seen each year also overlapped substantially and 38 hectares encompassed all the sightings. There was an appreciable overlap between the areas used by both these does. Although both animals probably covered a larger area than calculated, much of their life must have been spent in these relatively small areas. It is unlikely that either doe would have gone unobserved if she had frequently visited other parts of the estate. Because does in general do leave and return to the estate, it is likely that both animals, particularly number 108, also did so. Therefore the above areas are best regarded as core areas of their home ranges, the sizes of their ranges being unknown. If doe 108 left the estate for long, she must have had at least one other core area. Neither the home ranges nor the life time ranges of any of the does are known. The furthest that a marked doe has been seen away from the estate is just under two kilometres. The home ranges and life time ranges of bucks are unknown.

Heidemann in his study at Salzau estimated that about 60 bucks, does and followers had an annual home range of at least 730 hectares. The home ranges of the bucks and of the does and fawns varied at different times of the year. The bucks wandered widely within the area from May to December but restricted their activities to smaller, forested areas from January to April when cover was poor and food was less plentiful. The doe herd was more flexible than that of the bucks and its home range was greater, but there was often an appreciable overlap of the two. The relative proportions of the time that the deer spent in the various types of habitat at Salzau at different seasons is given in Table 12. The does often visited fields even in winter, when the bucks usually remained in dense cover in the woods. In summer, both bucks and does spent much more time in fields of corn and rootcrops where both food and cover were plentiful.

The home range of fawns depends on that of their dams, at least in the early months of life. Doe number 33 was caught as a newly born fawn in June 1967 but was not seen again until the following November. Apart from December, she was then seen on the estate every month until a year old. A buck fawn also caught in June 1967 was seen on the estate in every month of his first year apart from July and December. All the observations on these two fawns were encompassed by areas of 22 and 16 hectares respectively and included the places where they had been caught. The ranges of these animals overlapped but not nearly so much as the ranges for the same doe from one year to the next. Doe number 108, was observed in areas in her first, second and third years which covered 28, 26 and 24 hectares respectively and included the place where she was found. The areas overlapped extensively and it was particularly noticeable that she was never seen in the eastern part of the estate, despite numerous observations on other marked deer being made in that area. This doe appears to have established a core area of her home range in her first year and to have returned to it in succeeding years. Fallow deer are certainly creatures of habit and regularly follow definite routes which lead to the formation of well-defined paths. (page 164). These paths may be used for only part of the year, depending upon changes in the animals' habits.

Table 12. Percentage of the time spent in different seasons by fallow deer in various habitats at Salzau in Germany

Habitat	Jan.-Feb.		Mar.-Apr.		May-Jun.		Jul.-Aug.		Sep.-Oct.		Nov.-Dec.	
	Buck	Doe	Buck	Doe	Buck	Doe	Buck	Doe	Buck	Doe	Buck	Doe
Wood	87	54	20	5	16	22	16	18	63	63	28	13
Wood edge	2	6	20	16	18	5	16	18	8	7	43	24
Open field	11	40	60	79	41	38	6	18	29	30	29	63
Field with cover	0	0	0	0	25	45	62	46	0	0	0	0

Limitation of Herd Size

At South Weald, the number of deer in winter and early spring has fluctuated between 23 and 54 over the past seven years. In January 1968, 38 deer were counted on the estate, of which approximately 24 were does. If we assume that all the female deer give birth to a single fawn from the age of two onwards and that numbers of males and females are equal, it can be calculated that by January 1974 there should have been 376 deer, or 253 does and fawns, on the estate if none had died or moved away. In fact, only 54 deer were counted. Very few dead deer or skeletons have been found and virtually no culling takes place on the estate. Therefore the deer must leave the estate and we have noted already that the bucks do. The death of deer on the main road bordering part of the estate provides further evidence of movement to and from it. In Epping Forest, young deer formed a high proportion of those killed in road traffic accidents and the same is probably true at South Weald.

Well-used deer path. Fallow are creatures of habit.

Buck grooming. Note velvet beginning to clean from trez tine.

A given area can accommodate only so many deer before it becomes overcrowded, whether it is an enclosed park or an open estate. What happens to the deer born on the estate? Do other deer move from the area to make way for them or do they themselves leave when old enough? Although these questions cannot be answered completely, our studies give some clues as to what happens. Some fawns, both male and female, stay on the estate until they are yearlings. Of the five newly born fawns, four male and one female, caught in June 1967, at least four were seen frequently during their first year. Only two newly born doe fawns have been marked and both were seen on the estate in their second, third and fourth years. Although they probably left the estate from time to time, they were using it for at least the first three years of their life. Six newly born buck fawns have been marked and the observations on these animals have been augmented by those on yearling bucks, which can be distinguished readily by their spike antlers. None of the four marked buck fawns caught in June 1967 was seen on the estate after November 1968 despite numerous observations of other tagged deer. Yearlings with hard antlers are seen only rarely between the end of March and late August, when the previous year's fawns shed the velvet from their antlers; this suggests that the majority of buck fawns leave the estate at about 18 to 20 months of age. By this time they are independent of their mothers although at the time of the rut lone yearling males looking rather "lost" are sometimes present. Whether these animals depart spontaneously or follow the adult bucks when they leave is unknown. In a study of 465 marked white-tailed deer, Hawkins and Klimstra found that 80 per cent of male fawns emigrated as yearlings but only 13 per cent of female fawns did so. Two marked male fallow yearlings, at least one of which was born on the estate, were not seen after October until they turned up as young bucks for the rut a year later, but neither has been seen on the estate again.

Therefore it appears that, whereas some doe fawns continue to frequent for several years the area where they were born, most, if not all, the buck fawns leave the area as yearlings, some returning as adults for the rut. Emigration of deer from the estate is the main factor in maintaining the population at a relatively stable level.

Behaviour

The daily behaviour of fallow deer, even more than their seasonal behaviour, is affected by weather, time of year, availability of food and disturbance as well as their sex and age. Consequently, the pattern of behaviour observed in one locality may be very different from that in another area.

Fallow do not like strong winds or driving rain, which cause them to seek shelter in the lee of a hedge or a wood. Light rain does not seem to worry them as they can often be seen grazing in fields during drizzle. They seem to appreciate the sun: even on a sunny winter's day, they may bask in a sheltered spot. Fallow are active both in the day and at night and are extremely wary: a strange object or even a change in the position of a familiar object results in great suspicion. In areas where disturbance is frequent, they may only emerge from cover at dusk, and return as dawn breaks, whereas in quieter areas they can be seen either grazing or resting in fields for much of the day. The various activities which comprise a day in the life of a fallow deer are feeding, resting, grooming, ruminating and moving from area to area. Few systematic observations appear to have been made on the proportions of the day fallow spend on these activities. As dawn breaks, they are usually to be found feeding and this is as good a time as any to watch them; light is increasing and the deer have had the night to become settled, although early-morning mist may reduce visibility. Gillian Puttick observed eight does each for one day, her observations being conducted from mid-May to the end of September during daylight hours only. She found that the deer spent their time as follows:

	Per cent
Grazing	27-50
Lying and ruminating	7-21
Lying without ruminating	5-31
Standing and moving	14-40
Other activities	2-20

The transition in a herd from feeding to resting is gradual, not sudden. First one deer stops feeding and lies down, then another and another until all the herd is at rest; this change in behaviour occupying up to half an hour or so, depending upon the size of the herd. During periods of rest the deer will often be seen grooming themselves. Mutual grooming by adults does not appear to be common although does and fawns groom each other. They scratch themselves with their hind feet or, in males, with their antlers even when in velvet (page 167). The teeth and mouth are used to groom their coats.

Fallow may assume many positions when resting and these appear to depend upon whether or not they are ruminating and the degree of rest involved. Page 189 shows the position usually adopted whilst resting and ruminating. Ruminating may be interspersed with periods of simply resting. On warm, sunny days some of the deer may lie with their necks and heads stretched forward so that their chins rest on the ground. They may also curl up, their heads turned back on their bodies and resting on their fore legs. These two positions are adopted when fallow are completely relaxed. Resting and ruminating, unlike grazing, are not synchronised among individuals. Occasionally an animal may stand, change position and lie down again or even graze for a few moments before resting again. Apparently responsibility for the security of the herd can be taken by any member of the group, even a fawn, and may change during the period of rest.

Antlers are useful for scratching.

Hand tame but apprehensive.

When alarmed, fallow bunch together and face the disturbance, with ears forward and tails raised.

The distance between individuals of a group at rest varies widely. Heidemann estimated that adult bucks each claimed an area of between 3.5 and 12.3 square metres whereas members of the doe herd each claimed only 1.5 to 2.1 square metres. Fallow may rest in all types of habitat, woods, copses, rank vegetation, pasture and arable fields, the choice depending on the sex of the animal, the degree of disturbance and weather conditions. Heidemann found that the fallow avoided areas near roads, fields used by cattle, and thick undergrowth. The opposite is true at South Weald, the deer frequently resting in open fields within 100 metres of a major road and in those occupied by cattle. Furthermore, they may retire to rest in patches of dense thorn scrub if there has been much disturbance. Clearly it is unwise to generalise on the behaviour of fallow. The resting areas may be the same as the grazing areas. It is perhaps wrong to refer to these places as traditional, but suitable ones may be used over many years. The does at South Weald often use the same fields to rest in the afternoon as they did when we first visited the area twelve years ago. The actual resting place on bare soil or on the forest floor may be scraped with the fore feet before the deer lies down but this is not done before resting on deep vegetation. Often this scraping is so superficial that the ground surface is unaffected. Some of these resting hollows are used repeatedly, those at Salzau sometimes attaining a depth of 20cm. Fallow may also rest standing up. One sees them frequently on the edge of a wood bordering a field, just standing and apparently doing nothing, although a certain amount of grooming may take place and, on hot days, ears and tails are being flicked continually. The resting period usually ceases as gradually as it started, if the herd is not disturbed. On getting up, the deer stretch and often raise their tails and defaecate.

When alarmed, all the herd may rise or stop feeding simultaneously. In doe herds, it is the adult and yearling does which appear most alert to suspected danger,

The cause of some accidents: dogs should be kept under control. The bucks' raised and flared out tails warn other deer of danger.

Up and over with ease. These young bucks prefer to jump a fence: often fallow push between the strands. *S. R. Worsfold.*

the fawns and yearling bucks apparently being less concerned. With wild bucks, the oldest ones are reputed to show the greatest mistrust. In captivity, the reverse appears to be the case: the mature bucks in a park are frequently the animals that become hand tame. Likewise, a fawn born to a tame doe in captivity is much more wary than its dam. The behaviour of deer is influenced by experience. The wary beast in the wild is more likely to survive to maturity whereas in parks, the older deer have become accustomed to man.

Fallow deer detect danger by sight, smell and sound. Heidemann considers that optical recognition of the enemy provides the chief impulse to flee. The flight distance is very variable, depending upon the individual animal and the circumstances and, in wild deer, may be as great as 700 metres. Cadman, however, considers that of these three senses, sight is the least keen and smell the most efficient because fallow will often overlook a person who remains still against a dark background. Fallow deer have a keen sense of smell. If unsure of a disturbance, they can be seen raising their heads and nosing the air; if they get a whiff of human scent, away they go. Scent probably also plays a very important part in communication between individual deer but little is known about the use of the various scent glands in fallow. Their hearing is acute and the snap of a twig under the foot of a careless observer will put them on the alert.

When alarmed, fallow have a wide range of signals, both vocal and non-vocal, with which to warn other members of the herd of danger. The action taken by fallow when disturbed depends on the habitat. They often appear to take little notice of people walking quietly along a path close to them in a wood, but one has only to stop and gesticulate or take a few steps towards them and off they run. If much noise is made when entering a wood, the deer usually move quietly away and will not be seen. In open fields, where they have no cover, they may flee when one is still a field or more away. Fallow can be approached much more closely on horseback or in a vehicle.

When aware of possible danger fallow usually move closer together, hold their necks vertical, ears cupped forward and all look in the direction of the disturbance (page 168). Fallow are very inquisitive and, if they are unsure of the cause of the disturbance, such as a motionless deer-watcher, they will take stiff, not relaxed, steps in a hesitating manner in the direction of the enemy. They may stamp a fore foot as well. This rigid stance, as opposed to their usual slow and easy movements, and the stamping are alarm signals and immediately warn others of danger. As they approach, their heads move from side to side and up and down, and give the impression that they are "peering". If the watcher remains still and the deer are convinced it was a false alarm, they will return to what they were doing previously. However, once they realise that danger is present, a doe gives a short, sharp bark which may be repeated a few times, and then they move off with their characteristic

A disturbed fallow leaping through standing corn. *K. E. Hoy.*

alarm gait, known as pronking, pause and then run quickly with tails raised. The bark is not repeated by the other members of the herd; it is limited to the animal which barked first. Does are capable of barking throughout the year, we have heard them in every month except November, December and February. It appears to be a common alarm signal particularly when they have fawns nearby. When alarmed, the raised tail is fluffed out but fallow do not have the ability to flare out their rump patches like a powder-puff in the same way as roe and sika deer.

The pronk is a characteristic aspect of fallow behaviour and consists of the animal bouncing stiff-legged on all four feet. It is used by many African ungulates such as antelopes and gazelles and also by wapiti and mule deer. Pronking is a very effective alarm signal, the sound of all four feet striking the ground at the same time can be heard readily in a wood in the still of the night. Pronking may also act as a visual alarm signal, in that in most colour varieties the leaps are accompanied by flashes of white from the rump patch and underside of the raised tail as well as the pale belly. The gait is used by fallow when disturbed unexpectedly but, if danger is close, the deer just run. Young fawns only a few days old can pronk; a doe moving in this manner with her tiny fawn pronking after her is an amusing sight. This gait does not always appear to be used as a sign of danger, a captive doe and her fawn have been seen chasing each other in playful mood around their paddock and then suddenly breaking into a pronk. Bucks also pronk.

The other gaits used by fallow are the walk, the trot, the bound and the gallop or run. When trotting, fallow usually place two diagonally opposite legs on the ground at the same time; the speed is intermediate between the walk and the gallop. Both the bound and the gallop are fast gaits. When bounding, both fore legs move in unison, as do both hind legs. Fallow can jump well (page 170) although, unless harassed, they push under or through a fence or hedge if possible, rather than go over it. They can swim well and will not hesitate to plunge into a stream to avoid danger, shaking themselves like dogs when they emerge.

CHAPTER ELEVEN

Ecology

FALLOW have a pronounced effect on the countryside, whether it is by providing sport and pleasure to those who hunt or watch them or by damaging the farmer's crops and the forester's trees. Likewise, the results of man's activities, such as increasing urbanisation and use of the countryside, have a profound effect on the deer. In the New Forest, the number of camping nights—one person camping for one night—increased six-fold between 1960 and 1970 when it reached about 600,000. This is the type of change with which the deer have to contend. The decline of fallow deer in Epping Forest and their move to surrounding agricultural estates is due, we believe, largely to the increasing use and disturbance of the Forest. The relationship between fallow deer and the plants and animals, including man, that share their environment, in other words their ecology, is an important aspect of their natural history.

Habitat

Fallow live in a wide variety of habitats. In Britain, they are predominantly forest animals inhabiting deciduous and mixed woodlands but less frequently mature coniferous ones, although they spend much of their time in nearby fields. Areas which are predominantly agricultural and devoid of woods are rarely frequented, because they lack cover and shelter. The woods need not be large; those of only five hectares can provide ideal fallow country, if they have plenty of undergrowth and are interspersed with agricultural land and not houses. Unlike red and roe deer, fallow are not at home on open, rugged moorland such as occurs in northern England and over much of the Scottish Highlands, although they may inhabit the wooded valleys.

Fallow appear to favour similar types of habitat in other countries in western Europe although in Holland they occur in some coniferous woods on the coastal dunes. In southern Spain, fallow inhabit the plans of the Coto Donaña where the vegetation is *Halium* thickets dotted with gorse and isolated cork oaks. According to Swift and Holloway, the fallow's principal habitat in Turkey is maquis scrub, with plants such as oak, evergreen oleander and strawberry trees; the deer occur also in the pine woods, but rarely go above 800 metres altitude.

Fallow are field-loving animals. Black, common and white does and fawns alerted whilst grazing.

The fallow deer in the Pacific Coastal Range of California, which has the same latitude as Turkey and southern Spain, inhabit the oak woodlands and the grasslands between 250 and 1,000 metres altitude but they usually avoid the coniferous forests and the chaparral, the American equivalent of the maquis. Further east in America, fallow live in agricultural land and small woods on the edge of the Nebraska sandhills much as they do in England, although the vegetation is different. On Little St Simons Island in Georgia, the fallow frequent both the salt marshes and the oak woods of the uplands. The fallow on Sidney Island near Vancouver, in British Columbia, inhabit fields and mixed deciduous and coniferous woods comprising mainly Douglas fir, red alder, garry oak, broadleaf oak and arbutus.

In South America, the fallow in Argentina inhabit mountainous areas, or sierra, whereas in Chile they live in eucalyptus, pine and southern beech forests. The fallow in New Zealand also live in the indigenous beech forest but most frequent the lower bush and scrub zones of the valley sides and river flats. In the Caples Valley, Otago, however, the deer may move higher up the sides of the valleys to the upper bush limit if the valley floor becomes snow covered in winter. The animals also move from the river terraces to the mountainous flax belt immediately above the timber line as spring progresses.

The many different types of habitat in which fallow deer live and breed are testimony to their adaptability, which is probably to their advantage in view of the radical changes taking place in the countryside.

Food

Throughout their range, fallow are predominantly grazing animals, feeding in fields, pastures and meadows although trees and shrubs are commonly browsed.

The only comprehensive study of the food eaten by fallow deer is that completed recently by Jackson for those in the New Forest. Firstly, he surveyed the vegetation to find what food was available and then he spent many hours not only watching fallow feeding but also examining the rumen contents of deer culled or killed accidentally. Some idea of the extensive nature of his work can be obtained from the fact that, from April 1971 to October 1972, he made 1,551 observations of fallow feeding and recorded the type of plant eaten in no less than 80,672 "bites". The contents of 325 rumina were analysed. Only those who have handled the chewed and partially digested contents of a deer's rumen will appreciate what a labour of love this work was.

What a fallow deer eats will obviously depend upon what is available and this varies both seasonally and annually as well as with the locality. In the New Forest, heather is common and forms an important part of the winter diet, accounting for about a quarter of the food consumed in February. At South Weald heather does not occur but the deer find other plant species to feed upon. Acorns form an important item in the autumn diet of the deer at South Weald and in the New Forest. In 1970 and in 1971, acorns were plentiful and, together with other fruit, accounted for 50 to 60 per cent of the November diet of the New Forest fallow. In 1972, however, the acorn crop was poor, so fruits accounted for under five per cent of their food in November: conifers, heather, holly and bramble were eaten in much larger amounts than in the previous two years. The proportions of grasses and herbs eaten varied little between the three years. The seasonal changes in the main types of food eaten by fallow deer in the New Forest are given in Figure 12.

The food of fallow determined by Jackson from analysis of rumen contents agreed well with his observations of food eaten, apart from leaves of coniferous trees. Large quantities of conifer leaves were found in the rumina although fallow were rarely seen to feed on conifer brashings and thinnings, probably because of the

Cornfields provide food and cover. The giraffe-necked posture gives the doe a better view of the photographer. *R. A. Cowlin.*

difficulty of finding and watching deer in these plantations without disturbing them.

The species of flowering plants and conifers eaten by fallow in the New Forest is given in Appendix III.

Grasses, rushes and sedges are among the principal foods of fallow deer throughout the year. Sweet grasses, such as species of *Agrostis, Festuca, Holcus* and *Poa,* are eaten readily whereas the purple moorgrass, tufted hair-grass and bristle agrostis are eaten much less frequently although the new shoots and the seed heads are often relished. Herbs are an important summer food and at least 60 species are eaten by the New Forest fallow; the only common ones apparently not eaten are foxglove, ragwort and stinging nettle. The first two species are extremely poisonous to many animals, which appear to have an innate sense about not eating certain plants which may prove harmful; perhaps they are deterred by taste or smell. Grasses and herbs appear to be important foods for fallow wherever they live, which is not surprising for animals that spend so much of their time grazing.

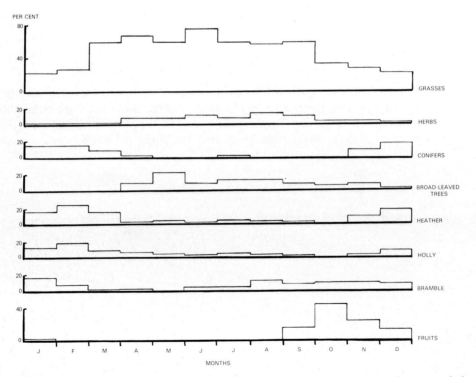

Seasonal changes in the main items of the diet of fallow deer in the New Forest, based upon analysis of rumen contents. (adapted from Jackson). Figure 12.

Fallow are also found frequently in woodland.

The leaves of bramble remain green through much of the winter, particularly in a mild climate like that of southern England. Consequently, this plant, although eaten throughout the year, forms a common item in the winter diet of fallow. Ivy is also eaten readily, particularly in winter. The leaves and shoots of broad-leaved trees and shrubs form a major item of the diet from spring to autumn. A wide variety of species is eaten, including apple, ash, beech, birch, hawthorn, hornbeam, horse chestnut, oak, pear, plum and willow. Fallow appear to prefer the soft, newly unfurled leaves to the older, more leathery ones. In the New Forest, birch was present in the rumina of over 90 per cent of the deer examined in April and accounted for two-thirds of the browse eaten. Beech became important when the buds opened in May and this was followed by oak. In May, the deer spent almost half their feeding time browsing. The branches of many species of tree which have not been browsed sweep down to the ground, whereas those that have been browsed by fallow deer end at a uniform height, a browse line, about one and a half to two metres from the ground (page 77). Dead leaves of many species of tree are also eaten and in November they may form almost a tenth of the diet. Many of the dead leaves, such as ash, are partly green when they fall. Holly, both prickled and plain leaved, is eaten throughout the year, particularly in winter and spring, when it may form up to a fifth of the diet.

Conifers are planted in many of the inclosures of the New Forest and brashings and thinnings from these were browsed by fallow mainly from November to February and in some animals accounted for up to 70 per cent of the rumen contents. Nine species of conifer were found by Jackson in the rumina but Scots pine, which covers about a quarter of the area of the inclosures, was by far the most frequent. Corsican pine, on the other hand, although occupying 12 per cent of the inclosures, was not found in the fallow rumina. However, much of the conifer eaten by the deer resulted from forestry operations such as brashing rather than being taken from the trees. Norway and sitka spruces, western hemlock and Douglas fir were also eaten to a smaller extent. Several deer culled in March and April had fed on yew; our captive fallow browse it frequently, although excessive amounts are said to cause fatal results.

The importance of fruits has been noted already. The deer select acorns and beech mast, which may be swallowed whole, but leave behind the cups and husks. Blackberries, chestnuts, crab apples, haws and holly berries have all been found in fallow stomachs. Barking of trees occurs in the winter and, in Essex, elm saplings seem particularly prone to attack. The barks of holly and various conifers were found in about a fifth of the rumina examined from the New Forest in winter. Ferns, mosses and 13 species of fungi were also taken in small amounts.

Some deer frequent litter bins near picnic sites and evidence of their forays can be seen in the stomachs on post-mortem examination. Polythene bags were the most frequently found foreign objects in the fallow of Richmond Park. Eleven whole

A browse line. Horse chestnut tree (a) browsed by deer and (b) the natural shape protected from deer and other grazing animals.

Norma Chapman.

polythene bags, some still advertising their original contents, were found in one five year old buck, together with a 40cm length of rubber, 3cm wide. Other articles found in the stomachs of fallow have included ribbon, parts of rubber balloons, silver paper, elastic bands, sweet wrappers, cigarette ends, string, cotton fabric and nylon thread. The results of examining the stomachs of 59 fallow killed accidentally in Richmond Park are summarised in Table 13. Although mature bucks were generally the most frequent scavengers around the litter bins, foreign articles were found just as often in does. There was, however, a far higher incidence of foreign objects in animals older than two years. Ten of the does, but only one buck, were over six years of age, probably reflecting the different age structures of the doe and buck herds in the park. Although the "pre-pack" age has accentuated this problem, it is not a new hazard. Early this century a dead fallow deer in Greenwich Park had two hatfuls of orange peel removed from its stomach and other members of the herd were said to have consumed large quantities of gooseberry tart, cloth and even mutton bones and venison cutlets!

Fallow deer appear to drink rarely, getting their water from dew and the vegetation.

Feeding Behaviour

Fallow deer probably feed sporadically throughout the twenty-four hours, periods of feeding being interspersed with periods of rest and rumination. The

Fallow does, common (left) and menil (right), in winter coat. The scattered long hairs are particularly noticeable on the menil.

proportions of the day and night spent feeding are unknown but probably vary with the time of year, the age and sex of the animal, and the degree of disturbance. In undisturbed places, fallow may be seen feeding at all hours of the day. They are usually grazing well before first light, when there appears to be a period of intense feeding which continues into the dawn. As the sun rises, the deer often retire to rest. There is frequently another more continuous period of feeding in the late afternoon or early evening. At South Weald, observations from a car fitted with a spotlight on the roof showed that fallow continued feeding after darkness fell. Later in the evening the deer were usually found resting and ruminating although some animals were grazing at midnight.

Table 13. Incidence of foreign objects in the stomachs of deer from Richmond Park

	3 months to 2 years		over 2 years	
	Male	Female	Male	Female
Number of deer examined	13	17	13	15
Per cent with foreign objects	8	24	62	80

When grazing, all the deer in the group usually move slowly in the same direction (see below) each plucking a bite here and there, so avoiding eating any particular plant completely. Deer searching for a particular food, such as acorns, move at random to and fro in different directions. Fallow also eat bark stripped from trees; by using their incisiform teeth as a chisel, the bark is loosened and then pulled off while gripped between the teeth and the dental pad.

Menil, white and common fallow deer, in winter coats, all grazing in the same direction.

Loss of weight and condition in males during the rut has been mentioned already and bucks killed whilst rutting have often had empty stomachs. Nevertheless, we have examined 14 mature bucks which were killed in road accidents in October and November but none had an empty stomach. This suggests that only mature animals at the peak of their rut may stop feeding. Young bucks hanging around the edge of a rutting territory certainly feed.

The diet of fawns changes gradually from liquid to solid as they develop. Soil is ingested and solid foods such as grasses are nibbled within a few days of birth, although rumination does not start until later. A fallow fawn observed by Burger first showed ruminating movements when seventeen days old. The animal lay in a sleeping position, with the side of the head resting on the body; five consecutive but irregular phases of chewing were observed. On the nineteenth day, while ruminating, the fawn adopted a normal resting position, with the head up, but the movements, although still irregular and initially similar to "munching", were more uniform than two days earlier. At twenty-four days the fawn ruminated, while in the normal resting position, for longer periods and the chewing movements had a regular pattern. By the time fawns are two or three months old they are grazing regularly with their dams.

Relations with Other Species

Fallow deer have been introduced so widely that they often live in the same area as either native deer, as in America, or with other introduced species of deer, as in New Zealand. How do fallow get on with these other species and is there any competition between them? The word 'competition' has a different meaning to different people, so we must clarify the term as used here. Milne defined competition between animals as that which occurs when animals of the same or different species endeavour to gain a common resource which is in short supply.

Roe deer are abundant throughout the coniferous woods which comprise Thetford Chase in eastern England. Yet fallow are rare there, occurring only in the King's Forest, a well-separated block of woodland where roe also occur and which contains deciduous trees. Only 60 kilometres away, in the coniferous woods of Aldewood Forest on sandy heathland near the coast, fallow occur but roe deer are absent. A similar pattern of distribution has been reported in other areas: fallow have not become well established in the coniferous woods of Kielder Forest on the borders of England and Scotland nor in those of the English Lake District but roe deer are abundant in both areas. On the other hand, both species of deer are common in the mixed woodlands of the New Forest. There are several possible reasons why the abundance of fallow in one area may coincide with the relative scarcity of roe and vice versa.

Carne believes that fallow, being alien to Britain, are intruders and usurpers and a powerful deterrent to roe. He claims that historical records show that, as fallow have increased in an area, roe have decreased or even become extinct. Delap goes one stage further and believes that there is antipathy and antagonism between the two species. One must remember, however, that although fallow deer were probably re-introduced, they were present in Britain in the Pleistocene interglacial periods. Furthermore, in many areas of England, the roe deer were re-introduced relatively recently, having died out in earlier centuries. Roe deer were liberated at Milton Abbas in Dorset in 1800, in Thetford Chase in the middle of the nineteenth century and elsewhere in Britain at other times before and since. It is the descendants of these animals that have colonised so much of southern England and resulted in their present widespread distribution. Fallow and roe deer are both indigenous to other countries, such as Turkey, so it seems unlikely that the mere act of introducing a species would change its behaviour. There also appears to be little evidence to substantiate the idea that the two species are antagonistic to each other. While studying the fallow in the New Forest, Jackson noticed on 41 separate occasions that their feeding areas were shared with roe deer. The only sign of social interaction noticed between the two species was that both responded to the others' alarm signals.

The changes in the relative proportions of the two species of deer over a period of years cannot be considered in isolation. The changes in a garden that meet one's return from holiday are obvious; look at a house that has been left empty for a few months and the once neatly kept garden is a veritable jungle. Heaths and woods change too, although not so rapidly: scrubland develops gradually into woodland and then into tall forest. A deer's habitat is changing all the time, a point which is often forgotten. Relations between fallow, red and roe deer in Drummond Hill Forest in Perthshire were studied by Batcheler. He concluded that the three species occupied different types of habitat and this, rather than interspecific antipathy or antagonism, was why roe and fallow were rarely found together. Roe are browsing animals and more adapted to a woodland existence than the field-loving fallow.

Another point to remember when considering the relative abundance of deer is that they do not just arrive; they must be introduced either intentionally or by natural spread. Thetford Chase was planted on the sandy heathlands, known as Breckland, where roe deer had been introduced the previous century. The roe were consequently well established when the young conifer plantations provided an ideal habitat with abundant food. Although fallow will live in young plantations, there were probably few fallow if any in the Thetford area. The Reverend Lubbock made no mention of them in his *Observations on the Fauna of Norfolk* although he mentioned roe deer. Roe were not present in the area when Aldewood Forest was planted although fallow were in the nearby park at Campsea Ashe and escapees were probably living in the adjacent woods. Opportunity and habitat are more likely to determine whether fallow or roe preponderate in an area rather than social interactions between the two species, in the sense of one species driving the other out.

Fallow deer have been seen feeding with native mule deer in California but the association was probably accidental, occurring when deer of one species enter or pass through an area occupied by the other. The habitats of these two species differ; whereas both frequent oak woodland and grassy areas, fallow are rarely found in the chaparral occupied by the mule deer. In Nebraska, fallow are said to compete to some extent with mule deer and the native white-tailed deer, presumably because they occur in the same type of habitat.

Fallow get on well with domestic stock which are allowed to share the grazing in parks. Frequently we have seen wild fallow, cattle and horses all grazing in the same field. The ancient right of pannage, whereby pigs are turned loose in the forest to feed on acorns, is still exercised in some areas. Here they may compete with fallow for this fruit, a favourite food of both species.

Relations with Man

For centuries, fallow deer have provided food, sport and pleasure for man and the same is still true today, although perhaps fewer people now eat venison regularly. The form of the sport has varied over the centuries, from stalking with bow and arrow and coursing with dogs, to hunting on horseback with horns and hounds, and now stalking with a rifle. Hunting fallow on horseback became popular in the fourteenth century when the first specific mention was made of the Royal Buckhounds. The pack was well exercised for several centuries and its last visit to Richmond Park was in 1753. Probably few race-goers today realise that the Ascot Races were instituted in 1711 primarily for a race for horses which had hunted with the Royal Buckhounds. A link to the present time survives in the name of one race, the Royal Hunt Cup. Other packs also existed but when the Savernake Buckhounds were disbanded in 1968 only one pack remained, the New Forest Buckhounds which hunt twice a week in September and from November to April. They take about ten bucks a year but on occasions, particularly in early spring, aim only at dispersing groups of bucks from agricultural land.

Deer management has always been a controversial topic and, no doubt, will remain so. There are two sides to every argument. For years, fallow were treated as vermin to be destroyed and eradicated; an understandable though perhaps short-sighted view for anyone whose trees, orchards or crops had been severely damaged. On the other hand, there are those who enjoy seeing these fine beasts, even if only a fleeting glimpse of them, and believe that they should be allowed to live in peace. However, we delude ourselves if we believe that deer will live in peace if left alone. There are probably more wild fallow today than at any time since the Elizabethan period and, with the absence of natural predators, they will increase dramatically if their numbers are not controlled. Six thousand fallow were culled in an 8,000 hectare forest in the Otago region of New Zealand in 1957 and 1958 because of the damage they had caused. This heavy cull far from exterminated the fallow; each year from 1962 to 1971, between 1,500 and 2,000 deer were culled in the three state forests of the Blue Mountains in Otago. If allowed to increase unchecked, fallow will eat themselves out of house and home, impoverish the countryside and eventually die of disease and starvation. This situation has already arisen with other species of mammal in various parts of the world where areas have been degraded by overgrazing followed by erosion of the soil.

This is perhaps easier to appreciate if one considers a typical, well-stocked deer park of 160 hectares containing 20 bucks and 60 does, or one animal per two hectares. Assuming the does are adult and breed each year, there will be 2,930 deer in the park after only ten years, or almost 37 deer per two hectares! This calculation makes no allowance for mortality, but even half that number of deer would mean almost 10 deer per hectare. Admittedly the area available to the deer in the park is restricted, but so it is for wild fallow in a heavily populated island like Britain. Furthermore, certain types of habitat are being reduced as hedgerows, scrub and copses disappear under the plough or the concrete of urbanisation. Even though the area under afforestation in Britain has increased greatly in the past 50 years, much of it is unsuitable for fallow. There are few fallow in the 42,300 hectares of conifer which make up the Border Forest, Britain's largest forest. There is no doubt that fallow must be managed and, whereas this usually means culling because natality outweighs mortality, this is not invariably so. A proper balance must be maintained between the interests of agriculture and forestry on the one side and amenity and conservation on the other, not forgetting the interests of the deer: aims that are easier stated than achieved.

Although it is not true that fallow deer cannot be exterminated, this would be both undesirable and impracticable. The great reduction in the numbers of wild deer in England in the nineteenth century has been mentioned already. The fallow deer in Turkey have been decimated and are now threatened with extinction, largely as a result of excessive hunting, and grazing by domestic animals. The fallow population of the southern part of Monavgat Forest in Turkey, comprising some 50,000 hectares, was thought to be about 25 animals when Swift and Holloway surveyed the area in 1967 for the United Nations. In contrast, over 50,000 goats, 10,000 sheep and numerous horses, oxen, donkeys and camels grazed the 232,000 hectares of the entire Forest.

Methods of control must be chosen carefully, for the wrong method may aggravate rather than alleviate the problem. In its early days, the Forestry Commission in Britain tried to reduce the number of fallow in forests by driving them towards shot-guns. They were not alone in this practice, but this method resulted in an even more rapid spread of deer in the countryside. Fortunately

In spite of roadside warnings, many deer are killed in road accidents . . . .
Norma Chapman

policies have changed and the Forestry Commission is now in the forefront of deer management, humane and selective control with a rifle being the order of the day. In certain other European countries, such as Germany, there is a much stronger tradition of deer hunting and management. The thrill of hunting and the possibility of acquiring an impressive head of antlers means that people will pay large sums of money just to shoot deer. Although paying to stalk red deer has been common in the Scottish Highlands for well over a century, the idea of paying to stalk fallow is a more recent innovation. This practice is developed better on the continent: in Hungary, the charge for shooting a prime buck with trophy-quality antlers may be £2,000; this includes neither the cost of the carcase nor the services of a professional guide. The antlers of Hungarian fallow are considered amongst the best in the world, hence the high fees. Stalking is rigorously controlled and the deer are managed to produce trophy antlers and to reduce damage in the forest to an acceptable level. At present, the antlers of fallow in Britain very rarely attain this quality, probably because of neglected management.

Less than ten years ago, venison could be bought in Britain for about 18p per kilogram but the price has risen greatly, wholesalers now paying 55p per kilogram. The letting of hunting and increased venison prices may make deer management a more economical proposition. The forester or farmer is more likely to tolerate some damage if he can see some return in sporting rights. Deer and venison sales perhaps should be regarded as a forest or farm crop, like timber and corn, to be managed accordingly.

Having accepted that management is necessary, the first requirement is to carry out a census of the fallow present. On occasions of severe marauding, however, it may be necessary to cull first and then to prepare a proper management plan for the future. It is as well to remember that deer do not respect man-made boundaries, so management calls for a co-operative approach among neighbouring landowners and their tenants. It is useless trying to reduce the numbers of deer in an area if, as soon as they are shot, animals from a neighbouring estate take up residence. The formation of local deer control societies in Britain is helping in this respect but there is still a long way to go to catch up with continental practice. The game laws of the German Federal Republic are based upon ownership of land. Two sorts of hunting grounds are distinguished, "the owned hunting area", which must be at least 75 hectares, and the "community area" of at least 150 hectares. All landowners who do not own the minimum of 75 hectares are required by law to join their local game society which administers and leases the community hunting area. The law allows for the above areas to be increased. A deer culling plan has to be agreed by the appropriate Game Council. Sportsmen must possess game licences which are granted only after they have passed the difficult huntsman's examination which requires a knowledge of game animals as well as weapons.

. . . . and others are lucky to survive.

There are several ways of carrying out a census of fallow deer, the choice depending upon the locality, the aims and the personnel available. Fallow, despite their size, are surprisingly difficult animals to count accurately, even in a park. Most censuses probably result in an under-estimate, possibly by as much as 60 to 70 per cent. For example, fallow on a wooded Danish island of 250 hectares were exterminated by Sporon-Fiedler: the population had been estimated as 30 deer but 42 were shot, an error of 32 per cent. Because the area was an island the probability of emigration and immigration during the culling period can be ruled out. If such a large error can be obtained in a small restricted area, how much greater the possible error must be in a large forest.

The best time to attempt to count fallow is in winter and early spring when ground cover is sparse and the leaves of deciduous trees have fallen. The precise date to be chosen will depend upon local conditions, remembering that the bucks move from the doe herds at this time of year. Once a procedure, including choice of dates, has been adopted it should be followed yearly unless altered circumstances demand a change. In this way any error should be consistent and trends in the population can be observed even if the count is somewhat inaccurate.

On the South Weald estate, complete counts of the fallow are attempted by driving the deer twice a year, at the end of January and again in mid-March. When disturbed, the deer usually move to a particular small wood and this is taken account of in the census procedure. A line of beaters walks through the various small woods on the estate, all the time attempting to move the deer in the direction of the wood used as a sanctuary. People familiar with the estate and the deer are placed at carefully selected vantage points around the edges of the woods, to watch for deer leaving or breaking back between the beaters. Finally, the deer are moved out of their sanctuary and counted as they cross the fields. The aim of the census is to obtain an estimate of the population and to see how this fluctuates from year to year. A method such as this is impracticable in large areas of woodland because of the very many people who would be required; up to 60 are used at South Weald. The idea that the number and sex of deer in a wood can be estimated from their tracks, although still widely believed, is a fallacy. When planning a census, one cannot do better than read *A Practical Guide to the Study of the Productivity of Large Herbivores* by Golley and Buechner. Although this book does not mention fallow, it outlines the methods and, more important, the pitfalls, in the various procedures which can be used to census deer.

How many fallow deer will the land support or how many can be tolerated? If deer are to be culled, the questions arise of how many, bucks or does, and what ages? The answers depend upon the aims of management. One buck will serve many does, so it is the females that need to be culled if the size of the population is to be reduced; this will have a far greater effect than culling the same number of males. The theoretical maximum increase in a stable fallow population each year is

Resting and ruminating.

73 per cent of *all* the females present if we assume that does reach puberty at about 16 months and give birth to a single fawn. This means that the population increases by 36 per cent each year if there are equal numbers of bucks and does in the herd. Therefore, about one third of the population should be culled each year if it is desired to keep the number of deer constant, due allowance being made for mortality from other causes. If there is a preponderance of does, the number of deer culled must be increased and vice versa.

If deer damage is to be prevented, consideration should be given to fencing the area to be protected, but this is expensive. When a wood or orchard is planted the presence of deer should be taken into consideration just as much as soil, drainage and climate. To plant young trees in traditional rutting areas is asking for trouble. Some species of tree are more prone than others to attack by deer. The use of chemical repellants to deter deer is costly, of limited duration and not particularly effective at present.

In Hungary, where the deer are managed for sport, their number is restricted, an equal sex ratio is aimed for and bucks of the desired quality are not shot before they have reached maturity. This intensive system of deer management is under Government control. Similar policies exist in the German Federal Republic and also in Poland where the density of fallow is limited to between one and three per 100 hectares.

Selective shooting of bucks is reputed to improve the antler quality of the deer but there is little evidence for this assumption in any species of deer, particularly fallow. Sometimes a few deer are introduced into a park herd because "there has not been any change of blood for many years". It should not be forgotten that, although antlers are carried only by bucks, the character is transmitted by both sexes. Only half of the buck's genes are passed to his offspring, which will only pass on a quarter and so on. Consequently the genetic influence of an imported animal soon becomes diluted out. There is nothing intrinsically wrong with inbreeding provided that culling is carried out intelligently. The herd of Père David's deer at Woburn Park in Bedfordshire must be the most inbred in the world, all being the descendants of a handful of deer, but they are still in excellent condition.

An extensive system of deer control operates in New Zealand, where licences to hunt in state forests are issued by the Government; the stalker may shoot whatever deer appears, young or old, good or bad. Trophy antlers comparable to those of the Hungarian bucks are not produced in New Zealand probably because the animals are not allowed to reach a sufficient age. Fallow are included in the Noxious Animals Act 1956, which is administered by the New Zealand Forest Service, making provision for the control and eradication of harmful species. In 1927, attempts were made to control the fallow by poisoning them with strychnine in salt licks and in carrots. Thirty years later, similar attempts were made but this time the poison was sodium fluoroacetate. The bait was dropped from an aeroplane onto clearings in the forest; 247 deer were later found dead, which were thought to represent between 60 and 90 per cent of those on the clearings when the bait was dropped. Red deer, rabbits, hares and opossums were also poisoned. The use of poison is unselective but, provided its action is humane, it may prove a useful form of controlling fallow in special circumstances.

Occasionally the need arises to catch deer either for marking or for moving them to other areas. Besides the long established technique of walking animals into nets, newer methods have been devised. In Kentucky, fallow deer have been caught in nets fired over them by small rockets, or cannons, whilst they were feeding, up to 11 animals being caught at one time. This method has been used most successfully to catch geese and its adaptation to catch deer appears promising. Fallow have also been captured with drugs injected from syringes fired from rifles or cross-bows. The technique is frequently thought to be simple, probably as a result of its wide publicity on television, but in fact it is fraught with problems and should only be undertaken by people aware of all the potential hazards. Some drugs, such as the muscle relaxant succinylcholine, are inhumane because the animal is fully conscious but paralysed, so cannot react to pain or fear. Other drugs such as etorphine, a derivative of morphine, may cause fatal reactions under certain conditions. Nevertheless, suitable drugs are available and, with proper precautions, the technique is valuable for catching individual fallow in special circumstances. Some of the problems of using drugs to capture fallow deer have been outlined by Tschirch.

If fallow are to be managed for meat, then the maximum number of deer that the area will support is required, assuming deer damage is unimportant. The deer at South Weald are not culled and so the density of between 18 and 43 per 100 hectares may represent an optimum for that type of locality. The density of fallow deer in parks is often much greater; 100 per 100 hectares is not uncommon but it must be remembered that in many parks the deer are given supplementary food such as hay and beans in winter. A preponderance of does will be required and yearlings should be culled heavily as this will result in greater productivity. The greatest increase in weight of a fallow occurs in its first year and, although the animals eat as much, or more, in subsequent years, the increase in weight is less. In Australia and New Zealand, this type of management has been taken one step further with the introduction of deer farming. One of the first deer farms in South Australia, at Ashbourne, accommodates eight fallow in five hectares of an 800 hectare cattle and sheep farm, although up to 14 deer have been kept in about half a hectare. Fallow deer farming in New Zealand is regulated by the Noxious Animals in Captivity Regulations 1969 and the Deer Farming Regulations 1969. The farms are confined to the area around North Auckland, which is one of the localities where feral fallow occur. Most of the farms are still building up their stock and have

Rutting bucks battle for supremacy.

fewer than 100 animals, although two established in 1969 and 1970 respectively hold 396 and 764 fallow. Deer farming is more expensive than beef or sheep farming in terms of fencing but the high price of venison and the revenue which can be obtained for antlers, tails, hides and ligaments may make it an economic proposition.

Whitehead in *Deer and their Management* records the weights of the various parts of the body of a buck reputed to be five years old, which was shot one July in Woburn Park. Some of these figures, together with those for bucks and does from Richmond Park and from Essex, indicate how much "waste" there is in a deer carcase (Table 14). Most organs form a relatively constant proportion of the body but fluctuations do occur, particularly with the stomachs and, to a smaller extent, the intestines and their contents. The proportions vary with the time of year and the health of the animal. Jackson found that in culled New Forest fallow the gralloched weight, the carcase less the alimentary tract, was about 84 per cent of the dead weight for a 100kg buck and about 76 per cent for a 50kg doe. The butcher's weight, namely the carcase and skin but less head, feet and all internal organs apart from the kidneys, was about 59 per cent of the dead weight for the same sized buck and about 56 per cent for a 50kg doe. These proportions are very similar to those found by Whitehead. A butchered carcase represents a surprisingly low proportion of a fallow deer. If, say, five per cent is allowed for the skin and ten per cent for the skeleton then the proportion of 'meat' is only about 40 to 45 per cent of the dead weight. Even allowing for the organs that are usually eaten, less than half the weight of a fallow deer is edible.

Table 14. Average weights and ranges of the various parts of fallow deer as a proportion of their body weight

| | | | Per cent of Body Weight | | | |
| | | MALES | | | FEMALES | |
	Number of Animals	Average	Range	Number of Animals	Average	Range
Skeleton (dried)	7	6.9	5.9-8.4	6	6.7	5.6- 8.2
Stomach and contents	26	9.9	3.5-20.1	20	11.0	6.6-19.4
Intestines and contents	26	4.7	2.0-7.9	20	5.5	3.1- 8.2
Spleen	23	0.3	0.2-0.7	14	0.4	0.2 0.7
Liver	3	2.1	1.9-2.2	3	1.8	1.5- 2.3
Heart	1*	0.5	—	7**	—	0.7- 0.8
Kidneys	1*	0.6	—	7**	—	0.2- 0.4
Lungs	1*	1.4	—	—	—	—
Skin	1*	5.4	—	—	—	—
Head with skin	1*	4.4	—	—	—	—

*Whitehead, 1950   **Piekarz, 1964

A fawn ventures out.

CHAPTER TWELVE

Mortality, Diseases and Parasites

THE EFFICIENT management of deer requires a knowledge of the various factors causing changes in the size of the herd. The birth of fawns and the movement of animals have been considered already. Because all deer must die it is important to consider the causes of mortality in fallow deer and the diseases and parasites which may contribute to their death.

In Britain, fallow deer nowadays have no predators apart from man and dog. Foxes are opportunist feeders and certainly eat carcases of young and adult fallow. Therefore the finding of deer remains in fox faeces or near fox earths is not evidence of predation. Some countries still have large mammalian predators: species such as the wolf, brown bear, lynx and jackal survive and may prey on fallow deer and their fawns. In Sweden, Borg found that 382 out of 2,827 roe deer examined died as a result of attacks by predators and that weak or diseased deer were selected preferentially. Wolves are important predators in North America and attack such large deer as moose and reindeer. Mountain lions, bobcats, blackbears and coyotes are also possible predators of fallow deer in that continent.

Mortality

In the absence of natural predators, fallow in Britain must die either from old age, disease or as a result of man's activities. Wild animals that are sick often try to hide and so they are less likely to be seen than healthy ones: consequently, wild deer dying from disease are often not found until they are just heaps of bones and it is too late to establish the cause of death. It is probably for this reason, coupled with the fact that culled deer are generally found to have been healthy, that so little is known of the causes of mortality in wild fallow.

A survey of 115 fallow deer found dead, sick or injured in Richmond Park from 1967 to 1973 showed that 61 per cent of both male and female deer examined had died as a result of accidents, mostly on the roads. About 25 per cent of the deer examined had died either from natural causes or were shot because they were sick (Table 15).

Table 15. Causes of death of 115 fallow deer, 57 males and 58 females, examined from Richmond Park, 1967-1973 (Numbers in brackets refer to diseased animals)

MALES	Per cent Under 1 year	1-7 years	Over 7 years	Total
Road accidents	26 (2)	12 (2)	5 (4)	43 (8)
Other accidents*	7 (2)	11 (9)	0	18 (11)
Disease**	21 (21)	5 (5)	0	26 (26)
Injuries from dogs	2 (2)	2 (2)	0	4 (4)
Injuries from deer	0	2	0	2
Unknown	2	5	0	7
TOTALS	58 (27)	37 (18)	5 (4)	100 (49)

FEMALES	Per cent Under 1 year	1-7 years	Over 7 years	Total
Road accidents	22 (2)	18 (2)	15 (4)	55 (8)
Other accidents*	2	2	2	6
Disease**	14 (14)	2 (2)	8 (8)	24 (24)
Injuries from dogs	7	2 (2)	2	11 (2)
Injuries from deer	0	0	2 (2)	2 (2)
Unknown	0	2	0	2
TOTALS	45 (16)	26 (6)	29 (14)	100 (36)

*Includes, for example, death as a result of getting caught in a fence.
**Includes deer shot because they were sick.

Not all the deer that died in the Park were received for examination and therefore the sample is probably biased somewhat in favour of natural mortality, because deer dying from unknown causes were more likely to be sent for examination. Therefore the true percentages for accidental death are likely to be slightly higher and those for natural mortality slightly lower than indicated above. Although these figures do not give the actual incidence of mortality because the total numbers of deer in the Park and those dying in any one year are unknown, they do give an indication of the causes of mortality and age of death. Similar numbers of male and female deer died although there are fewer bucks than does in the Park, which suggests there was a higher incidence of mortality in the male deer. It is a generally accepted fact that in mammals, including man, mortality is higher in males than in females. Put another way, the natural expectation of life of bucks is less than that of does.

Figure 13 shows that there was a very high mortality in the first year of life of both bucks and does as half the deer examined were less than one year old. There was also a higher mortality in does older than seven years compared with bucks but this is a reflection of the age of the deer in the herd in which there were more older

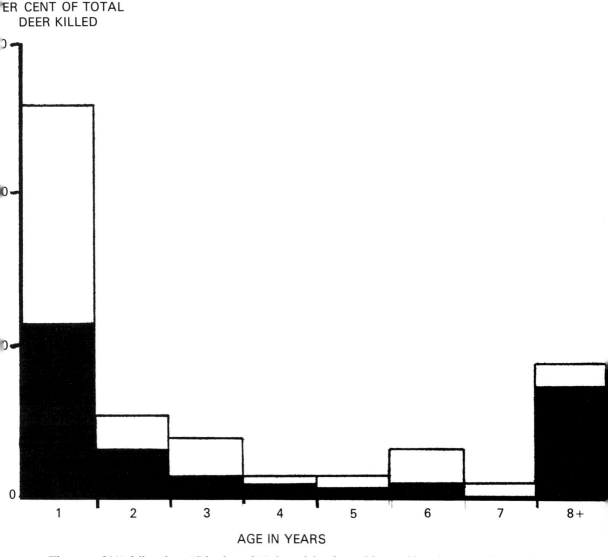

The ages of 115 fallow deer, 57 bucks and 58 does, dying from either accidental or natural causes in Richmond Park, 1967 to 1973.   Figure 13.

females than older males. On the whole, these older does were less healthy than the does which died between one and seven years of age. Hence most natural mortality in these fallow deer appears to occur in the very young and the old; a picture similar to that found in other species of deer that have been studied.

Adult deer of both sexes died in all months of the year, whereas many more fawns died in spring and summer (Figure 14). In spring, natural food and shelter are scarcest and the fawns have been exposed to the rigours of winter. Many of the

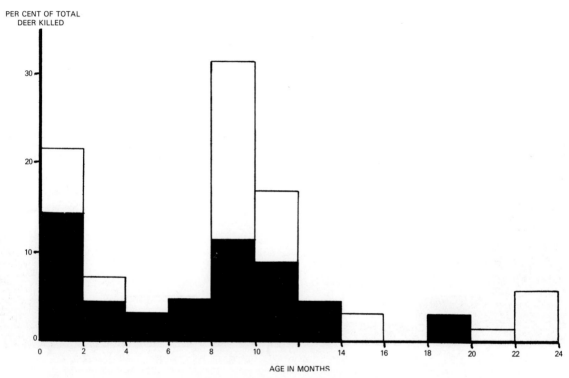

PER CENT OF TOTAL
DEER KILLED

AGE IN MONTHS

The ages of 70 fallow deer, 37 males and 33 females, dying from either accidental or natural causes in the first two years of life in Richmond Park, 1967 to 1973.   Figure 14.

fawns that died were obviously in poor health, being very emaciated. The average weight of 24 fawns which died in February and March was 18kg (range 13.6-29.5) compared with an average weight of 27kg (range 20-34) of 31 fawns culled in the previous November and December. The deer that were culled were on average half as heavy again as those that died in the spring even though they were up to five months younger. A high mortality of fawns in late winter and early spring has been reported from other parks and it may be influenced by management practices as well as by environmental conditions. Does are usually culled in the winter and motherless fawns may be more likely to succumb in adverse conditions. Fallow fawns may be suckled as late as February and March and this source of nourishment is denied to orphans.

Parturition in fallow deer occurs mainly in June and early post-natal mortality accounts for the peak of deaths in mid-summer. Eleven of the 15 deer which died were newly born and six of these were grossly underweight, each weighing between 1.8 and 2.7 kg compared with an average weight of newly born fawns of 4.5 kg. One underweight fawn was stillborn and another was deformed with an undershot lower jaw. The remaining four underweight animals probably were too weak to suck or were deserted by their dams. The causes of this low birth-weight are not known but

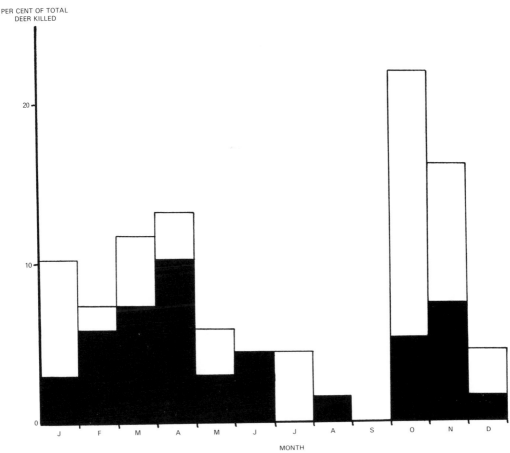

The seasonal distribution of 87 fallow deer, 45 bucks and 42 does, older than one year dying from either accidental or natural causes in Epping Forest and Essex, 1963 to 1973.   Figure 15.

Ueckermann and Hansen have implied that even ill-nourished does have fawns of normal weight. The other five newly born fawns were of normal weight. Three of these were deserted, two probably because of excessive human disturbance and one having been born in November, one had a liver abscess and the cause of death was not discovered for the fifth. Of the four fawns which died between one and eight weeks of age, one had a lung infection and three were killed in road accidents.

A survey of the deer found dead or injured in south-west Essex and in Epping Forest from 1963 to 1973 showed that 86 per cent of the 87 deer examined had been killed in road accidents. This high proportion is not surprising in view of the many main roads in the area and the great density of traffic. Two bucks were killed by trains, seven deer were injured in miscellaneous accidents and had to be shot, one died from a tumour and two died from unknown causes. About 21 per cent of the deer examined were less than one year old and 37 per cent were less than two whereas only 16 per cent were estimated to be about seven years or older.

Fawn deaths were distributed throughout the year whereas there was a peak in October and November in the number of adult deer killed. Over twice as many adults were killed from October to March as were killed from April to September (Figure 15). The high numbers of deer killed in October and November are probably associated with the rut, particularly as almost twice as many adult bucks were killed as adult does. It is well known that the rut is a time of great activity for the bucks. At the peak of this slaughter, deer were being killed in road accidents at the rate of one every three and a half days although this did not occur every year. In Kansas, there was a sharp increase in the numbers of mule deer killed during the rut, when twice as many males as females were killed. Other American States have also reported a sharp increase in "road kills" of deer around the time of the rutting season. The higher number of fallow killed in the winter and early spring compared with the number killed in late spring to early summer may be due to the reduced cover of vegetation in the Forest in the former period, causing the deer to be more readily disturbed. The duration of darkness, which reduces the motorist's chance of seeing deer, may also be a contributory cause of the higher winter mortality. Many of the deer were killed in the evening or at night. Most of the accidents were on the main roads in the area and, in Epping Forest, several "black spots" became apparent where deer were killed most frequently.

Many fallow deer are killed in road accidents in other areas of Britain and Europe. Between 20 and 50 a year were killed in Cannock Chase in Staffordshire between 1962 and 1966. Similar numbers were killed in the New Forest in both 1971 and 1972.

In April 1973 in the Rhein-Main area of West Germany, which covers about 40,000 hectares, the fallow deer population was estimated to be 1,370, of which 650 animals were bucks. During the period 1962 to 1973, 663 fallow died as a result of road accidents and 2,480 were culled. Of the bucks killed in accidents, 27 per cent were less than two years old and 73 per cent were under five years old. The highest mortality of bucks (41 per cent) occurred in the winter between 1st November and 1st February; least accidents (12 per cent) occurred between 1st May and 1st August. This picture is very similar to that observed for deer killed in road accidents in Epping Forest. Unfortunately, Geissler did not publish the corresponding figures for does killed in road accidents in Rhein-Main.

An article in *Wild and Hund* of 5th October 1969 estimated that in the German Federal Republic about 700 to 800 fallow deer were killed annually in road accidents. Although this figure may appear high, it should be remembered that the estimated mortality of roe deer in road accidents was 40,000 to 60,000 a year.

Many of the fallow deer killed in Epping Forest and Essex had been involved in accidents prior to the fatal one, judging from the old fractures, and many had degenerative lesions in one or more bones. It is amazing what severe injuries fallow deer can survive, still managing to lead more or less normal lives. One buck had lost its left hind leg above the hock in a previous accident but the wound had healed completely (page 202). A doe had lost her left fore leg above the elbow, which again had healed, yet she was pregnant, with a well-developed foetus. Three-legged fallow deer have also been seen in other areas of Britain. A wild fallow doe involved in a road accident showed no external injuries but, although well cared for, eventually died 32 days later. She was found to have a fractured jaw, a pelvis fractured in thirteen places and a ruptured diaphragm (pages 203 and 204). On humane grounds, it is generally better to kill deer injured in accidents rather than to try to save them. Three bucks had been caught in fox snares and had escaped, with the remains of the wire nooses embedded in the bones of their fore legs (page 209). Shot gun pellets were found in almost a third of the deer, being just as prevalent in does as in bucks. One buck had been blinded in one eye and the hind quarters of a three month old fawn had been peppered with at least 24 shot gun pellets. The incidence of deer with shot gun pellets was higher in the earlier years of the survey than in the latter ones and one hopes that the cruel practice of taking "pot shots" at deer is dying. Only one case of natural mortality was found and that was a 19 month old doe which had died from a malignant tumour.

Eleven of the 79 wild deer killed in road accidents were previously incapacitated. Missing legs, blindness and wire nooses embedded in legs, which have also been recorded in fallow deer in other areas of Britain and in Europe, must obviously hinder the animals to some extent and make them more liable to accidents.

Although road accidents are major causes of death in fallow deer in Richmond Park and also in Essex and Epping Forest, the proportions of the various age groups and the seasonal distribution of deaths were quite different. No planned culling of the wild deer occurs and the age structure of the population is unknown. Moreover, deer dying from natural causes are much less likely to be found in the wild than in

Young buck which lost his left hind leg in an accident and had a plastic ring stuck on his other hind foot before being killed in a road accident. *Dr D. Chapman.*

the Park. Skeletons of wild deer were found during the course of the survey but only one freshly dead animal not killed accidentally was found. Other causes of accidental death in both wild and park fallow deer are the entanglement of antlers in fences or old wire, or even with those of another buck. Stab wounds inflicted by a buck's antlers followed by infection have also caused the death of both does and bucks; clostridial bacteria, which produce gas gangrene, have been detected in several animals dying in this way. Bad management and overcrowding in deer parks can also lead to high mortality in fallow deer.

Diseases

On the whole, fallow deer are healthy animals and one does not hear of large numbers of deer dying nowadays from "murrain", as occurred in previous centuries. Murrain was the name given in former times to almost any disease affecting animals. A fascinating account of these plagues, which affected domestic stock and other wild animals as well as deer, has been given by Fleming in his monumental work *Animal Plagues*. He records that there was a very severe winter in England in 1254 and that "also there chanced the same year a great murrain, and death of sheep and deer, so that of whole flocks and herds scarce the half escaped". Anthrax, rabies and other severe diseases, although not recognised as such at that time, were rife. The murrain was not restricted to Britain but also struck deer in many other countries of Europe and no doubt in other parts of the world. Cox in *The Royal Forests of England* records that in 1485 in Melksham and Pewsham Forests in Wiltshire, 27 fallow bucks, 35 does and 20 fawns died of murrain; 140 bucks and 200 does died in the following year; and 50 bucks and 90 does and fawns died in

Wild yearling doe which showed no fear after being injured in a road accident. Her looks belie her severe injuries.   *C. W. Hutchings.*

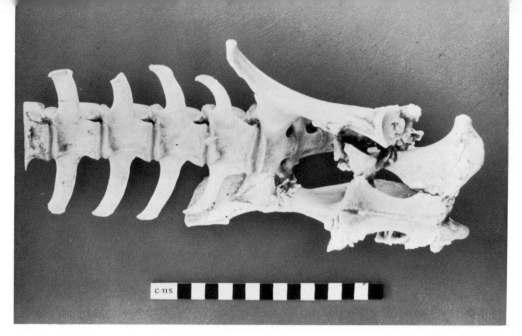

Pelvis of the injured doe, fractured in 13 places.   *Dr D. Chapman.*

1487. In Clarendon Forest, also in Wiltshire, 2,209 deer are reputed to have died of murrain in 1470. Wiltshire was not exceptional and other areas of the country where many deer died are also mentioned by Cox. It should be remembered, however, that there were very large numbers of fallow deer in the country at that time and those dying may have represented only a small proportion of the population. For example, in 1777, 300 deer were found dead from starvation in Boldrewood Walk in the New Forest, but the total population in the Forest was considered to be about 6,000 fallow.

Several diseases have been recorded in fallow deer but many of these cases involved only a single animal in a zoo. Although such occurrences are important to the zoo concerned, of more interest is the frequency with which diseases are found in herds of deer. Very few surveys appear to have been carried out on disease in fallow deer; such surveys are important even if only to show that the deer are healthy and not likely to infect domestic stock. Potentially pathogenic micro-organisms can exist in mammals which may show no clinical signs of the disease. Animals exposed to certain diseases may acquire some immunity, even if they have not exhibited clinical signs which can be detected by examination of a blood sample.

Evidence of avian tuberculosis was found in 13 per cent of fallow deer from the New Forest which were examined by McDiarmid. Bovine tuberculosis caused by *Mycobacterium bovis* was found in almost a quarter of the herd of about 200 fallow deer in a park in Michigan. Pseudotuberculosis, due to *Corynebacterium pyogenes,* has been found in fallow deer in Germany and pseudotuberculosis due to *Pasteurella pseudotuberculosis* in fallow deer in a zoo. McDiarmid also found evidence of brucellosis or contagious abortion in a few fallow, but despite extensive investigations he did not find the causative organism.

Evidence of erysipelas, caused by *Erysipelothrix rhusiopathiae,* was found by Munday in two out of 74 Tasmanian fallow deer. In Britain the bacterium affects pigs in particular but it has been found also in red grouse in Scotland and in wood-pigeons. Leptospirosis, which is widespread in wildlife in Britain, is caused by a large family of bacteria, one species of which causes Weil's disease in man, sometimes with fatal results. Only one out of 94 fallow deer from southern England examined by Twigg and his colleagues gave evidence of past infection and that was with *Leptospira icterohaemorrhagiae.* A similar number of fallow deer examined in New Zealand by Daniel showed no evidence of past infection and only one animal out of 127 examined in Tasmania showed such evidence and that was by *L. grippotyphosa.*

Rickettsia are a group of micro-organisms which can be regarded as being mid-way between bacteria and viruses. Tick-borne fever, a rickettsial-like disease infecting sheep on tick infested pastures, has also been found in fallow deer in Hampshire and Wiltshire in England.

Rabies used to be rife in England, and Fleming gives a dramatic description of the behaviour of rabid fallow bucks in a park in the early nineteenth century. In

The right antler of this buck was broken whilst in velvet.

1886 many fallow deer died of rabies virus in Richmond Park. This outbreak appears to have been the first authenticated example of rabies in deer and experimental work by Horsley showed that fallow could infect each other by biting. In 1889, the fallow in Ickworth Park in Suffolk became infected and within three months about 450 animals out of an estimated 600 to 700 had died. Infected animals usually left the herd and, once this stage had been reached, death usually occurred within 30 hours. These outbreaks are thought to have resulted from bites by rabid dogs. Rabies has been gradually spreading westwards in Europe and is now a serious problem in countries such as Denmark where it occurs in the deer and other wildlife, particularly foxes. Fortunately, rabies has not been found in wildlife in Britain for many years, which emphasises the importance of rigid adherence to our importation laws. Cattle in Tasmania are frequently infected with mucosal disease according to Munday, who found evidence of it in 11 out of 76 fallow deer. It was thought that the deer were infected, either directly or indirectly, from the cattle. Foot and mouth disease has been found in deer in Europe although it does not appear to have been recorded for wild fallow deer. Recent work by Forman and his colleagues at the Animal Virus Research Institute at Pirbright in Surrey has shown that fallow deer are susceptible to foot and mouth disease virus, either by innoculation or by contact with diseased animals. The clinical disease, however, was usually mild or unapparent. Red deer reacted in a similar way whereas roe deer developed severe clinical signs.

Ringworm is probably the best known of the fungal diseases. Skin brushings from 11 fallow deer, examined for us by Mary English for the presence of these fungi, were all negative.

A few fallow deer have been found with tumours but, in general, these appear to be rare in wild deer. A lymphosarcoma, a rapidly progressive malignant tumour, was present in the 19 month old fallow doe found dead from natural causes in the survey of deer in Epping Forest and Essex. Other examples of this tumour have been seen in fallow deer from Savernake Forest and the New Forest. A young buck found shaking its head in a Berkshire deer park, had a tumour of the ethmoid bone of the skull which had spread into the naso-pharynx, impeding breathing.

Cerebrocortical necrosis, first reported less than 20 years ago, occurs mainly in cattle and sheep but was diagnosed recently in a six to eight week old captive fallow fawn, which was staggering around in circles and was unable to suck.

Enzootic ataxia is a disease which has been known to affect red deer in parks for many years and, more recently, rare cases have been reported in fallow deer. The symptoms are similar to those of swayback in sheep in that there is a progressive weakness and incoordination of the hind quarters and this has led to the disease being referred to as "staggers". The condition, which results from degenerative changes in the spinal cord although the underlying causes are unknown, is fatal if allowed to run its course.

Bone abnormalities range from minor deviations from normal to chronic arthritic conditions. The former, unless they are the beginning of a more severe condition, are probably of no importance whereas the latter are certainly evidence of disease and may well increase the chances of such normally agile animals as deer being involved in accidents. The survey of the fallow deer in Epping Forest and Essex indicates that around 53 per cent of the 30 deer whose skeletons were examined had degenerative lesions of one or more bones. Similar lesions have also been found in the skeletons of fallow deer from Richmond Park. The surface of bones forming a joint should be covered with articular cartilage and present a smooth, polished appearance. In many of the lesions, erosion of the cartilage and even of the bone itself had occurred but complete fusion of the bones was rare. Bony growths or exostoses occurred frequently at the edges of joints and often accompanied erosion of the joint surfaces. These lesions have been found between the vertebrae and at their junctions with the ribs, at the hip, knee, shoulder, elbow and wrist, and at the distal ends of the metacarpal and metatarsal bones and the phalanges. The vertebrae, the wrist and ankle joints seem particularly susceptible. The erosion of the bones of the hock joints may be so severe that they are deeply scored and gross exostoses may render the joint almost immovable. It is not surprising that deer with these severe lesions (page 208) get killed in road accidents. Slight lesions have been found in three month old fallow deer but they are very much more extensive in the adults, particularly the aged ones.

Many of the fallow deer in Richmond Park, older than seven years, had abscesses of the bone surrounding the roots of the molariform teeth, whereas very few of the younger deer had them. These abscesses, which often expose the roots of the teeth, usually occurred around M_1 and M_2 in the lower jaws and around M_2 and M_3 in the upper jaws. Most animals with abscesses had them in both jaws although a few had them in only one. In many of these deer, some of the molariform teeth were missing, only the roots remaining, whilst other teeth were unevenly worn and fibres of vegetation, rubber, or string were wedged between them. One fallow doe had an abscess of the lower jaw reminiscent of "lumpy jaw" which, in cattle, is caused by the bacterium *Actinomyces bovis*. Kober has described a case of "lumpy jaw" in a German fallow deer which had a lump the size of an orange on the right lower jaw due, apparently, to the bacterium *Corynebacterium israeli*.

Ectoparasites

The lice, *Damalinia tibialis* (211, 212, 213), which occur on fallow deer are flattened, wingless, off-white insects which belong to the order Mallophaga or biting lice. These small insects, about 2mm long, live on the skin and among the hairs of the host, feeding on epidermal debris. Only females of this louse have been found, and it is probably parthenogenetic. The eggs are laid on the hairs of the host and

Arthritic changes incapacitate these normally agile animals.   *J. R. Mercer*

hatch into nymphs which undergo two further nymphal stages before they become adults. The distribution of this louse in Britain is unknown. It has been found on fallow bucks and does in Epping Forest, Essex, Greenwich Park and Richmond Park.

The louse is often extremely common on debilitated animals dying in Richmond Park, particularly fawns which die in the spring. Although lice may be found on all parts of the animal's body they seem to congregate in the axillary areas, the groins and around the genital region of males. Whether the animals become debilitated and this enables the lice to multiply or whether the high louse burden causes the deer's debility is unknown. The following figures for fallow deer infected with lice were obtained from an examination of 64 bucks, does and fawns either killed in accidents or dying naturally in Richmond Park.

	Jan.-Feb.	Mar.-Apr.	May-Jun.	Jul.-Aug.	Sep.-Oct.	Nov.-Dec.
No. of Deer	12	18	10	7	11	6
Per cent infested	42	72	50	14	0	17

The incidence of infection varies at different times of the year, being high in late winter, spring and early summer and low in late summer, autumn and early winter.

Similar seasonal fluctuations in the proportion of animals carrying lice have been recorded for other species of deer.

A species of sucking louse, *Solenopotes burmeisteri,* which belongs to the order Siphunculata, has been found on fallow deer in Germany although it does not appear to have been found on them in Britain.

The deer ked, *Lipoptena cervi* (page 211), is a parasitic, blood-sucking fly and belongs to the family Hippoboscidae. This insect, which is flattened dorso-ventrally so that it looks as if it has been squashed, is dark reddish-brown, about 2.5mm long; it scuttles among the hairs of the host like a small crab. The life cycle and distribution of this parasite have been studied by Haarløv in the Jaegersborg Deer Park near Copenhagen. The egg hatches and develops within the body of the female until it is a third stage larva. It is then voided, drops to the ground where it

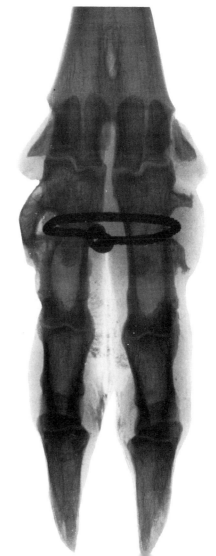

This deer was caught by the foot in a fox snare some time before being killed in a road accident. *Dr D. Chapman.*

pupates over winter and hatches in the spring. When the adult emerges it is winged but within a few days of reaching its host the wings are broken off by rubbing them against the hairs of the host.

The adult ked may be found throughout the year but fallow deer are most heavily infested in autumn and early winter, as is shown by the following figures for 64 fallow from Richmond Park.

	Jan.-Feb.	Mar.-Apr.	May-Jun.	Jul.-Aug.	Sep.-Oct.	Nov.-Dec.
No. of Deer	12	18	10	7	11	6
Per cent infested	50	44	0	29	91	100

In Britain and in Europe, the winged ked has been found only from August to December, when the adults hatch from the pupae; this explains why infestation of fallow deer is highest at this time of year. Fallow appear to be less susceptible than red deer to infestation with this ked and, in contrast to fallow deer, sick red deer may be extremely heavily infested.

Warble flies, species of *Hypoderma,* do not appear to trouble fallow deer in Britain. Only one fallow from Epping Forest was found to be infected and that had only one abscess which was caused by the larva. No other reports of this fly on fallow in Britain have been found although it has been reported as a parasite of German fallow deer. The larvae of the nasal bot flies, *Cephenomya multispinosa* and *C. rufibarbis,* which are closely related to the warble flies have been found on fallow in Germany, although apparently not in Britain.

Ticks, the adults of which have eight legs, are not insects like the ectoparasites previously mentioned but belong to the order Acarina which also includes mites. Ticks are important parasites because they can harbour and transmit pathogenic micro-organisms; so one tick bite may kill the host. Tick-borne fever in fallow deer has been mentioned already. The deer or sheep tick, *Ixodes ricinus* (page 213), varies in colour from dark brown to bluish grey and its size depends upon its sex, whether it is mature and whether it is gorged with blood. Ticks have complicated life cycles which may be quite lengthy because the adults can survive without feeding for several years. The deer tick is not particular about which species of animal it feeds on and will attack any warm-blooded one that passes its way. After mating, which occurs on the host, both sexes drop to the ground and the tiny male dies. The female lays her eggs in the ground and after about two months they hatch into six-legged larvae known as seed ticks. The larvae crawl up the vegetation and wait for a passing host from which to take their first meal. After feeding, the larvae drop to the ground and change into eight-legged nymphs. The nymphs also climb vegetation and wait for a host to pass in order to be able to obtain a meal. Once more they drop to the ground and this time change into mature ticks. The

Ectoparasites. (a) deer keds, *Lipoptena cervi.*

G. B. Thompson.

time taken at each stage depends upon environmental conditions and the chances of a suitable host passing by. All stages of the tick have been found on deer.

The presence of the deer tick on fallow deer in Britain was apparently first recorded as recently as 1963 and its distribution is unknown. Ticks are common on fallow in the New Forest and yet they are extremely rare on fallow in Epping Forest and in Richmond Park and then usually only a single tick is present.

Two other ticks, which are very catholic in their choice of host, have been found on fallow deer. The tick, *Haemaphysalis punctata,* has been found on them in Italy and France and the tick, *Dermacentor reticulatus,* has been found on fallow in California.

A mite, *Sarcoptes,* which causes mange has been found on fallow deer in Germany but apparently not in Britain.

Endoparasites

Deer are hosts to a wide range of endoparasites such as the parasitic worms or helminths, the larvae of insects and certain protozoa. However, virtually nothing is known about the occurrence of these parasites, apart from the helminths, in fallow deer. The importance of helminth parasites is that they may provide and maintain a reservoir of infection for domestic livestock, particularly as fallow are so very widely distributed in Britain.

Ectoparasites. (b) a deer louse, *Dama-linia tibialis* grasping a hair.

J. B. Mercer.

Three main groups of parasitic worms occur in fallow deer, namely round-worms or nematodes, flukes or trematodes and tapeworms or cestodes. Most live in the deer's alimentary canal and each type is concentrated in a particular region of it, although they occur also in the bladder, liver and lungs. The eggs of these worms are usually passed in the faeces and contaminate both pasture and water. These parasitic worms have complex life cycles and most of them have to pass through one or more intermediate hosts before being swallowed by deer along with food or water. A detailed discussion of all the helminths which occur in fallow deer is outside the scope of this book but a list of the species which have been found is given in Appendix IV.

Of 26 fallow deer examined from Epping Forest and Essex, 81 per cent were infected with helminths; in Denmark, 81 per cent of 21 fallow were found to be infected. In Holland, 100 per cent of 14 fallow examined were infected with nematodes but in Czechoslovakia only 33 per cent of 323 deer were infected. Most fallow deer are probably infected with some parasitic worms and, provided the infestations are not extremely high, they appear to be well tolerated and, with the exception perhaps of the liver fluke and lung worm, they do not contribute greatly to deer mortality. In the fallow from Epping Forest and Essex, the youngest animal found to be infected was a three month old buck; a 17 month old buck had the highest infestation, with 310 worms. Pathological lesions attributable to the presence of worms were not found in any of the gastro-intestinal tracts examined.

Roundworms are the commonest helminth parasites in the alimentary canal and at least 58 species have been found in fallow deer. Many of these species occur also in domestic ruminants but nothing appears to be known about cross infection between them and fallow deer. The number of worms found is usually much lower than that in domestic stock. It is interesting that introduced fallow deer in Alabama have acquired some of the nematode parasites which infect the native white-tailed deer.

Ectoparasites. (c) deer ticks, *Ixodes ricinus:* left, female; right, male.   *G. B. Thompson.*

Two species of lungworm, *Dictylocaulus viviparus* and *D. filaria*, have been found in fallow deer although only the former has been recorded in them in Britain. The eggs of the worm are laid in the lungs and they and first stage larvae are coughed up and swallowed. The larvae pass out of the deer with the faeces where they develop until the third stage larvae are swallowed by the host grazing contaminated pastures. The larvae bore through the wall of the intestine and are then carried in the blood to the lungs where they mature and the cycle is repeated. This is an important parasite and may give rise to parasitic pneumonia which can have a high mortality rate in some species such as the roe deer but its effect on fallow is unknown.

Six species of tapeworm have been found in fallow deer although only the dog tapeworm, *Taenia hydatigena*, has been isolated from them in Britain. The larval stage of this worm, which was given a different name, *Cysticercus tenuicollis*, before the connection with the adult worm was known, is found in fallow deer as a small fluid-filled cyst or bladderworm up to 3cm in diameter. The cyst often occurs attached to the exterior of the alimentary tract but it may also be found partially embedded in the liver or lungs. Unless large numbers of larvae migrate into these two organs, little harm comes to the deer. The adult worm occurs in dogs and foxes and the presence of the larval cyst in fallow indicates that they have grazed over ground on which these animals have been. The extent to which fallow are infested varies in different parts of the country. Cysts are rarely foun in fallow deer from either Richmond Park or Epping Forest and Essex but 28 per cent of 25 fallow from Holkham Park in Norfolk were infected.

The eggs of the dog tapeworm pass out with the faeces of the host and are swallowed by an intermediate host such as fallow deer or domestic ruminants. The eggs hatch and the larvae bore through the wall of the intestines and develop into the cysts that are found in the abdominal cavity. The further development of the parasite depends upon the dog or fox consuming the cyst when eating infected carcases. The hydatid cyst, *Echinococcus granulosus*, another canine tapeworm, has been found in fallow in Germany. This is a far more serious parasite because man is also a host but it is not known how widespread the infection is in fallow deer.

At least four species of fluke can occur in fallow deer, all of which have been found in them in Britain. Liver fluke disease also occurs in domestic ruminants as well as in many small mammals. The degree of infestation in fallow deer varies in different parts of the country. Liver flukes are rare in them in Richmond Park, and in Epping Forest and Essex whereas, according to McDiarmid, nearly every fallow examined from the New Forest showed evidence of past or present infection, yet the roe deer in that area were hardly affected.

CHAPTER THIRTEEN

Persian Fallow Deer

THE PERSIAN or Mesopotamian fallow deer is one of 25 species or subspecies of deer under threat of extinction. In the Red Data Book, compiled by the International Union for Conservation of Nature and Natural Resources, it is listed as *endangered,* a term applied to animals which survive in such low numbers that they could become extinct within 15 years unless conservation measures enable the population to increase. It is a handsome animal, larger than its European relation and its antlers typically have a flattened base but little palmation at the end. Only a few specimens of modern Persian fallow bones are available for study and most of the fossil bones found so far are incomplete; consequently the ranges of size in both sexes are unknown. Since the forms of the bones in the European and Persian fallow are so alike and size is of little guidance, particularly as the European fallow in Pleistocene times were larger than those of to-day, antlers are the only reliable means of distinguishing between the two subspecies from fossil or archaeological remains. Fortunately such remains have been found and, with historical evidence as well, indicate that formerly the Persian fallow had a wider distribution to the east of the Mediterranean, in Palestine, Lebanon, Syria and Iraq as well as Persia (Iran) where it still survives. Possibly it may also have extended its range into the African continent, as suggested by inscriptions on ancient monuments in Egypt and Ethiopia.

Prehistorical Times

Persian fallow remains are known from sites, principally caves, occupied by Palaeolithic man in the Late Pleistocene and by Mesolithic and Neolithic man in early Postglacial times. The most numerous finds of Pleistocene Persian fallow were the 10,000 specimens of jaws, antlers, limb bones and teeth in the Wad and Tabun caves in the Wady el-Mughara, Mount Carmel, in Palestine. Here remains of 51 other species of mammals were also found, including red deer bones, sometimes difficult to distinguish from those of fallow, particularly as most of the bones were fragmentary because the animals had been used as food by Palaeolithic man. The fallow bones occurred in various levels of deposits to a depth of 16 metres. A few limb bones were complete but antlers were represented only by the basal portions which, although very variable, were mostly of two main types. Some had a small brow tine with a comparatively wide and flat second tine just above it. Others, geologically older, had a large brow tine, about 14cm long, which was not closely followed by another tine but the beam flattened immediately above the coronet. Dorothea Bate, who studied all the remains and the few available modern Persian antlers, considered the possibility that these types could represent more than one species but, in the absence of more complete specimens, concluded that the evidence was inadequate.

Other Palestinian sites where ancient remains of Persian fallow have been found are the Kebara cave at Mount Carmel; the Athlit caves; Shukbah; the Zuttijeh cave near Galilee; and Oumn Qatafa which is 12 kilometres from Bethlehem. In Lebanon, sites for Persian fallow remains include caves at Antélias, Nahr Ibrahim, Ras el Kelb, Adloun, Beirût, Nahr el Djoz, Djaita and Ksar-Akil. In 1865, ten years before the description and naming of the living Persian fallow, a piece of jaw with teeth and the ends of limb bones found in the Nahr el Kelb caves were described as European fallow. In the light of later neighbouring finds it seems probable that these too may have been from Persian fallow. The adjacent countries of Syria and Iraq also have evidence of Persian fallow in Palaeolithic deposits, as at Goz and at Barda Balka, dating from about 100,000 years ago, and in younger deposits at Uruk and Tell al-Halaf. These countries where Persian fallow remains have been found in late Pleistocene and early Postglacial times were not subjected to the same climatic conditions as Europe. They probably had alternating wetter and drier periods during the Pleistocene but were not directly influenced by the cold from glaciated northern Europe. So whilst the European fallow disappeared from most, if not all, of Europe during the Last, or Würm, Glaciation its Persian relation was able to survive in south-west Asia right through the Late Pleistocene and into the Postglacial epoch.

Of the Postglacial remains of Persian fallow the best documented findings are from several prehistoric sites on Cyprus, in the Mediterranean roughly equidistant from Turkey and Syria. Neither living nor fossil deer have been found on the island but Persian fallow bones were found during excavations of Neolithic sites at Erimi, Sotira and Khirokitia and a Bronze Age Sanctuary at Pigadhes, dating from the thirteenth century B.C., also yielded remains of this animal. An almost complete pair of antlers, of which the lower parts were flattened but the free ends had no palm, clearly showed the identity of the animal. Cyprus probably originated as an island about 15 million years ago and the once postulated land bridge to Turkey is now thought never to have existed. If the deer were not indigenous to Cyprus they must have been imported in Neolithic and perhaps again in Bronze Age times, presumably from Lebanon or Syria, the nearest areas on the east Mediterranean coast and where Persian fallow are known to have lived, rather than from Turkey where the European fallow lived. Whether the animals were used only for religious practices or for meat as well is unknown.

Engraved by W. Holl.

Larger-than-life winged figure carrying a buck, probably Persian, depicted on a relief in the Palace of Ashurnasirpal II at Nimrud. Plate 35 from Layard's *Monuments of Ninevah*.

Cambridge University Library.

Persian fallow buck with antlers in velvet, at Dasht-e-Naz National Park in Iran. Similarities of the coat to that of a common European fallow are striking. Antlers have broad distal palms and also flattened bases.   *Dr S. Hess*

Historical Times

Coming into historical time, deer must have been well-known in Palestine when the books of the Old Testament were written. Although these contain many references to deer the identity of the species is not clear. The Hebrew word *yachmur* was interpreted as fallow deer in the Authorised Version of the Bible but later versions translate this word as roe buck. Support for the former view comes from the dialect of the area where the Persian fallow still survives. Ilany, of the Israeli Nature Reserves Authority, informed us that there the animal is called a *yachmoor* although its Iranian name is *gavazne zard,* meaning "yellow deer". If the translation of the Authorised Version is correct, fallow deer were amongst the cloven-hooved animals that the Israelites were commanded to eat and furthermore there may have been Royal deer parks about 900 B.C. for the vast daily supply of animals for King Solomon's household included fallow deer. Several places called Ajalon give some support to this possibility for the word means "the place of the deer" or "deer pasture". *Ayyal* and the feminine form *ayyalah* are translated as hart and hind and probably meant deer in general. To the Hebrews, as to most people to-day, probably a deer was just a deer and they did not distinguish between the different species occurring in Palestine, which could have been fallow, roe and red deer, although the latter may already have been extinct there.

The ancient works of art in eastern countries provide clues to the former existence of Persian fallow over a wide area. Animals which can be identified as Persian fallow are depicted on many objects, particularly from Iraq and Persia. In Iraq one of the most spectacular portrayals was at Nimrud, the ancient Assyrian city of Calah, where a larger-than-life winged figure carrying a deer was depicted on a relief at the Palace of Ashurnasirpal II who ruled in the ninth century B.C. (page 217) and whose hunting extravaganzas are recorded in words and pictures on the Black Obelisk of Shalmaneser III now in the British Museum. The spotted coat and long tail indicate a fallow deer and the antler, with some palmation at the end but also a broadening at the base, probably represents a Persian fallow. This relief has been lost but an almost identical one is in the British Museum.

Portrayals of Persian fallow are not confined to the large spectacular stone monuments. Amongst the small objects some chariot rein-rings found at Kish, near Babylon in Iraq, are of particular interest. One of these depicts a buck with large fallow-like antlers, hobbled by the feet to the nose, suggesting domestication. The animal surmounting a rein-ring generally was thought to indicate the species of animal that was harnessed to that particular vehicle. This theory breaks down in the case of a ring which depicts a dragon! Nevertheless, the possibility remains of fallow deer pulling a cart four or five thousand years ago. Reindeer and wapiti have proved useful draught animals and as recently as 1750 Lord Orford was driven through Suffolk in a carriage pulled by four red deer stags.

Goblets, gaming boards, a lyre and seals found at the royal cemetry at Ur, in southern Iraq, also depict deer and date from about 2,700 B.C. Many of these

Persian fallow buck.   *Dr S. Hess.*

portrayals clearly show a spotted coat, palmate antlers, brush and tail of about the right proportion so undoubtedly they represent fallow deer which were presumably well known to the artists. On these small objects it is sometimes difficult to decide whether European or Persian fallow are portrayed but one particularly fine chequer board clearly depicts Persian bucks. The skill needed by a craftsman to show the details on which we distinguish the two forms can be judged by comparing the antlers of the two subspecies on pages 101 and 218. Such skill was possessed by the makers of the Pasirik carpet, the oldest in the world, made in Persia about 500 B.C. and taken to Siberia where, fortuitously, it was preserved in a frozen state. The pattern included twenty-four grazing bucks which their antlers show to be Persian fallow. The antlers are also the clue to the identity of Persian bucks in two Roman mosaics, one from Antioch, the ancient capital of Syria and the other from Tyre in Lebanon. The antlers show some flattening near the base and also at the end. They are therefore completely different from the antlers depicted on floors such as the Lion and Stag mosaic at Verulamium, St Albans, where a red deer stag is obviously being shown.

Of all the ancient representations of Persian fallow the one which conveys the most information about the use of the animal is the relief on the Taki-Bustan monument which shows a Royal hunt. This cliff-carving in the Zagros Mountains of Persia, just east of the present-day location of this animal, was probably erected in the fifth to seventh centuries A.D. Reed's interpretation of the scene is that the deer, all Persian fallow and mostly bucks, were driven into holding compounds from which men on elephants urged them into the arena where the King galloped across and shot them with arrows. The carcases were carried away on dromedaries. Reed does not say how many deer are shown; his photographs indicate about 50 deer. For many animals to be herded into an enclosure for one hunt they must have been abundant in the wild, or bred in captivity for the purpose.

From the art record left by the ancient civilisations in Iraq and Persia and the fossil and archaeological records from the neighbouring countries of Palestine, Lebanon and Syria, it seems clear that the Persian fallow was distributed over these areas. In relatively recent times there have been reports of the animal in three of these countries. The most northerly record is from Zakho which is 37 degrees north and close to the Turkish and Syrian border. North of this latitude records of fallow are of the European form. Its southernmost extensions is more debatable for its infiltration into Egypt and up the Nile Valley to Ethiopia have been postulated but not proved. Many monuments in ancient Egypt are decorated with numerous figures and some do show deer. Although the stylised representations rarely have enough detail to indicate which species is portrayed, a hieroglyph believed to mean fallow deer has been identified and Joleaud published illustrations of many of the small figures of deer. With these as his evidence, Joleaud postulated the arrival of the Persian fallow, across the Suez isthmus from Palestine, during the Late

Pleistocene times and before 3,500 B.C. and its subsequent semi-domestication. He believed that by the time of the New Kingdom, about 1,580 to 1,075 B.C., this deer had declined as a result of hunting pressures and climatic changes. Some antler fragments found at Thebes were regarded by Joleaud as belonging to a Persian buck but proof was lacking. Deer are featured also in ancient Ethiopian inscriptions and these, Joleaud believed, represented the Persian fallow which had spread up the Nile Valley, through Nubia to south-east Ethiopia, during the wetter phases of the Pleistocene when the area supported grassland and shrubs.

An alternative explanation of these ancient representations of deer was offered by Dawson who believed that fallow never had been indigenous to Egypt. He maintained that the animals the ancients knew well, they drew well. Deer are drawn relatively poorly, representing a generalised deer rather than a particular species, so were probably known to the artists only as captive animals imported from other countries, the Barbary red stag and the Persian fallow being the nearest and most likely candidates.

Another explanation for the deer represented on ancient monuments was suggested in 1896 when a fallow buck, possibly from Tripoli, was taken from Egypt to Germany. When it died a year later its cast antlers, skin, skull and in-velvet antlers were taken to Berlin Zoological Museum but these specimens no longer exist. Although its antlers and coat colour were similar to those of the European buck, Hilzheimer named it *Dama schaeferi*. The "new species" was, he believed, the animal depicted in ancient Egyptian carvings, the most recent example of which was on the tomb of Mentuhirkhopshef, dated about 1475 B.C. If he were correct, the Berlin specimen would have been an exciting "living fossil". As it was, at the time of *schaeferi's* discovery, which was shrouded in some mystery, the European fallow was living in Tripoli, Libya and also in the Zoological Gardens at Giza, near Cairo, from 1894 to 1902. Just possibly it was wild in Egypt for there are reports of the introduction of fallow in Egypt in the sixteenth century and their survival until the nineteenth century. Little importance can be attached to *Dama schaeferi* which was almost certainly an aberrant European fallow buck, not a Persian fallow or a relic species from the past. Whether or not the Persian fallow did ever inhabit these north-east African countries remains in doubt, which only fossil or archaeological findings could elucidate. Even if such discoveries were made, the problem of whether the animal had arrived there naturally or been imported would probably remain. The proximity of Egypt to Palestinian sites for Persian fallow gives plausibility to the theory of their natural presence there but in the absence of proof the matter remains one of intriguing speculation. Despite the evidence that the Persian fallow was widely known to some ancient civilisations, there is a vast gap in its record from the early centuries A.D. until its "re-discovery" in modern times. In 1866 Canon Tristram reported deer near Mount Tabor in Palestine. As this date was before the Persian fallow had been described, he reported them just as "fallow deer", assuming them to be European. In 1882 he saw deer which he believed to be fallow, not red deer, near Shara and said that they were well known to the natives.

Although many invertebrates and even small vertebrates must still await their first scientific description and naming, it has been for many decades a rare event for a large mammal to be declared "new to science". Within the present century, the discovery of the okapi was the outstanding such occasion. Not until 1875 was the Persian fallow described scientifically, by Brooke. His description was based on the skin and skull with half-grown antlers of an animal shot in south-west Persia. With these specimens as his model, Wolf painted an attractive picture, cautiously depicting the animal with its head half concealed in vegetation. Brooke regarded the deer as a new species and called it *Cervus mesopotamicus*; fallow deer were at that time included in the genus *Cervus*. The name *mesopotamicus* is somewhat misleading as originally Mesopotamia referred only to the Land Between Two Rivers, the Euphrates and Tigris, and even when Brooke first described this animal it probably did not exist in that region. However, the name Mesopotamia was also used locally for the whole plain of the Tigris, extending eastwards into Persia, close to the area where the animal occurred.

The specimens were sent to London by a Vice Consul, Robertson, based at Basra in Mesopotamia, who acquired them whilst hunting across the border in Persia. Robertson had encountered the animal before, for in 1871 he reported the presence near the Karun River of two kinds of deer, one of which was spotted. He believed the latter occurred only in south-west Persia where they descended from the Luristan Hills during the dry season to live in the jungle bordering the Rivers Karun, Dez and possibly the Karkheh. The size of the population was unknown but natives said the Hills abounded in sheep and deer of various kinds: roe deer and a red deer, called the maral, do occur in Persia although even a century ago the latter was restricted to the northern part of the country. A few more antlers were received by Brooke and in 1893 a mounted head and skin of a buck from the Upper Karun were presented to the Natural History Museum in London. One animal was seen in the upper reaches of the River Dez in 1906 and in 1917 a buck was obtained from Zakho in the extreme north of Iraq, the only record from that country, and another was recorded from north of Kermanshah in western Persia. An antler from a young male from Jerash, in northern Jordan, was on sale in a shop in 1923 but no further information came from Persia and it was thought that the animal had become extinct.

Re-Discovery

In 1955, Talbot, working for the International Union for Conservation of Nature and Natural Resources, heard rumours of the Persian fallow's survival where the Sirwan River crosses the Persian border into Iraq, between Maidan and Halabja, and the same year there was a report from near Jebel Baradust. Their survival was confirmed the following year by Trense who believed there were two small populations, each of about a dozen animals. A later figure of 200 to 400 by Haltenorth was probably a considerable over-estimate. In 1957 and 1958 three expeditions visited south-west Persian and reported the animal from Harmala, Ahmad Mollah and Karkheh, all near Shushtar on the Karun. They collected some cast antlers and captured two fawns, one of each sex, which were taken to the late Georg von Opel's Zoo at Kronberg, near Frankfurt-am-Main, in Germany. In time, the male fathered two daughters but in 1960 he died of a surfeit of sugar provided by over-indulgent Sunday visitors, before a pure-bred son had been sired although he had fathered sons born to European fallow does.

The Iranian Government organised an expedition in 1963 which, with the help of villagers, netted two adult deer of each sex in an area of the Karkheh River where the population was estimated at 60 to 100. These four deer were taken to northern Persia where a game park had been established on land presented by His Imperial Highness Prince Abdorreza. The park is at Dasht-e-Naz, near Sari on the south-east coast of the Caspian Sea. In 1965 one fawn was born there and another expedition captured one doe and two more bucks, one of which was sent to Kronberg as a mate for the doe already there. The other three went to Dasht-e-Naz. In 1965 an expedition, which had planned to use a cross-bow loaded with an immobilising drug, was unsuccessful. The dense vegetation was apparently unsuitable for this technique and attempts at netting were curtailed by torrential rain and excessive flooding. The number of Persian fallow deer remaining in the wild was estimated at 25 in 1973, all within a strictly protected area which now forms two adjoining wildlife reserves, Dez and Karkheh, so further loss of suitable habitat should not occur. In the past, land development has encroached on the area of dense cover available to the deer and poaching may have contributed to the decline of the species.

Biology

Attempts to study the Persian fallow in its native habitat are fraught with problems. The forest areas are long strips, ranging from a few metres to several kilometres in width, which follow the courses of the rivers. Desert borders the forest. Dense growth of tamarisk, willows and poplars characterise its habitat, which is shared by wild boars, wolves, jackals, jungle cats, hares and porcupines with a few domesticated water buffaloes and camels too. Some fawns may fall victims to the predatory species. At dusk the deer emerge into clearings or venture on to the fringes of the forest and desert to graze, but return to dense cover in the morning. Their food plants include the white poplar and a moss which grows where rain has lain in the desert. Haltenorth reported that the deer's coat assumes an olive-green colour from constant brushing against the tamarisk bushes. Further evidence of this would be interesting for mammals do not usually become discoloured by contact with vegetation: the well-known case of the green coat of sloths is due to the presence of algae in grooves in the hairs. The climate in south-west Persia is hot and dry in summer with intermittent rains from October to May, different from that at Kronberg, Germany where the first studies were made on captive Persian fallow. Although these captive animals have provided much useful information, as well as serving their prime function as a breeding herd, the limitations of extrapolating from captive animals far removed from their homeland are severe; little is known of their biology but this is now being studied by the Iranian Department of Environmental Conservation in the 55 hectares of semi-natural habitat at the Dasht-e-Naz National Park. In 1974 the herd here numbered approximately 32, which included seven animals, two males and five females, which had been sent from Kronberg, where another seven remained. As a further safeguard in the endeavours to prevent the extinction of this animal, there are plans to establish another herd in captivity in Persia.

Although the basic coat pattern of the Persian fallow has been known since it was first described by Brooke, observations of captive animals have provided further details, including the seasonal variation. The fawn-coloured summer coat is heavily spotted and on either side of the chocolate-brown vertebral stripe, which is three to four centimetres wide, a row of partly merged white spots forms a continuous line. The coalescing of these spots is but a minor distinction from the pelage of the common and menil varieties of the European fallow for these animals frequently have the spots very close, almost touching if not actually fusing together. In both sub-species of fallow a white line runs along the mid-line of the flanks and over the haunches. The face of the Persian fallow is lighter and greyer than the body and has whitish areas round the muzzle and eyes. The chest and belly are also whitish. The tail, about 16cm long, is white with a black line down its dorsal side but this is less distinct than in the European fallow except at the base and, to a lesser extent, at the end.

In October the greyish-brown winter coat is assumed. The spots become less obvious, the belly becomes cream but the vertebral stripe remains prominent. A captive animal in Germany, some twenty degrees of latitude north of its home area, acquired a darker, longer coat in which the spots and stripes became very indistinct. Closer examination of the heads of the two subspecies of fallow reveals a difference in their rhinaria. In the Persian the area of naked skin on the nose has an evenly concave upper edge whereas in the European deer the rhinarium has a short, straighter central edge with obtusely angled outer margins. In the Persian fallow the hairs on the muzzle radiate from one central point but in the European they radiate from two points.

The main differences between the two kinds of fallow and the reasons for separating them into two subspecies lie in the antlers and body size. Much emphasis was placed on the type of palmation of the Persian bucks' antlers when

European fallow bucks occasionally grow extra tines. The second head of buck 145 with a small left brow tine and a large extra tine.

The third head of buck 145, back to normal.

they were first described. A fan-shaped, not very broad palm arose above the base of the brow tine, not at the free end as in European bucks. However, relatively few Persian antlers have been described but as more become available they indicate that some are not so dissimilar to European fallow antlers as once may have been thought. A typical Persian antler may differ considerably from a typical European one but the great variation in antlers shown within a species, or even one population, must be remembered: for individual variation, no other bone can equal that of an antler. Haltenorth, who studied Persian fallow as intensively and extensively as material allowed, assembled a collection of their antlers. The average length of the antlers from 23 adult bucks was 58cm, the range being from 51 to 66, and the average weight was 1.1 kg, the range being from 0.8 to 1.4. In all of them the forward-pointing brow tine arose immediately above the coronet and was much shorter than in European fallow, being only five to nine centimetres long. Higher on the front edge of the beam arose a longer, trez tine measuring between nine and 22 cm. In many of the antlers a small third tine was present near the base, close to the brow tine. A comparable tine is not usually present in European fallow although bucks of this subspecies may have a bump, or offer, or occasionally even a well developed tine in a similar position. Pages 225 and 226 show a European buck with an extra basal tine on one antler and his antlers the following year without an extra tine. The European buck on page 106 has two offers near the brown tine of his right antler. In Persian fallow the part of the beam adjacent to the trez tine is flattened, usually in a fan-shape, and the extent of the flattening is in contrast to the rounded lower part of the beam in European bucks and is generally regarded as a major point of distinction between the two forms. Above the trez tine the beam becomes more rounded but the front edge of the beam on some specimens has one or more offers giving the appearance of a jagged edge if the antler is seen in side-view. The distal portion of the antlers shows some flattening, the extent being very variable from almost none to a palm comparable with that seen in some European bucks.

Apart from antler shape, the main distinction between the two subspecies of fallow is reputed to be size. The Persian form has been described as a giant among fallow deer but this rather overstates the case. In 1959, Haltenorth compared two or three Persian bucks with a couple of European bucks. Several measurements of the Persian deer were greater than those of the European deer but the reverse was true for other measurements. The greatest reputed difference was the length of the body which for two Persian bucks, measured from nose to the tail tip, was 223 and 241 cm whereas the European bucks were about 170 cm long. A buck, about five years old, was measured recently at Dasht-e-Naz Park. The total length, measured along the backbone was 197cm; it was thus appreciably shorter than Haltenorth's bucks although the method of measurement seems to have been similar. Yet this buck was about 107cm high at the shoulder whereas Haltenorth's first buck was only 97cm, which is within the range found for European bucks. Clearly further measurements, taken by a uniform method, are required before conclusions can be reached regarding the relative sizes of the two subspecies. Similarly, information is required on body weights. The one published weight for a Persian buck, 200kg, seems an improbably high figure which must be regarded with suspicion.

Some minor differences in skull structure between the two forms have been described, namely that the Persian's nasal bones have broader upper ends and that the suture between the malar and maxilla bones is different. Skull structure, however, is not constant in European fallow, even within one population. In some animals in Richmond Park the premaxilla meets the nasal bone but in others the maxilla intervenes.

Studies at Dasht-e-Naz are providing interesting information about the behaviour and annual events of the Persian fallow's biology. The rut begins in August, probably reaching a peak late in the month and early September although some activity has been seen in December. These dates are ahead of those of the European fallow living on the island of Rhodes and at Mendocino County, California which are both at the same latitude as the Persian deer. In both these places the rut takes place in October and November. The birth of Persian fawns is correspondingly advanced, beginning at the end of March or early April and continuing into May whereas European fawns on Rhodes and in California are born in June. The rut of European fallow in Andalusia in southern Spain is reported by Sartorius to occur in the first half of September, fawns being born from about 20th May. In other areas of Spain, the rut occurs in the first half of October. These dates are intermediate between those for Persian fallow and those for the European fallow on the island of Rhodes and in California, so it is not clear whether there is a difference in the reproductive physiology of the two subspecies or whether climatic conditions may account for the differences in rutting dates. Some of the apparent variation may even result from different definitions of when the rut occurs: whether it is when the bucks start groaning or when the peak of conceptions occurs. The birth of fawns from 20th May suggests that conceptions occur from early October, not the first half of September, assuming that the gestation period is about 229 days. Haltenorth gives mid-March to mid-April as the fawning period for the wild Persian fallow in south-west Persia, about 500km south of the captive herd. The gestation period for both subspecies appears to be similar. As with European fallow, occasional late births do occur: at Dasht-e-Naz a male was born in November 1973. In close captivity considerable variation in the birth dates has been recorded. Six Persian fawns born in the London Zoological Gardens between 1880 and 1887 were dropped from June to September. In Kronberg Zoo the birth of a Persian fawn on 17th July 1960 was photographed and described by Löffler and Walther.

The bucks not only rut earlier than their European relations but also cast their antlers earlier. Casting begins in February, peaks late in the month and is completed by mid-March, except in the case of yearling males. The original buck shot in March from which Brooke described the Persian fallow had half-grown antlers in velvet.

Much remains to be discovered about the Persian fallow deer and, despite protection, the wild population exists only in perilously low numbers. Nevertheless, studies on the captive herds should answer many of the questions and it is to be hoped that this handsome animal will not die out. Perhaps time will tell another success story such as those of the Père David's deer and the ne-ne goose which were bred in captivity and thus saved from extinction. Better still would be to ensure this animal's survival in the wild as well as in captivity. The Iranian Government, as well as the International Union for Conservation of Nature and Natural Resources, is aware of the problem and is to be congratulated on its active steps towards saving this animal.

Parks containing Fallow Deer in the British Isles in 1975

ENGLAND

Avon
Ashton Court, Bristol
Badminton

Bedfordshire
Woburn

Berkshire
Englefield House, Theale

Cambridgeshire
Burghley House, Stamford

Cheshire
Tatton, Knutsford

Cornwall
Boconnoc, Lostwithiel
Prideaux Place, Padstow
Tregothnan, Truro
Werrington, Launceston

Cumbria
Dalemain, Penrith
Dallas Tower, Milnthorpe
Gowbarrow, Ullswater
Holker Hall, Cark-in-Cartmel
Levens Hall, Kendal

Derbyshire
Calke Abbey, Ticknall
Chatsworth, Bakewell
Locko, Spondon

Devonshire
Powderham, Exeter

Dorset
Charborough, Wareham
Melbury, Evershot
Sherborne
Stock Gaylard

Durham
Beamish, Chester-le-Street
Raby Castle, Staindrop
Whitworth, Spennymoor

East Sussex
Buxted
Eridge

Essex
Quendon
St. Osyth Priory, Clacton

Gloucestershire
Berkeley, Whitcliffe
Brockhampton
Lydney, Chepstow

Greater London*
Bushey, Teddington
Hampton Court
Heriots, Stanmore
Richmond

Greater Manchester
Dunham Massey

Hampshire
Bramshill, Hartley Wintney
Hackwood, Basingstoke

Hereford and Worcester
Elmley Castle, Pershore
Kentchurch Court
Moccas, Hereford
Spetchley, Worcester

Hertfordshire
Knebworth

Humberside
Normanby,
Scunthorpe

Kent
Boughton, Maidstone
Knole, Sevenoaks
Mersham Hatch, Ashford

Leicestershire
Bradgate, Newtown Linford
Donington

Lincolnshire
Belton, Grantham
Revesby Abbey, Boston
Scrivelsby, Horncastle

Norfolk
Holkham, Wells-next-the-Sea
Houghton, King's Lynn
Melton Constable

*Several parks (Battersea, Clissold, Golders Hill, Greenwich, Maryon, Victoria) have enclosures
containing fallow deer.

Northamptonshire
Althorp, Northampton
Castle Ashby
Lichborough Hall, Towcester
Whittlesbury Lodge, Towcester
Yardley, Yardley Hastings

North Yorkshire
Allerton, Knaresborough ,
Ripley Castle, Harrogate
Studley Royal, Ripon
Swinton, Masham

Nottinghamshire
Thoresby, Ollerton
Welbeck, Worksop
Wollaton, Nottingham

Oxfordshire
Barrington, Burford
Buckland
Cornbury, Charlbury
Magdalen College, Oxford
Stonor, Henley-on-Thames

Shropshire
Attingham
Longnor Hall, Shrewsbury
Loton, Shrewsbury
Weston, Shifnal

Somerset
Hatch Court, Taunton

Staffordshire
Aqualate, Newport

Suffolk
Helmingham, Stowmarket

Surrey
Parkhatch, Godalming

Warwickshire
Alscot, Stratford-on-Avon
Charlecote, Warwick
Goldicote House, Stratford-on-Avon
Shuckburgh, Daventry

West Midlands
Packington Hall, Coventry

West Sussex
Petworth
Warnham, Horsham

Wiltshire
Donhead Hall, Shaftesbury
Dyrham, Chippenham
Longleat, Warminster
Tottenham, Marlborough

WALES
Dyfed
Dynevor Castle, Llandeilo
Golden Grove, Llandeilo

Mid Glamorgan
Dunraven, Bridgend

Powys
Powis Castle, Welshpool

West Glamorgan
Margam Castle, Port Talbot

SCOTLAND
Angus
Kinnaird Castle, Brechin

Caithness
Langwell, Berriedale

Kircudbrightshire
Cumloden, Newton Stewart

Perthshire
Dodcote, Kinmouth

West Lothian
Hopetoun House, South Queensferry

IRELAND
Co. Cork
Castle Mary, Cloyne
Mallow Castle, Mallow

Co. Dublin
Phoenix Park, Dublin

Meath
Balrath Burry, Kells

Co. Monaghan
Lough Fea, Carrickmacross

Co. Tipperary
Archerstown, Thurles

Co. Waterford
Ballynatray

Co. Wicklow
Grange Con, Baltinglass

Age Estimation of European Fallow Deer

This appendix describes diagnostic features which enable fallow deer to be divided into age classes on the basis of the wear of the molariform teeth in the lower jaw. It should be read in conjunction with page 232 and it must be remembered that it is strictly applicable only to fallow deer in Richmond Park killed in September to December, on which animals it is based. Its possible application to other populations of fallow deer has already been discussed.

Attrition of teeth is continuous and so there is no well-defined difference that enables an animal of, for example, just under three years to be distinguished clearly from one just over three years. The characteristic features for one age class merge gradually into those characteristics for the succeeding age class. Furthermore, the older the animal the greater the variation in tooth wear that could have occurred; consequently the more in error the estimate of age is likely to be. No attempt has been made to provide criteria for fallow deer beyond their seventh year because of insufficient data. For animals in which the full permanent dentition has not been attained, reference should be made to Table 5 in Chapter Six.

3rd Year

a) The third pair of cusps of M_3 are unworn and unstained.
b) There is only slight wear on the first and second pairs of cusps of M_3 with, at most, only a very thin line of dentine showing.
c) There is very little wear on P_4 which is as wide as it is high, that is, it has a more or less square appearance.

4th Year

a) The third pair of cusps of M_3 show slight wear and some staining although in occasional specimens the cusps may be unworn.
b) The crests on the third pair of cusps of M_3 on the cheek side are higher or level with the crests on the side nearest the tongue but are lower than those on the second pair of cusps. Dentine is often not visible on the third pair of cusps of M_3 but, if present, is separated from that on the cheek crests of the second pair of cusps.
c) Dentine is visible on both cheek and tongue sides of the first and second pairs of cusps of M_3. The upper halves of the second pair of cusps of M_3 are stained on the cheek side. All cusps of P_4 show wear and in most a thin line of dentine is visible. On the cheek side P_4 is wider than it is high, that is, it has a rectangular appearance.

5th Year

a) The third pair of cusps of M_3 show definite signs of wear and the crests on the cheek side are lower than those nearest the tongue.
b) The surfaces of the crests of the third pair of cusps of M_3 nearest the cheek are at more or less the same level as those of the second pair of cusps and the dentine usually forms a continuous line.
c) The infundibulum of the third pair of cusps of M_3 is connected with that of the second pair of cusps.
d) The crown of M_2 is clear of the alveolus but the crown of M_3 is not clear.

FALLOW DEER

6th Year

a) The infundibulum of the third pair of cusps of M3 is present as a hole and is separated from that of the second pair of cusps.

b) The crown of M3 is not yet completely clear of the alveolus.

7th Year

The infundibulum of the third pair of cusps of M3 is absent and dentine is visible in the centre of this pair of cusps. The crown of M3 is clear of the alveolus.

 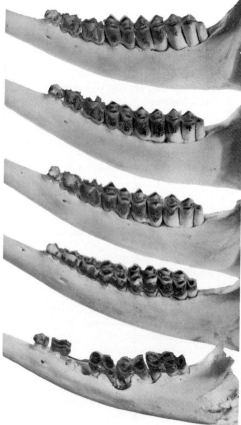

Lower jaws of male fallow deer from Richmond Park illustrating tooth eruption.

(a) 2 months. All teeth are deciduous; tip of M1 just visible.

(b) 7 months. M1 erupted.

(c) 13 months. Permanent I1 and I2 erupted, M2 erupting.

(d) 17 months. Permanent I3 and C erupted, tip of M3 just visible.

(e) 21 months. Permanent P3 and P4 erupted, tip of permanent P2 just visible.

(f) 26 months. Full set of permanent teeth.

J. R. Mercer.

Molariform teeth in the lower jaws of male fallow deer from Richmond Park illustrating tooth eruption and wear. Animals (a) to (d) were killed in August and September.

(a) 4th year.

(b) 5th year.

(c) 6th year.

(d) 7th year.

(e) "Aged" P4 missing, abscess between M1 M2.

J. R. Mercer.

Flowering Plants and Conifers eaten by Fallow Deer in the New Forest

The following plants have been recorded by Jackson as being eaten by the deer. Plants marked * form important items of food; availability and the amount eaten have been taken into account. The nomenclature is that used by Clapham, Tutin and Warburg in *Flora of the British Isles.*

Grasses, rushes and sedges
*Agrostis canina	Brown bent-grass
,, setacea	Bristle agrostis
* ,, tenuis	Common bent-grass
*Brachypodium sylvaticum	Slender false-brome
Carex spp.	Sedges
,, echinata	Star sedge
,, panicea	Carnation-grass
*Cynosurus cristatus	Crested dog's-tail
Dactylis glomerata	Cock's-foot
Deschampsia cespitosa	Tufted hair-grass
* ,, flexuosa	Wavy hair-grass
Festuca ovina	Sheep's fescue
*Holcus lanatus	Yorkshire fog
,, mollis	Creeping soft-grass
Juncus articulatus	Jointed rush
* ,, bulbosus	Bulbous rush
,, effusus	Soft rush
*Lolium perenne	Rye-grass
Melica uniflora	Wood melick
Molinia caerulea	Purple moor-grass
*Poa annua	Annual poa
* ,, pratensis	Meadow-grass
*Sieglingia decumbens	Heath grass

Herbs
Ajuga reptans	Bugle
Anagallis arvensis	Scarlet pimpernel
Bellis perennis	Daisy
Betonica officinalis	Betony
Campanula rotundifolia	Harebell
Chamaenerion angustifolium	Rosebay willow-herb
Cirsium dissectum	Meadow thistle
,, palustre	Marsh thistle
,, vulgare	Spear thistle
Endymion non-scriptus	Bluebell
Epilobium montanum	Broad-leaved willow-herb
,, palustre	Marsh willow-herb
Euphrasia nemorosa	
Fragaria vesca	Wild strawberry
Galium saxatile	Heath bedstraw
Hieracium spp.	Hawkweeds
Hydrocotyle vulgaris	Pennywort
Hypericum humifusum	Trailing St John's wort
Hypochoeris radicata	Cat's ear
Lathyrus montanus	Bitter vetch
Leontodon taraxacoides	Hairy hawkbit
Lotus corniculatus	Birdsfoot-trefoil
,, pedunculatus	Large birdsfoot-trefoil
,, nummularia	Creeping jenny
Lysimachia nemorum	Yellow pimpernel
Melampyrum pratense	Common cow-wheat
Mentha aquatica	Water mint
Odontites verna	Red bartsia
Oxalis acetosella	Wood-sorrel
Plantago lanceolata	Ribwort
,, major	Great plantain
,, media	Hoary plantain
Polygala serpyllifolia	Common milkwort
Polygonum aviculare	Knotgrass
Potentilla erecta	Common tormentil
Ranunculus acris	Meadow buttercup
,, bulbosus	Bulbous buttercup
,, ficaria	Lesser celandine
,, repens	Creeping buttercup

FALLOW DEER

Rumex acetosa	Sorrel	*Erica cinerea*	Bell-heather
,, *acetosella*	Sheep's sorrel	,, *tetralix*	Cross-leaved heather
Saponaria officinalis	Soapwort	*Fagus sylvaticus*	Beech
Scrophularia nodosa	Figwort	*Frangula alnus*	Alder buckthorn
Senecio vulgaris	Groundsel	*Fraxinus excelsior*	Ash
Stellaria graminea	Lesser stitchwort	*Hedera helix*	Ivy
Succisa pratensis	Devil's-bit scabious	*Ilex aquifolium*	Holly
Taraxacum officinale	Common dandelion	*Larix* spp.	Larches
Teucrium scorodonia	Wood sage	*Ligustrum vulgare*	Common privet
Trifolium campestre	Hop trefoil	*Malus sylvestris*	Crab apple
,, *pratense*	Red clover	*Picea abies*	Norway spruce
,, *repens*	White clover	*Picea sitchensis*	Sitka spruce
Veronica chamaedrys	Germander speedwell	*Pinus nigra laricio*	Corsican pine
,, *officinalis*	Common speedwell	* ,, *sylvestris*	Scots pine
Viola spp.	Violets	*Prunus spinosa*	Blackthorn
Wahlenbergia hederacea	Ivy campanula	*Pseudotsuga menziesii*	Douglas-fir
		Quercus spp.	Oaks
		Rhododendron ponticum	Rhododendron
		Rosa spp.	Roses
Trees and shrubs		*Rubus fruticosus agg.*	Bramble
Abies grandis	Giant fir	*Ruscus aculeatus*	Butcher's broom
,, *procera*	Noble fir	*Salix* spp.	Willows
Acer pseudoplatanus	Sycamore	*Sambucus nigra*	Elder
Alnus glutinosa	Alder	*Sarothamnus scoparius*	Broom
Berberis sp.		*Sorbus aucuparia*	Rowan
Betula pendula	Silver birch	*Thelycrania sanguinea*	Dogwood
Calluna vulgaris	Heather	*Thuja plicata*	Western red cedar
Castanea sativa	Sweet chestnut	*Tsuga heterophylla*	Western hemlock
Chamaecyparis lawsoniana	Lawson's cypress	*Ulex europaeus*	Gorse
Corylus avellana	Hazel	,, *minor*	Dwarf furze
Crataegus monogyna	Hawthorn	*Vaccinium myrtillus*	Bilberry
		Viburnum opulus	Guelder rose

Endoparasites found in Fallow Deer

	Austria	Czechoslovakia	Denmark	Germany	Great Britain	Netherlands	New Zealand	Poland	USA Alabama
Nematodes									
Apteragia quadrispiculata			+	+	+	+	+	+	
Artionema altaica		+							
Bicaulus sagittatus		+		+					
*Bunostomum phlebotomum									+
Capillaria sp.									+
* ,, bovis	+	+		+	+			+	
* ,, longipes					+				
*Chabertia ovina	+	+	+	+					
*Cooperia curticei			+	+					
* ,, oncophora						+			
* ,, pectinata		+	+	+	+			+	
* ,, punctata								+	+
*Dictylocaulus filaria					+				
* ,, viviparus	+	+	+	+		+		+	
*Gongylonema pulchrum					+				+
**Grosspiculagia lasensis					+	+	+		
*Haemonchus contortus	+	+	+	+			+	+	
* ,, placei									+
*Muellerius capillaris				+					
**Muflonagia podjapolski				+					
*Nematodirus filicollis	+	+	+	+	+				
* ,, helvetianus						+			
,, roscidus			+	+				+	
* ,, spathiger			+	+					
Oesophagostomum cervi								+	
* ,, radiatum			+						
,, sikae	+							+	
* ,, venulosum			+	+	+	+	+	+	
Onchocerca flexuosa		+		+					

The sources of the information are given in the bibliography.
*Domestic ruminants are the prime hosts.
**Also recorded from domesticated cattle, goats or sheep.

	Austria	Czechoslovakia	Denmark	Germany	Great Britain	Netherlands	New Zealand	Poland	USA Alabama
Ostertagia asymmetrica					+				
* ,, circumcincta			+	+	+	+			
** ,, leptospicularis			+	+	+	+		+	
* ,, lyrata				+					
,, mossi				+		+			
* ,, ostertagi	+		+	+		+			
* ,, trifurcata	+				+	+			
Pentastomum taeniodes				+					
Protostrongylus sagittatus			+						
Rinadia mathevossiani				+	+	+		+	
,, schulzi		+							
Setaria tundra									+
*Skrjabinagia kolchida								+	+
,, odocoilei									
Spiculopteragia asymmetrica			+	+	+	+	+	+	
,, schulzi		+		+					
* ,, spiculoptera			+	+	+	+		+	
*Teladorsagia davtiani				+		+			
*Trichostrongylus axei			+	+		+		+	
* ,, capricola		+		+					
* ,, colubriformis			+	+		+			
,, ventricosus				+					
* ,, vitrinus			+		+	+			
**Trichuris cupreoli	+			+					
* ,, globulosa	+			+					
* ,, ovis	+		+	+					
Wehrdikmansia cervipedis					+				
,, flexuosa					+				
Cestodes									
*Echinococcus granulosus larva				+					
*Moniezia expansa				+				+	
* ,, benedini		+							
Taenia cervi larva				+					
* ,, hydatigena larva	+			+	+		+	+	
* ,, multiceps larva				+					
Trematodes									
*Dicrocoelium dendriticum		+		+	+				
*Fasciola hepatica		+	+	+	+			+	
**Fascioloides magna		+		+	+				
*Paramphistomum cervi		+		+	+				

APPENDIX V

Mammals mentioned in the Text

With the exception of fossil species*, the nomenclature is that used by Morris in *The Mammals: A Guide to the Living Species.*

Axis deer, *Axis axis*
Badger, *Meles meles*
Barasingha, *Cervus duvauceli*
Barbary red deer, *Cervus elaphus*
Bighorn sheep, *Ovis canadensis*
*Bison, *Bison priscus*
Black bear, *Ursus americanus*
Blackbuck, *Antilope cervicapra*
Boar, *Sus scrofa*
Bobcat, *Felis rufa*
Brocket deer, *Mazama* spp.
Brown bear, *Ursus arctos*
Brown rat, *Rattus norvegicus*
Camel, *Camelus bactrianus*
Cat, *Felis catus*
*Cave lion, *Panthera spelaea*
Civet, *Viverra* spp.
Coyote, *Canis latrans*
Dog, *Canis familiaris*
Donkey, *Equus* sp.
Dromedary, *Camelus dromedarius*
*Elephant, *Elephas antiquus*
Fox, *Vulpes vulpes*
Gaur, *Bos gaurus*
*Giant deer, *Megaloceros giganteus*
Giraffe, *Giraffa camelopardalis*
Goat, *Capra hircus*
Grey squirrel, *Sciurus carolinensis*
Guemal, *Hippocamelus* spp.
Hare, *Lepus europaeus*
*Hippopotamus, *Hippopotamus amphibius*
Hog deer, *Axis porcinus*
Horse, *Equus caballus*
*Hyaena, *Crocuta crocuta*
Impala, *Aepyceros melampus*
Jackal, *Canis aureus*
Jungle cat, *Felis chaus*
Leopard, *Panthera pardus*
Lynx, *Felis lynx*
Maral, *Cervus elaphus*
Marsh deer, *Blastocerus dichotomus*

Moose, *Alces alces*
Mountain goat, *Oreamnos americanus*
Mountain lion, *Felis concolor*
Mouse, *Mus musculus*
Mule deer, *Odocoileus hemionus*
Muntjac deer, *Muntiacus muntjak*
Musk deer, *Moschus moschiferus*
Musk ox, *Ovibos moschatus*
Nilgai, *Boselaphus tragocamelus*
Okapi, *Okapia johnstoni*
Opossum, *Trichosurus vulpecula*
Ox, *Bos taurus*
Pampas deer, *Ozotoceros bezoarticus*
Panther, *Panthera pardus*
Père David's deer, *Elaphurus davidianus*
Pig, *Sus scrofa*
Porcupine, *Hystrix indica*
Pronghorn antelope, *Antilocapra americana*
Pudu, *Pudu* spp.
Rabbit, *Oryctolagus cuniculus*
Red deer, *Cervus elaphus*
Reindeer, *Rangifer tarandus*
*Rhinoceros, *Rhinoceros* sp.
Rocky Mountain goat, *Oreamnos americanus*
Roe deer, *Capreolus capreolus*
Rusa deer, *Cervus timorensis*
Sable antelope, *Hippotragus niger*
Sambar, *Cervus unicolor*
Sheep, *Ovis aries*
Sika deer, *Cervus nippon*
Sloth, *Choleopus* spp.
*Straight-tusked elephant, *Palaeoloxodon antiquus*
Tiger, *Panthera tigris*
Wapiti, *Cervus canadensis*
Water buffalo, *Bubalus bubalus*
White-tailed deer, *Odocoileus virginianus*
Wild boar, *Sus scrofa*
Wild cat, *Felis sylvestris*
Wolf, *Canis lupus*

Legislation

DEER ACT 1963

The following summary covers those aspects concerning deer; other parts of the Act deal with the apprehension of offenders, penalties and forfeitures. The Act applies to England and Wales only.

1.   Deer shall not be taken or wilfully killed
   - (a) during the close seasons which for fallow deer are:
       - Buck 1 May to 31 July inclusive
       - Doe   1 March to 31 October inclusive;
   - and (b) between the expiration of the first hour after sunset and the commencement of the last hour before sunrise.

2.   The use of the following articles to injure, kill or take deer is prohibited:
   - (a) Firearms: smooth bore guns of less gauge than 12 bore; rifles having a calibre of less than 0.240 inches or a muzzle energy of less than 1,700 foot pounds; any air gun, air rifle or air pistol;
   - (b) Ammunition: cartridges for use in a smooth bore gun loaded with shot of less than 0.269 inches in diameter; any rifle bullet other than soft-nosed or hollow-nosed;
   - and (c) Traps, snares, poisoned or stupefying baits, poisons, stupefying drugs or muscle-relaxing agents, and arrows, spears or similar missiles.

3.   Shooting from mechanically propelled vehicles or using such vehicles to drive deer is prohibited except by, or with the written authority of, the occupier of enclosed land where deer are usually kept in relation to deer on that land.

4   Under certain exemptions from parts of the Act it is permissible to prevent:
   - (a) Suffering by injured or diseased deer;
   - and (b) Serious damage to crops, vegetables, fruit, growing timber or any other form of property on any cultivated land, pasture or enclosed woodland. Under this section of the Act, the person taking or killing the deer must also be able to prove that he is the occupier of that land, pasture or woodland, or that he acted with the written authority of the occupier.

5.   The Nature Conservancy Council may licence the use of nets, traps, stupefying drugs, muscle-relaxing agents and any missile carrying such compounds for the purpose of removing deer from one area to another or of taking deer alive for scientific or educational purposes.

DEER (SCOTLAND) ACT, 1959
DEER (CLOSE SEASONS) (SCOTLAND) ORDER 1966
DEER (AMENDMENT) (SCOTLAND) ACT 1967

This legislation is concerned primarily with red deer but the following applies to fallow deer in Scotland.

1. Deer shall not be taken or wilfully killed
   (a) during the close seasons which for fallow deer are:
       Buck 1 May to 31 July inclusive
       Doe   16 February to 20 October inclusive;
   and (b) between the expiration of the first hour after sunset and the commencement of the last hour before sunrise.

2. Deer shall not be taken or wilfully killed on any land without the legal right to do so or without permission from a person having such right.

3. Deer shall not be taken or wilfully killed otherwise than by shooting. Shooting means discharging a firearm, as defined in the Firearms Act 1968, other than a prohibited weapon.

4. There are certain exemptions from parts of the legislation:
   (a) Any act done to prevent suffering by an injured or diseased deer, or by any deer calf deprived of its mother, is not an offence against this legislation;
   (b) An occupier of agricultural land or of enclosed woodlands, or any person authorised by him in writing in that behalf, may take or kill during a close season any deer found on any arable land, garden grounds or land laid down in permanent grass (other than moorland and unenclosed land) forming part of that land, or on such woodlands;
   and (c) An occupier of agricultural land or of enclosed woodlands may take or kill during the night-time any deer found on any such arable land, garden grounds or land laid down in permanent grass or on such woodlands;

5. The Secretary of State may authorise in writing the taking or killing of deer during a close season for scientific purposes.

Anyone concerned with the management of deer is strongly advised to consult the relevant legislation for the full details.

Glossary

Words which are in *The Concise Oxford Dictionary* are, in general, not included in the glossary if used in the text in accordance with the dictionary definition.

Age class	A group of animals *estimated* to be of similar age; used when the actual ages are unknown.
Androgen	A compound with male sex hormone activity.
Anointing post	A tree on which an area of the trunk is oily and worn smooth by deer depositing scent.
Antler	A deciduous bony outgrowth on the head of male deer.
Antorbital gland	*see* Suborbital gland.
Bachelor group	A herd of male animals.
Barking (of trees)	Removal of bark from trees by the teeth.
Beam	The stem of the antler below the palm from which the brow and trez tines grow. See Figure 5.
Bez tine (or bay)	The second tine of an antler, usually absent in European fallow deer, in which the second tine is therefore the trez (q.v.).
Brashings	A forestry term referring to the lower branches removed from a tree at the end of the thicket stage (q.v.).
Breeding season	The period during which fertile matings occur. Not to be confused with rutting season.
Brow tine	The lowest tine of an antler. See Figure 5.
Browse line	The levels up to which the branches of a tree are eaten.
Brush	The tuft of hairs at the end of the penis sheath.
Buck	A male of various species, including fallow deer.
Burr	The edge of the coronet of the antler. See Figure 5.
Butcher's weight	The weight of a deer carcase without head, feet and all internal organs except the kidneys, but with skin on.
Calcification	The deposition of calcium salts; part of the process of ossification (q.v.).
Cannon bone	The elongated bone of the lower leg. See Figure 2.
Centimetre	Equals 0.394 inches.
Chase	Unenclosed land, other than a Royal Forest (q.v.), formerly used for hunting.
Clean (of antlers)	Antlers free of velvet.
Clean weight	Various definitions but, in general, the weight of a deer carcase without lungs and gastro-intestinal tract. Some people also exclude heart and/or liver.
Cleave	One half of a cloven foot.
Close season	The part of the year when the taking or wilful killing of deer is prohibited. Varies in different countries.
Core area	A part of an animal's home range which it uses frequently.
Coronet	The base of an antler. See Figure 5.
Crest (of teeth)	The highest points of a tooth. See Figure 4.
Crotties	An ancient term for heaps of deer faeces, still sometimes used.

Crown (of teeth)	The part of a tooth protruding beyond the gum.
Cryptic colouration	Colouration which conceals animal by camouflaging it.
Cryptorchid	The condition in which a testis is in the abdomen rather than in the scrotum; can be unilateral or bilateral.
Cull	To kill surplus deer.
Cusp (of teeth)	Projection on upper surface of molar and premolar teeth. See Figure 4.
Deciduous teeth	Milk teeth.
Deer leap	A mound constructed to enable deer to leap into, or out of, an enclosure.
Dental pad	The hard pad of tissue at the front of the upper jaw against which the front teeth of the lower jaw bite.
Dentine	The main constituent of teeth. See Figure 4.
Diastema	The gap between the incisiform and premolar teeth in the lower jaws.
Doe	A female of various species, including fallow deer.
Double head	The condition in which a buck carries both the current and previous year's antlers.
Ectoparasite	A parasite living on the outside of an animal. (cf. endoparasite).
Enamel	The hard material covering the exposed surface of a tooth. See Figure 4.
Endoparasite	A parasite living inside an animal. (cf. ectoparasite).
Epiphysis (plural: epiphyses)	The terminal part of a growing bone which is separated from the rest of the bone by a layer of cartilage.
Eructation	The mechanism whereby fermentation gases are lost from the rumen.
Exotoses	Bony growths on the surface of a bone.
Faeces	Droppings or excrement.
Fat buck season	The time of year when bucks in prime condition are killed (August in Britain).
Fawn	A deer in its first year, including fallow deer.
Fewmets	An ancient term for deer faeces, still sometimes used.
Flehmen	A behaviour reflex sometimes exhibited by males, usually after savouring the female's urine. It consists of raising the head, curling back the upper lip and dropping the lower lip.
Followers	The fawns and yearlings following a doe.
Forest Law	Laws, as distinct from Common Law, which provided for the control and management of Royal Forests (q.v.).
Fraying	The act of removing the bark of a tree by a deer rubbing his antlers on it.
Gralloch weight	The weight of a deer carcase without the gastro-intestinal tract except the gullet.
Groan	The sound (like a resonant belch) made by male fallow when rutting.
Ground flora	The lower layer of plants growing on the floor of a wood.
Growth rings	The concentric layers sometimes seen in sections of pedicles and of the cement of teeth.
Hart	An ancient term for a six-year old red deer stag.
Havier	A castrated male deer.
Head (of antlers)	A buck with, for example, his second set of antlers has his second head.
Hectare	Equals 2.47 acres.
High seat	An elevated platform from which to watch or shoot deer.
Hind	A female red or sika deer; also used for some other species.
Hog-dressed	The weight of a deer carcase without head, feet and all internal organs but with skin on.
Home range	The area to which an animal confines itself in its day-to-day activities.
Hummel	An entire male deer which does not produce antlers, Chinese water deer excepted.
Incisiform	A term used to describe both incisor and canine teeth when of similar shape.

Inclosure	An area in the New Forest in England set aside for planting of trees, fenced to exclude domestic grazing animals.
Infraorbital gland	*see* Suborbital gland.
Infundibulum	The area between the cusps of a molar or premolar tooth. See Figure 4.
Interdigital gland	A scent gland between the cleaves of the feet.
Kilogram	Equals 2.2 pounds.
Lifetime range	The total area with which an animal becomes familiar.
Lumpy jaw	A swollen lump on the jaw caused by bacterial infection.
Master buck	A buck holding a rutting territory.
Menil	A colour variety of fallow deer.
Metacarpal	The cannon bone (q.v.) of the fore leg.
Metatarsal	The cannon bone (q.v.) of the hind leg.
Metre	Equals 1.09 yards or 39.4 inches.
Mewing	The sound made by fallow deer during submissive behaviour but particularly by very young fawns, when it is also referred to as peeping or pheeping.
Mixed woodland	A wood comprising both coniferous and deciduous trees.
Murrain	An ancient term for diseases.
Netting	A method of catching deer by guiding them into nets.
Oestrus	"Season" or "heat". The period in which the female is receptive.
Ossification	The conversion to bone.
Palm	The flat portion of an antler. See Figure 5.
Pedal gland	*see* Interdigital gland.
Pedicle	The permanent column of bone, from the skull, which supports the antler. See Figure 5.
Peep	*see* Mewing.
Pelage	The hair of mammals.
Perruque	Malformed antlers grown after castration or damage to the testes, normally retained for life.
Pheep	*see* Mewing.
Pheromone	The behaviourally active component(s) of the secretions of scent glands used as a means of communication.
Plantation	A group of trees all planted at the same time.
Plesiometacarpalian	The condition in which the splint bones are at the upper end of the cannon bone e.g., as in fallow and red deer.
Points	An alternative term for the tines and spellers of an antler. See Figure 5.
Preorbital gland	*see* Suborbital gland.
Pricket	A male deer with his first head of antlers. Used by some people only for a male deer in his second year.
Pronking	The gait in which the animal bounces stiff-legged on all four feet.
Reproductive cycle	The annual cycle of changes that occur in the reproductive organs.
Rhinarium (plural, rhinaria)	The area of naked skin on the nose.
Ride	A wide track separating woodland into blocks.
Rig	A colloquial term for cryptorchid (q.v.)
Royal Forest	A tract of land, not necessarily wooded, previously subject to Forest Law (q.v.) and used by the king or his favourites for hunting.
Rut	A period of sexual hyper-activity associated with mating. Not to be confused with breeding season (q.v.).
Scent gland	A specialised area of skin producing odoriferous compounds.
Scoring	The grooves made by antlers in the bark of trees.

Reed, C. A. (1965) Imperial Sassanian hunting of pig and fallow-deer, and problems of survival of these animals today in Iran. Postilla, No. 92, 1-23.

Sartorius, O. (1970) *Stärkste Damschaufler der Welt.* Hannover: Verlag M. & H. Schaper.

Scrape	An area of ground disturbed by a buck's forefeet; usually associated with the rut.
Season (in female animals)	The period of heat or oestrus.
Sexual dimorphism	Difference in form between the sexes.
Soar (Sore)	An ancient term for a male fallow in its fourth year.
Social hierarchy	A graded organisation regulating social behaviour; "peck-order".
Sorrel (Sorel)	An ancient term for a male fallow in its third year.
Speculum	The area around the tail on the rump of a deer.
Spellers	The tines or points along the edge of the palm of an antler. See Figure 5.
Stag	A male red or sika deer; also used for some other species.
Staggers	A disease of deer in which coordination of the hindquarters is lost, resulting in a staggering gait.
Stand (rutting)	The territory of a rutting fallow buck.
Stripping	Removing the bark of trees with the teeth.
Suborbital gland	Scent gland situated near the corner of the eye.
Suture line	Line of demarcation between adjacent bones which comprise the skull.
Teleometacarpalian	The condition in which the splint bones are at the lower end of the cannon bones e.g., as in roe deer.
Territory	An area which is defended, hence rutting territory.
Thicket	A forestry term; the stage of growth of woodland between the closing of the canopy and the first thinning (q.v.) but commonly an area of dense bushes or trees.
Thinning(s)	A forestry term. Selective removal of inferior stems from a plantation, usually repeated at 3-6 year intervals.
Thrashing	An activity in which a buck flays bushes or small trees with his antlers.
Tine	A prong or point of an antler. See Figure 5.
Trez tine (or tray)	The third tine of an antler. Usually the second tine in European fallow deer because the bez tine (q.v.) is generally absent. See Figure 5.
Trophy (of antlers)	A pair of antlers which merit an award in a hunting competition.
Velvet	The skin covering the growing antlers.
Venison	The flesh of a deer.
Vertebral stripe	The darker line along the middle of the back.
Villi (singular, villus)	Short, finger-like projections from the skin or other surface, such as lining of rumen.
Waster	An emaciated animal.
Whickering	A sound made by fallow does during the rut.
Yearling	A deer in its second year.

Bibliography

The titles of papers in foreign languages, but not books, have been translated into English: the original language is indicated. In Britain, most items are obtainable from the British Library at Boston Spa: applications should be made through local libraries.

Chapter One   Introduction

Anon. (1961) *Trees in Richmond Park; Fifth Report of the Advisory Committee on Forestry.* (Contains information on the fauna and the geology). London; H.M.S.O.

Chapman, D. (1966) Deer of Epping Forest. Animals, **8**, 394-397.

Chapman, N. & Chapman, D. (1970) *Fallow Deer.* —; The British Deer Society.

Chapman, D. I. & Chapman, N. (1969) Observations on the biology of fallow deer (*Dama dama*) in Epping Forest, Essex, England. Biological Conservation, **2**, 55-62.

Collenette, C. L. (1937) *A History of Richmond Park with an Account of its Birds and Animals.* London; Sidgwick & Jackson Ltd.

Darling, F. F. (1937) *A Herd of Red Deer: A Study in Animal Behaviour.* London; Oxford University Press.

Gulliver, G. (1842) Observations on the semen and seminal tubules of mammalia and birds. Proceedings of the Zoological Society of London, 95-102.

Heidemann, G. (1973) *Zur Biologie des Damwildes* (*Cervus dama* Linné 1758). Hamburg and Berlin; Verlag Paul Parey.

Millais, J. G. (1897) *British Deer and their Horns.* London; Henry Sotheran & Co.

Prior, R. (1968) *The Roe Deer of Cranborne Chase: An Ecological Survey.* London; Oxford University Press.

Qvist, A. (1971) *Epping Forest.* (revised edition) London; The Corporation of London.

Russell, R. (1755) *The Oeconomy of Nature in Acute and Chronical Diseases of the Glands.* London; J. & J. Rivington, and Oxford; J. Fletcher.

Tegner, H. (1951) *The Roe Deer: Their History, Habits and Pursuit.* London; The Batchworth Press.

Ueckermann, E. & Hansen, P. (1968) *Das Damwild.* Hamburg and Berlin; Verlag Paul Parey.

Chapter Two   Classification and General Characteristics

Anon. (1960) Opinion 581. Determination of the generic names for the fallow deer of Europe and the Virginia deer of America (class Mammalia). The Bulletin of Zoological Nomenclature, **17**, 267-275.

Baker, K. (1973) *Reproductive Biology of Fallow Deer* (*Dama dama*) *in the Blue Mountains of New Zealand.* M.Sc.Thesis, University of Otago, Dunedin, New Zealand.

Buxton, A. (1954) The deer of Epping Forest. Oryx, **2**, 241-245.

Fitzinger, L. J. (1874) A critical examination of the species of the natural deer families (Cervidae). Sitzungsberichte der Mathematisch—Naturwissenschaftlichen Classe der Kaiserlichen Akademie der Wissenschaften, **69**, 519-604. (Ger.)

Jackson, J. E. (1974) *The Feeding Ecology of the Fallow Deer* (*Dama dama L.*) *in the New Forest.* Ph.D.Thesis, University of Southampton, England.

Lascelles, G. (1915) *Thirty-five Years in the New Forest.* London; Edward Arnold.

Leland, J. see Smith

Letts,·M. (ed.) (1957) *The Travels of Leo of Rozmital through Germany, Flanders, England, France, Spain, Portugal and Italy, 1465-1467.* Cambridge; Cambridge University Press.

Linnaeus, C. (1758) *Systema Naturae. Tomus 1 (Regnum Animale).* Tenth edition. (Photographic facsimile, 1939). London; Trustees of the British Museum (Natural History).

Millais, J. G. (1897) *British Deer and their Horns.* London; Henry Sotheran & Co.

Rozmital, L. see Letts.

Shirley, E. P. (1867) *Some Account of English Deer Parks with Notes on the Management of Deer.* London; John Murray.

Smith, L. T. (ed.) (1910) *The Itinerary of John Leland in or about the Years 1535-1543, Parts IX, X and XI.* London; G. Bell & Sons Ltd.

Springthorpe, G. (1969) Long-haired fallow deer at Mortimer Forest. Journal of Zoology, London, **159**, 537.

Ueckermann, E. & Hansen, P. (1968) *Das Damwild.* Hamburg and Berlin; Verlag Paul Parey.

Whitaker, J. (1892) *A Descriptive List of the Deer-Parks and Paddocks of England.* London; Ballantyne, Hanson & Co.

Whitehead, G. K. (1950) *Deer and their Management in the Deer Parks of Great Britain and Ireland.* London; Country Life Ltd.

Winans, W. (1913) *Deer Breeding for Fine Heads with Descriptions of many Varieties and Crossbreeds.* London; Rowland Ward Ltd.

Chapter Three   Fossil and Early History

Arambourg, C. (1958) The large mammals of the Tayaciennes beds. (La Grotte de Fontéchevade). Archives de l'Institut de Paléontologie Humaine, Mémoire 29, 185-229. (Fr.)

Arnold-Bemrose, H. H. & Newton, E. T. (1905) On an ossiferous cavern of Pleistocene age at Hoe-Grange quarry, Longcliffe, near Brassington (Derbyshire). The Quarterly Journal of the Geological Society of London, **61**, 43-63.

Azzaroli, A. (1948) The fossil deer of Tuscany with particular reference to the Villafranchian species. Palaeontographia Italica, **43**, 45-81. (Ital.)

Azzaroli, A. (1953) The deer of the Weybourn Crag and Forest Bed of Norfolk. Bulletin of the British Museum (Natural History), Geology, **2**, No. 1.

Bate, D. M. A. (1937) Notes on recent finds of *Dama clactoniana* (*Cervus browni* auctt.) in London and Swanscombe. Proceedings of the Prehistoric Society, new series, **3**, 460-463.

Bökönyi, S. (1971) Information on the occurrence of early Holocene fallow deer *Cervus (Dama) dama* (Linné, 1758), in Europe. Säugetierkundliche Mitteilungen, **19**, 206-217. (Ger.)

Boule, M. (1910) *Les Grottes de Grimaldi (Baoussé-Roussé), Volume 1, Part 3 Géologie et Paléontologie.* Imprimerie de Monaco.

Bulleid, A. & Jackson, J. W. (1938) The Burtle sand beds of Somerset. Proceedings of the Somersetshire Archaeological and Natural History Society, **83**, 171-195.

Cuvier, G. (1823) *Recherches sur les Ossemens Fossiles.* (Nouvelle Edition) Paris; Chez G. Dufour et E. D'Ocagne, Libraires.

Dawkins, W. B. (1868) On a new species of fossil deer from Clacton. The Quarterly Journal of the Geological Society of London, **24**, 511-516.

Ducos, P. (1965) The fallow deer in Cyprus to the prehistoric era. In: *Report of the Department of Antiquities, Cyprus,* Pages 1-8. (Fr.)

Falconer, H. see Murchison.

Fisher, W. R. (1887) *The Forest of Essex its History, Laws, Administration, Ancient Customs and the Wild Deer which lived in it.* London; Butterworths.

Freudenberg, W. (1914) Mammals of the older Quaternary of central Europe with special regard to the fauna of Hundsheim and Deutschaltenburg in Lower Austria together with comments about related forms of other species which were discovered. [*Dama priscus*]. Geologische und Palaeontologische, **16**, (nF 12), 1-219. (Ger.)

Hutchinson, H. G. (1904) *The New Forest.* London; Methuen & Co.

Jarman, M. R. (1972) European deer economies and the advent of the Neolithic. In: *Papers in Economic Prehistory.* Higgs, E. S. (ed.) Pages 125-147. Cambridge; Cambridge University Press.

Jennison, G. (1937) *Animals for Show and Pleasure in Ancient Rome.* Manchester; The University Press.

Kenyon, K. M. (1948) Excavations at the Jewry Wall site, Leicester. Report of Research Committee of the Society of Antiquaries of London, No. 15.

Melentis, J. K. (1966) The Pleistocene deer of Beckens of Megalopolis in Peloponnes (Greece). Annales géologiques des pays helleniques, **16**, 1-92. (Greek and Ger.)

Møhl, U. (1961) Survey of the animal bones from Naesholm. In: *Naesholm.* Cour, V. la (ed.) Pages 398-427. Copenhagen; National Museum. (Dan.)

Møhl-Hansen, U. (1954) Marrow-split bones in interglacial deposits in Jutland. Aarbøger for Nordisk Oldkyndighed og Historie, 101-126. (Dan. and Eng.)

Murchison, C. (1868) *Palaeontological Memoirs and Notes of the late Hugh Falconer, A.M., M.D.* Volume 2, page 478. London; Robert Hardwicke.

Oakley, K. P. & Leakey, M. (1937) Report on excavations at Jaywick Sands, Essex (1934), with some observations on the Clactonian industry, and on the fauna and geological significance of the Clacton Channel. Proceedings of the Prehistoric Society, new series, **3**, 217-260.

O'Neil, H. E. (1945) The Roman villa at Park Street, near St. Albans, Hertfordshire. The Archaeological Journal, **102**, 19-109.

Pohlig, H. (1892) The deer from the Thuringian diluvial-Travertines with contributions on other diluvial and recent types of stag. [*Dama gastaldii*]. Palaeontographica, **39**, 215-263.

Portis, A. (1920) List of the species of fossil deer in and around Rome. Bollettino della Società Geologica Italiana, **39**, 123-139. (Ital.)

Ringe, D. (1959) *On the Indigenous Post Glacial Occurrence of Fallow Deer, Cervus (Dama) dama L. in Europe.* Inaugural-Dissertation zur Erlangung der veterinärmedizinischen Doktorwürde der Tierärztlichen Fakultät der Lugwig-Maximilians-Universität München, Germany. (Ger.)

Schmid, E. (1965) Fallow deer in Roman Augst. Ur-Schweiz-La Suisse Primitive, **29**, 53-63. (Ger.)

Sickenberg, O. (1965) *Dama clactoniana* (Falc.) in the Middle Terrace of Rhume-Leine near Edesheim (Landkreis Northeim). Geologisches Jahrbuch, **83**, 353-396. (Ger.)

Sutcliffe, A. (1960) Joint Mitnor Cave, Buckfastleigh. Torquay Natural History Society. Journal of Transactions and Proceedings, **13**, 1-26.

Sutcliffe, A. J. (1964) The mammalian fauna. In: *The Swanscombe Skull. A Survey of Research on a Pleistocene Site.* Ovey, C. D. (ed.). London; Royal Anthropological Institute, Occasional Paper No. 20, pages 85-111.

Tebbutt, C. F., Rudd, G. T. & Moorhouse, S. (1971) Excavation of a moated site at Ellington, Huntingdonshire. Proceedings of the Cambridge Antiquarian Society, **63**, 31-73.

Teilhard de Chardin, P. & Trassaert, M. (1937) The Pliocene Camelidae, Giraffidae and Cervidae of South-eastern Shansi. [*Dama sericus*]. Palaeontologia Sinica, Whole series No. 102, (New series C1) 1-68.

Toynbee, J. M. C. (1973) *Animals in Roman Life and Art.* London; Thames & Hudson.

Twici, W. (1908) *The Art of Hunting.* Revised edition by H. Dryden, 1844. Edited by Alice Dryden. Northampton; William Mark.

Vekna, A. K. (1960) Remains of *Cervus (Dama)* sp. from Pleistocene deposits of southern Georgia. Soobshcheniya Akademii nauk Gruzinskoı SSR, **24**, 45-47. (Russ.)

Chapter Four   Distribution, Past and Present

Alex-Hansen, B. (1965) Denmark's cloven-hooved game 1965. Dansk Jagttidende, **82**, 139-144. (Dan.)

Anon. (1952) *Census of Woodlands 1947-1949.* Forestry Commission Census Report No. 1. London, H.M.S.O.

Bentley, A. (1967) *An Introduction to the Deer of Australia with special reference to Victoria.* Melbourne, John Gartner at the Hawthorn Press.

Caboń-Raczyńska, K. (1965) Personal communication.

Cantor, L. M. (1970-1) The medieval parks of Leicestershire. Transactions of the Leicestershire Archaeological and Historical Society, **46**, 9-24.

Caughley, G. (1963) Dispersal rates of several ungulates introduced into New Zealand. Nature, **200**, 280-281.

Chapman, D. & Chapman, N. (1973) *Deer of East Anglia.* Ipswich; F. W. Pawsey and Sons.

Cox, J. C. (1905) *The Royal Forests of England.* London; Methuen & Co.

Donne, T. E. (1924) *The Game Animals of New Zealand. An Account of their Introduction, Acclimatization, and Development.* London; John Murray.

Heidemann, G. (1973) On the introduction of fallow deer (*Cervus dama* Linné, 1758) in the district Schleswig. Zeitschrift für Säugetierkunde, **38**, 341-347. (Ger.)

Heptner, V. G., Nasimovič, A. A. & Bannikov, A. G. (1966) *The Mammals of the Soviet Union. I Artiodactyla and Perissodactyla.* (German edition). Jena; Gustav Fischer Verlag. (Ger.)

Joleaud, L. (1935) The antlered ruminants of Africa. Mémoires présentés a l'Institut d'Égypte, **27**, 1-85. (Fr.)

Laver, H. (1898) *The Mammals, Reptiles, and Fishes of Essex: A Contribution to the Natural History of the County.* London; Simpkin, Marshall & Co. Ltd.

Mulloy, F. (1970) Wild deer: their status and distribution, 1970. (iii) A note on the occurrence of deer in Ireland. Deer, **2**, 502-504.

Nicholls, H. G. (1858) *The Forest of Dean: An Historical and Descriptive Account.* London; John Murray.

Patten, J. (1971) How the deer parks began. The chase and the English landscape -1. Country Life, **150**, 660-662.

Reinhardt, S. and Schenk, H. (1969) On the distribution of large mammals in Sardinia. Bonner Zoologische Beiträge, **4**, 429-436. (Ger.)

Sartorius, O. (1970) *Stärkte Damschaufler der Welt.* Hannover: Verlag M. & H. Schaper.

Taylor, W. L. (1948) The distribution of wild deer in England and Wales. The Journal of Animal Ecology, **17**, 151-154.

Taylor, W. L. (1949) The distribution of wild deer in Scotland. The Journal of Animal Ecology, **18**, 187-192.

Tubbs, C. R. (1968) *The New Forest: An Ecological History.* Newton Abbot; David & Charles.

Whitaker, J. (1892) *A Descriptive List of the Deer-Parks and Paddocks of England.* London; Ballantyne, Hanson & Co.

Whitehead, G. K. (1950) *Deer and their Management in the Deer Parks of Great Britain and Ireland.* London; Country Life Ltd.

Whitehead, G. K. (1964) *The Deer of Great Britain and Ireland: An Account of their History, Status and Distribution.* London; Routledge & Kegan Paul.

Wodzicki, K. A.(1950) *Introduced Mammals of New Zealand: An Ecological and Economic Survey.* Wellington; Department of Scientific and Industrial Research.

Chapter Five   Structure, Function and Growth

Baillie-Grohman, W. A. & F. (eds.) (1904) *The Master of Game, by Edward, Second Duke of York.* London; Ballantyne, Hanson & Co.

Baker, K. (1973) *Reproductive Biology of Fallow Deer (Dama dama) in the Blue Mountains of New Zealand.* M.Sc.Thesis, University of Otago, Dunedin, New Zealand.

Chapman, D. I. & Chapman, N. G. (1969) Geographical variation in fallow deer (*Dama dama*). Nature, **221**, 59-60.

Chapman, D. I. & Chapman, N. (1970) Development of the teeth and mandibles of fallow deer. Acta Theriologica, **15**, 111-131.

Gaston de Foix. see Baillie-Grohman.

Giesecke, D. (1970) Comparative microbiology of the alimentary tract. In: *Physiology of Digestion and Metabolism in the Ruminant*. Phillipson, A. T. (ed.) pages 306-318. Newcastle-upon-Tyne; Oriel Press.

Jackson, J. E. (1974) *The Feeding Ecology of the Fallow Deer (Dama dama L.) in the New Forest*. Ph.D.Thesis, University of Southampton, England.

Jenkinson, D. M. (1972) The skin structure of British deer. Research in Veterinary Science, **13**, 70-73.

Jenkinson, D. M., Blackburn, P. S. & Proudfoot, R. (1967) Seasonal changes in the skin glands of the goat. British Veterinary Journal, **123**, 541-549.

Larsen, K. (1971) Danish endocoprophilous fungi, and their sequence of occurrence. Saertryk af Botanisk Tidsskrift, **66**, 1-32.

Mehlitz, S. & Siefke, A. (1973) Physical and antler development of fallow deer *Cervus (Dama) dama* L. Beiträge zur Jagd-und Wildforschung, **8**, 49-74. (Ger.)

Prins, R. A. & Geelen, M. J. H. (1971) Rumen characteristics of red deer, fallow deer, and roe deer. The Journal of Wildlife Management, **35**, 673-680.

Prins, R. A., Hungate, R. E. & Prast, E. R. (1972) Function the omasum in several ruminant species. Comparative Biochemistry and Physiology, **43A**, 155-163.

Short, H. L. (1964) Postnatal stomach development of white-tailed deer. The Journal of Wildlife Management, **28**, 445-458.

Tempel, M. (1897) The gland of the interdigital skin of artiodactyla. Archiv für wissenschaftliche und praktische Tierheilkunde, **23**, 1-48. (Ger.)

Twici, W. (1908) *The Art of Hunting*. Revised edition by H. Dryden, 1844. Edited by Alice Dryden. Northampton; William Mark.

Ueckermann, E. & Hansen, P. (1968) *Das Damwild*. Hamburg and Berlin; Verlag Paul Parey.

Wherry, G. (1902) Observations on the horns of animals. The British Medical Journal, 27 September, 973-974.

Yalden, D. W. (1971) The functional morphology of the carpus in ungulate mammals. Acta Anatomica, **78**, 461-487.

Zeitzschmann, E. H. (1903) Contribution to the morphology and histology of the skin organs of deer. Zeitschrift für Wissenschaftliche Zoologie, **74**, 1-63. (Ger.)

Chapter Six   Age Estimation and Teeth

Baker, K. (1973) *Reproductive Biology of Fallow Deer (Dama dama) in the Blue Mountains of New Zealand*. M.Sc.Thesis, University of Otago, Dunedin, New Zealand.

Chapman, D. I. & Chapman, N. G. (1969) The incidence of congenital abnormalities in the mandibular dentition of fallow deer (*Dama dama* L.). Research in Veterinary Science, **10**, 485-487.

Chapman, D. I. & Chapman, N. (1970) Development of the teeth and mandibles of fallow deer. Acta Theriologica, **15**, 111-131.

Chapman, D. I. & Chapman, N. G. (1973) Maxillary canine teeth in fallow deer, *Dama dama*. Journal of Zoology, London, **170**, 143-147.

de Nahlik, A. J. (1959) *Wild Deer*. London; Faber and Faber Ltd.

Hansen, I.-E. (1971) *Damwildhege mit der Büchse*. Hamburg and Berlin; Verlag Paul Parey.

Mitchell, B. (1967) Growth layers in dental cement for determining the age of red deer (*Cervus elaphus* L.) Journal of Animal Ecology, **36**, 279-293.

Morris, P. (1972) A review of mammalian age determination methods. Mammal Review, **2**, 69-104.

Rieck, W. (1973) *Damwildalter-Merkblatt*. Herausgegeben vom Schalenwildausschuss des Deutschen Jagdschutz-Verbandes.

Ueckermann, E. & Hansen, P. (1968) *Das Damwild*. Hamburg and Berlin; Verlag Paul Parey.

Chapter Seven Antlers
Aristotle. see Cresswell.
Bedford, Duke of (1948) Clean of velvet. The Field, **192,** 468.
Beninde, J. (1937) The natural history of red deer. Zentrablatt für Kleintierkunde und Pelztierkunde, **13,** (10), 1-223. (Ger.)
Bernard, R. (1963) Specific gravity, ash, calcium and phosphorus content of antlers of cervidae. Le Naturaliste Canadien, **90,** 310-322.
Billingham, R. E., Mangold, R. & Silvers, W. K. (1959) The neogenesis of skin in the antlers of deer. Annals of the New York Academy of Sciences, **83,** 491-498.
Bruhin, H. (1953-1954) The biology of the frontal attachments of ungulates. Physiologia Comparata et Oecologia, **3,** 63-127. (Ger.)
Bubenik, A. (1959) The fine structure of fallow deer antlers — Cervus (Dama) dama Linné, 1758 and mesopotamicus Brooke, 1875 — and their stage of development. Säugetierkundliche Mitteilungen, I, Special Number, 90-94. (Ger.)
Bubenik, A. B. (1966) Das Geweih; Entwicklung, Aufbau und Ausformung der Geweihe und Gehörne und ihre Bedeutung für das Wild und für die Jagd. Hamburg and Berlin; Verlag Paul Parey.
Cadman, W. A. (1966) The Fallow Deer. London; H.M.S.O.
Cresswell, R. (1862) Aristotle's History of Animals in Ten Books. London; Henry G. Bohn.
Dunn, A. M. (1968) The wild ruminant as reservoir host of helminth infection. Symposia of the Zoological Society of London, **24,** 221-248.
Geist, V. (1966) The evolution of horn-like organs. Behaviour, **27,** 175-214.
Gilbert, B. K. (1964) Social Behaviour and Communication in Fallow Deer (Dama dama). M.A.Thesis, Duke University, N. Carolina, U.S.A.
Goss, R. J. (1970) Problems of antlerogenesis. Clinical Orthopaedics, **(69),** 227-238.
Hansen, P., Bülow, D. v. & Lotz, K. (1974) Das Ansprechen des Damschauflers; Herkunft und Verbreitung des Damwildes Lebensweise, Hege und Bejagung Merkmale guter und schlechter Veranlagung. Hannover; Verlag M. & H. Schaper.
Jaczewski, Z. (1958) Free transplantation and regeneration of antlers in fallow deer (Cervus dama (L.)). Bulletin de l'Académie Polonaise des Sciences, Série des Sciences Biologiques Class VI, **6,** 179-182.
Jaczewski, Z. (1961) Observations on the regeneration and transplantation of antlers in deer Cervidae. Folia Biologica, **9,** 47-99.
Jaczewski, Z. (1967) Regeneration and transplantation of antlers in deer, Cervidae. Zeitschrift für Säugetierkunde, **32,** 215-233.
Jaczewski, Z. & Topiński, P. (1970) Effect of human chorionic gonadotrophin on the antler cycle in fallow deer. Bulletin de l'Académie Polonaise des Sciences, Série des Sciences Biologiques, Class II, **18,** 731-732.
Kober, W. (1966) Thoughts and pictures about double head formation. Zeitschrift für Jagdwissenschaft, **12,** 85-87. (Ger.)
Lojda, Z. (1956) Histogenesis of the antlers of our cervidae and its histochemical picture. Ceskoslovenská Morfologie, **4,** 43-62. (Czech., Eng. summary)
Macewen, W. (1920) The Growth and Shedding of the Antler of the Deer. Glasgow; Maclehose, Jackson & Co.
Mehlitz, S. & Siefke, A. (1973) Physical and antler development of fallow deer Cervus (Dama) dama L. Beiträge zur Jagd - und Wildforschung, **8,** 49-74. (Ger.)
Müller, H. (1970) On the Influence of Artificial Variation to the Antler of Fallow Deer (Dama dama) upon the Behaviour of Others of the same Species. Thesis, University of Zurich, Switzerland. (Ger.)
Nüsslein, F. (1966) Die Formelmässige Bewertung der Europäischen Jagdtrophäen. Hamburg and Berlin; Verlag Paul Parey.

Pavlansky, R. & Bubenik, A. (1955) From which tissue does the essential stimulus to antler development originate? I An experiment in transplantation of a piece of antler in a fallow staggie, *Dama dama dama* (Linné, 1758). Säugetierkundliche Mitteilungen, **3**, 49-53. (Ger.)

Pavlansky, R. & Bubenik, A. (1960) From which tissue does the essential stimulus to antler development originate? IV Experiments with auto- and homo-transplantation of the antler. Säugetierkundliche Mitteilungen, **8**, 32-37. (Ger.)

Ratky, F. (1972) Fallow hummel. Deer, **2**, 827.

Rehn, E. (1955) Our deer seen by a surgeon and a huntsman. Wild und Hund, **58**, 216-219 & 239-240. (Ger.)

Riney, T. (1954) Antler growth and shedding in a captive group of fallow deer (*Dama dama*) in New Zealand. Transactions of the Royal Society of New Zealand, **82**, 569-578.

Sartorius, O. (1970) *Stärkste Damschaufler der Welt.* Hannover: Verlag M. & H. Schaper.

Ueckermann, E. & Hansen, P. (1968) *Das Damwild.* Hamburg and Berlin; Verlag Paul Parey.

Whitehead, G. K. (1964) *The Deer of Great Britain and Ireland: An Account of their History, Status and Distribution.* London; Routledge & Kegan Paul.

Wislocki, G. B., Weatherford, H. L. & Singer, M. (1947) Osteogenesis of antlers investigated by histological and histochemical methods. Anatomical Record, **99**, 265-295.

Zawadowsky, M. M. (1926) Bilateral and unilateral castration in *Cervus dama* and *Cervus elaphus.* Transactions of the Laboratory of experimental Biology of the Zoopak of Moscow, **1**, 1-31. (Russ.)

Chapter Eight   The Rut and Male Reproduction

Baker, K. (1973) *Reproductive Biology of Fallow Deer (Dama dama) in the Blue Mountains of New Zealand.* M.Sc. Thesis, University of Otago, Dunedin, New Zealand.

Cadman, W. A. (1966) *The Fallow Deer.* London; H.M.S.O.

Chapman, D. I. (1970) Observations on the sexual cycle of male deer in Britain. Mammal Review, **1**, 49-52.

Chapman, D. I. (1972) Seasonal changes in the gonads and accessory glands of male mammals. Mammal Review, **1**, 231-248.

Chapman, D. I. & Chapman, N. G. (1970) Preliminary observations on the reproductive cycle of male fallow deer (*Dama dama* L.) Journal of Reproduction and Fertility, **21**, 1-8.

Espmark, Y. & Brunner, W. (1974) Observations on rutting behaviour in fallow deer, *Dama dama* (Linné, 1758). Säugetierkundliche Mitteilungen, **22**, 135-142.

Frankenberger, Z. (1957) Circumanal and circumgenital glands of our cervidae. Československá Morfologie, **5**, 255-265. (Czech., Eng. summary)

Gilbert, B. K. (1964) *Social Behaviour and Communication in Fallow Deer (Dama dama).* M.S.Thesis, Duke University, N. Carolina, U.S.A.

Hinz, K. (1930) *Anatomical and Histological Examination of Testes, Vas Deferens and the pelvic part of the Urethra with the Accessory Glands of Fallow Deer in the Rut.* Dissertation, Anatomischen Institut der Tierärztlichen Hochschule zu Berlin, Germany. (Ger.)

Lincoln, G. A. (1971) Puberty in a seasonally breeding male, the red deer stag (*Cervus elaphus* L.). Journal of Reproduction and Fertility, **25**, 41-54.

Lincoln, G. A., Youngson, R. W. & Short, R. V. (1970) The social and sexual behaviour of the red deer stag. Journal of Reproduction and Fertility, Supplement, **11**, 71-103.

Packard, R. L. (1955) Release, dispersal, and reproduction of fallow deer in Nebraska. Journal of Mammalogy, **36**, 471-473.

Schloeth, R. (1968) Analysis of rubbing and thrashing of red deer stags (*Cervus elaphus* L.) in an alpine habitat (Swiss National Park). Ergebnisse der wissenschaftlichen Untersuchungen im schweizerischen Nationalpark, **11**, (59), 45-75. (Ger.)

Weiss, F. W. (1929) Histology and spermatogenesis of fallow deer testes outside of the rutting season. Zeitschrift für mikroscopisch-anatomische Forschung, 16, 21-54. (Ger.)

Chapter Nine   Female Reproduction and Maternal Behaviour

Armstrong, N., Chaplin, R. E., Chapman, D. I. & Smith, B. (1969) Observations on the reproduction of female wild and park fallow deer (*Dama dama*) in southern England. Journal of Zoology, London, **158**, 27-37.

Baker, K. (1973) *Reproductive Biology of Fallow Deer (Dama dama) in the Blue Mountains of New Zealand.* M.Sc.Thesis, University of Otago, Dunedin, New Zealand.

Cadman, W. A. (1966) *The Fallow Deer.* London; H.M.S.O.

Cowan, I. Mc.T. (1956) Life and times of the coast black-tailed deer. In: *The Deer of North America.* Taylor, W. P. (ed.), Pages 523-617. Harrisburg, Pennsylvania; The Stackpole Co. & Washington, D.C.; The Wildlife Management Institute. Institute.

Donne, T. E. (1924) *The Game Animals of New Zealand. An Account of their Introduction, Acclimatization, and Development.* London: John Murray.

Flerov, K. K. (1952) *Fauna of USSR. Mammal Volume 1, Number 2, Musk Deer and Deer.* English translation published by The Israel Program for Scientific Translations in 1960.

Gilbert, B. K. (1964) *Social Behaviour and Communication in Fallow Deer (Dama dama).* M.A.Thesis, Duke University, N. Carolina, U.S.A.

Gilbert, B. K. (1968) Development of social behaviour in the fallow deer (*Dama dama*). Zeitschrift für Tierpsychologie, **35**, 867-876.

Gray, A. P. (1971) *Mammalian Hybrids: A Check-list with Bibliography.* Farnham Royal, Slough; Commonwealth Agricultural Bureaux.

Guinness, F., Lincoln, G. A. & Short, R. V. (1971) The reproductive cycle of the female red deer, *Cervus elaphus* L. Journal of Reproduction and Fertility, **27**, 427-438.

Gustavsson, I. & Sundt, C. O. (1968) Karyotypes in five species of deer (*Alces alces* L., *Capreolus capreolus* L., *Cervas elaphus* L., *Cervus nippon nippon* Temm. and *Dama dama* L.). Hereditas, **60**, 233-248.

Hamilton, W. J., Harrison, R. J. & Young, B. A. (1960) Aspects of placentation in certain cervidae. The Journal of Anatomy, **94**, 1-33.

Harrison, R. J. & Hyett, A. R. (1954) The development and growth of the placentomes in the fallow deer (*Dama dama* L.). The Journal of Anatomy, **88**, 338-355.

Hawkins, R. E. & Klimstra, W. D. (1970) A preliminary study of the social organization of white-tailed deer. The Journal of Wildlife Management, **34**, 407-419.

Heidemann, G. (1973) *Zur Biologie des Damwildes (Cervus dama Linné 1758).* Hamburg and Berlin; Verlag Paul Parey.

Jackson, J. E. (1974) *The Feeding Ecology of the Fallow Deer (Dama dama L.) in the New Forest.* Ph.D.Thesis, University of Southampton, England.

Jensen, B. (1967) Sex- and age-composition, growth, and turnover in populations of red deer in Denmark, based on game yield. Danske Vildtundersøgelser, **13**, 77-106. (Dan.)

Lau, D. (1968) Contribution to the antler development and reproductive biology of deer. Zeitschrift für Säugetierkunde, **33**, 193-214. (Ger.)

Meier, E. (1973) A contribution to the parturition of the fallow-deer (*Cervus dama* L.). Zeitschrift für Säugetierkunde, **38**, 348-373. (Ger.)

Meier-Mühlemann, E. (1973) *Contribution to the Birth, Mother-Young Relation and Adolescent Behaviour of Fallow Deer.* Thesis, University of Zurich, Switzerland. (Ger.).

Prell, H. (1938) The gestation of native game animals. Tharandter Forstliches Jahrbuch, **89**, 696-701. (Ger.)

Puttick, G. (1972) *Analysis of Fallow Deer Population on Groote Schuur Estate.* Dissertation, University of Cape Town, South Africa.

Rieck, W. (1955) The Birth of roe -, red - and fallow deer in central Europe. Zeitschrift für Jagdwissenschaft, 1, 69-75. (Ger.)

Zuckerman, S. (1953) The breeding season of mammals in captivity. Proceedings of the Zoological Society of London, 122, 827-950.

Chapter Ten   Social Organisation and Behaviour

Bencze, L. (1972) Qualitative development of the existence of fallow deer in Hungary. Pol'ovnícky Zborník (Folia venatoria), 2, 211-221. (Hung., Germ. summary)

Cadman, W. A. (1966) The Fallow Deer. London, H.M.S.O.

Calhoun, J. B. & Casby, J. U. (1958) Calculation of home range and density of small mammals. Public Health Monograph No. 55., (Public Health Service Publication No. 592).

Collier, R. V. (1965) Some aspects of fallow deer (Dama dama) at Castor Hanglands National Nature Reserve. Journal of the Northamptonshire Natural History Society, 35, 360-364.

Dagg, A. I. (1973) Gaits in mammals. Mammal Review, 3, 135-154.

Dahlberg, B. L. & Guettinger, R. C. (1956) The white-tailed deer in Wisconsin. Wisconsin Conservation Department Technical Wildlife Bulletin, No. 14.

Gilbert, B. K. & Hailman, J. P. (1966) Uncertainty of leadership-rank in fallow deer. Nature, 209, 1041-1042.

Hawkins, R. E. & Klimstra, W. D. (1970) A preliminary study of the social organization of white-tailed deer. The Journal of Wildlife Management, 34, 407-419.

Heidemann, G. (1973) Zur Biologie des Damwildes (Cervus dama Linné 1758). Hamburg and Berlin; Verlag Paul Parey.

Jewell, P. A. (1966) The concept of home range in mammals. Symposia of the Zoological Society of London, 18, 85-109.

Jurek, R. M. (1970) A population of wild fallow deer in Mendocino County, California. Cal-Neva Wildlife, 54-62.

Puttick, G. (1972) Analysis of Fallow Deer Population on Groote Schuur Estate. Dissertation, University of Cape Town, South Africa.

Sparrowe, R. D. & Springer, P. F. (1970) Seasonal activity patterns of white-tailed deer in eastern South Dakota. The Journal of Wildlife Management, 34, 420-431.

Taylor Page, F. J. (1962) Fallow Deer. London; Sunday Times Publications Ltd.

Chapter Eleven   Ecology

Batcheler, C. L. (1960) A study of the relations between roe, red and fallow deer, with special reference to Drummond Hill Forest, Scotland. The Journal of Animal Ecology, 29, 375-384.

Burger, M. (1966) The ruminating of ruminants in the reflex theory and its origin in ontogenesis. Wissenschaftliche Zeitschrift der Karl-Marx-Universität Leipzig, 3, 483-489. (Ger.)

Carne, P. H. (1954) Roe deer, fallow and sika. Oryx, 2, 388-391.

Chapman, D. I. (1974) Reproductive physiology in relation to deer management. Mammal Review, 4, 61-74.

Daniel, M. J. (1962) Control of introduced deer in New Zealand. Nature, 194, 527-528.

Delap, P. (1955) Roe deer and fallow. Oryx, 3, 38-39.

Golley, F. B. & Buechner, H. K. (1968) A Practical Guide to the Productivity of Large Herbivores. Oxford and Edinburgh; Blackwell Scientific Publications.

Hore, J. P. (1893) The History of the Royal Buckhounds. London; Rimington & Co. Ltd.

Jackson, J. E. (1974) The Feeding Ecology of the Fallow Deer (Dama dama L.) in the New Forest. Ph.D.Thesis, University of Southampton, England.

Jackson, J. E. (1974) Feeding habits of deer. Mammal Review, 4, 93-101.

Jones, D. M. (1973) The use of drugs for immobilization, capture and translocation of non-domestic animals. The Veterinary Annual 1972, 320-352.

Lubbock, R. (1845) *Observations on the Fauna of Norfolk and more particularly on the District of the Broads.* Norwich; Charles Muskett, and London; Longman & Co.

Milne, A. (1961) Definition of competition among animals. Symposia of the Society for Experimental Biology, **15,** 40-61.

Morcan, L. (1973) Deer farming for profit or conservation. New Zealand Journal of Agriculture, **127,** 39-46.

Nall, R. W., Philpot, L. S., Smith, R. D. & Sturm, P. W. (1971) Use of the cannon-net for capturing fallow deer. Proceedings of the Twenty-Fourth Annual Conference, Southeastern Association of Game and Fish Commissioners, September 27-30, 1970 Atlanta, Georgia, 282-284.

Piekarz, R. (1964) Size of the gastro-intestinal tracts and weight of the internal organs of fallow deer. Acta Theriologica, **9,** 25-29.

Sporon-Fiedler, I. (1930) When the fallow deer on the island had to be removed. Danske Jagttidende, **47,** 39-43. (Dan.)

Swift, L. W. & Holloway, C. W. (1967) *Report to the Government of Turkey on Wildlife Management.* Rome; Food and Agriculture Organization of the United Nations. Report No. TA 2391.

Tschirch, W. (1973) Problems and results of wild animal narcosis. Beiträge zur Jagd - und Wildforschung, **8,** 155-170. (Ger.)

Wayre, P. (1967) Artificial rearing of red deer and fallow deer at Norfolk Wildlife Park. International Zoo Yearbook, **7,** 168-171.

Whitehead, G. K. (1950) *Deer and their Management in the Deer Parks of Great Britain and Ireland.* London; Country Life Ltd.

Chapter Twelve   Mortality, Diseases and Parasites

Adami, J. G. (1889) Notes on an epizoötic of rabies; and on a personal experience of M. Pasteur's treatments. [Rabies in fallow deer in Ickworth Park.] The British Medical Journal, 808-810.

Anderson, D. D. (1964) The status of deer in Kansas. University of Kansas Museum of Natural History, Miscellaneous Publication No. 39.

Baston, R., Baston, R., Chapman, D. & Chapman, N. (1970) Accidental injury and subsequent post-mortem observations on a wild fallow deer. Deer, **2,** 461-462.

Borg, K. (1970) On mortality and reproduction of roe deer in Sweden during the period 1948-1969. Viltrevy (Swedish Wildlife), **7,** 121-149.

Chapman, D. I. & Chapman, N. (1969) Observations on the biology of fallow deer (*Dama dama*) in Epping Forest, Essex, England. Biological Conservation, **2,** 55-62.

Cope, A. C. & Horsley, V. (1888) *Reports on the outbreak of rabies among deer in Richmond Park during the years 1886-7.* London; H.M.S.O.

Cox, J. C. (1905) *The Royal Forests of England.* London; Methuen & Co.

Daniel, M. J. (1967) A survey of disease in fallow, Virginia and Japanese deer, chamois, tahr, and feral goats and pigs in New Zealand. New Zealand Journal of Science, **10,** 949-963.

Fleming, G. (1871, 1882) *Animal Plagues: Their History, Nature, and Prevention.* London; Chapman & Hall (Volume 1); Baillière, Tindall & Cox (Volume 2).

Forman, A. J. & Gibbs, E. P. J. (1974) Studies with foot - and - mouth disease virus in British deer (Red, fallow and roe). I. Clinical Disease. Journal of Comparative Pathology, **84,** 215-220.

Forman, A. J., Gibbs, E. P. J., Baber, D. J., Herniman, K. A. J. & Barnett, I. T. (1974) Studies with foot - and - mouth disease virus in British deer (red, fallow and roe). II. Recovery of virus and serological response. Journal of Comparative Pathology, **84,** 221-229.

Geissler, B. (1973) Loss of fallow deer due to traffic near a population centre. Zeitschrift für Jagdwissenschaft, **19,** 205-209. (Ger.)

Haarløv, N. (1964) Life cycle and distribution pattern of *Lipoptena cervi* (L.) (Dipt., Hippobosc.) on Danish deer. Oikos, **15,** 93-129.

Horsley, V. see Cope & Horsley

Kober, W. (1965) Actinomycosis in the fallow deer. Zietschrift für Jadgwissenschaft, **10**, 110-111. (Ger.)

Markson, L. M. & Giles, N. (1973) Cerebrocortical necrosis in a fallow deer (*Dama dama*). The Veterinary Record, **93**, 243-246.

McDiarmid, A. (1962) *Diseases of Free-living Wild Animals*. Rome; Food and Agriculture Organization of the United Nations.

McDiarmid, A. (ed.) (1969) *Diseases in Free-living Wild Animals*. Symposia of the Zoological Society of London, **24**.

Munday, B. L. (1972) A serological study of some infectious diseases of Tasmanian wildlife. Journal of Wildlife Diseases, **8**, 169-175.

Thompson, G. B. (1963) The parasites of British birds and mammals. XL. Ectoparasites of deer in Britain. The Entomologist's Monthly Magazine, **99**, 186-189.

Towar, D. R., Scott, R. M. & Goyings, L. S. (1965) Tuberculosis in a captive deer herd. American Journal of Veterinary Research, **26**, 339-346.

Twigg, G. I., Hughes, D. M. & McDiarmid, A. (1973) The low incidence of leptospirosis in British deer. Veterinary Record, **93**, 98-100.

Ueckermann, E. & Hansen, P. (1968) *Das Damwild*. Hamburg and Berlin; Verlag Paul Parey.

Chapter Thirteen   Persian Fallow Deer

Bate, D. M. (1927) See Turville-Petre.

Bate, D. M. A. (1937) see Garrod.

Brooke, V. (1875) On a new species of deer from Mesopotamia. Proceedings of the Zoological Society of London, 261-266.

Brooke, V. (1876) Supplementary notes on *Cervus mesopotamicus*. Proceedings of the Zoological Society of London, 298-303.

Dawson, W. R. (1934) Deer in ancient Egypt. The Journal of the Linnean Society of London, Zoology, **39**, 137-145.

Garrod, D. A. E. & Bate, D. M. A. (1937) *The Stone Age of Mount Carmel. Excavations at the Wady el-Mughara*. Volume 1. Oxford; The Clarendon Press.

Goodwin, H. A. & Holloway, C. W. (1972) *The Red Data Book. Volume 1, Mammals*. Morges; International Union for Conservation of Nature and Natural Resources.

Haltenorth, T. (1959) Contribution to the knowledge of the Mesopotamican fallow deer (*Cervus (Dama) mesopotamicus* Brooke, 1875) and to the original and historical distribution of the common fallow deer. Säugetierkundliche Mitteilungen, **7**, Special Number, 1-89. (Ger.)

Haltenorth, T. (1961) Habitat behaviour and distribution of Mesopotamian fallow deer, *Cervus mesopotamicus* Brooke, 1875. Säugetierkundliche Mitteilungen, **9**, 15-39. (Ger.)

Harrison, D. L. (1968) *The Mammals of Arabia*. **Volume 2.** London; Ernest Benn Ltd.

Hilzheimer, M. (1927) *Dama schaeferi* Hilzh. Zeitschrift Saugetierkunde, **2**, 68-73. (Ger.)

Joleaud, L. (1935) The antlered ruminants of Africa. Mémoires présentés a l'Institut d'Égypte, **27**, 1-85. (Fr.)

Kraft, H. (1959) The nasal speculum of fallow deer (*Cervus (Dama) mesopotamicus* Brooke, 1875, and *dama* Linné, 1758. Säugetierkundliche Mitteilungen, **7**, Special Number, 95-98 (Ger.)

Layard, A. H. (1849) *The Monuments of Nineveh from Drawings made on the spot*. London; John Murray.

Löffler, G. & Walther, F. (1959-60) About our Mesopotamian. Georg von Opel-Freigehege Jahrbuch 1959-60, 12-21. (Ger.)

Picard, L. (1937) Inferences on the problem of the Pleistocene climate of Palestine and Syria drawn from flora, fauna and stratigraphy. Proceedings of the Prehistoric Society, new series, **3**, 58-70.

Red Data Book. see Goodwin & Holloway.

Talbot, L. M. (1960) A look at threatened species: a report on some animals of the middle east and southern Asia which are threatened with extermination. Oryx, 5, 153-293.

Trense, W. (1958) The forgotten fallow deer. Die Pirsch, München, No. 10, 279-283. (Ger.)

Tristram, H. B. (1866) Report on the mammals of Palestine. Proceedings of the Zoological Society of London, 84-93.

Tristram, H. B. (1822) *The Land of Israel.* London; Christian Knowledge Society.

Turville-Petre, F. (1927) *Researches in Prehistoric Galilee 1925-1926.* London; The Council of the British School of Archaeology in Jerusalem.

Van Buren, E. D. (1939) The fauna of ancient Mesopotamia as represented in art. Analecta Orientalia, **18**, 1-113.

Zeuner, F. E. (1958) Animal remains from a late Bronze Age sanctuary on Cyprus, and the problem of the domestication of fallow deer. Journal of the Palaeontological Society of India, **3**, 131-135.

Appendix III
Clapham, A. R., Tutin, T. G. & Warburg, E. F. (1962) *Flora of the British Isles.* (2nd. ed.). Cambridge; University Press.

Appendix IV
Batty, A. F. & Chapman, D. I. (1970) Gastro-intestinal parasites of wild fallow deer (*Dama dama* L.). Journal of Helminthology, **44**, 57-61.

Brugh, Jr., T. H. (1971) A survey of the internal parasites of a feral herd of fallow deer (*Dama dama*) in Alabama. Journal of the Alabama Academy of Science, **42**, 133.

Christie, A. H. C. & Andrews, J. R. H. (1966) Introduced ungulates in New Zealand, (d) Fallow deer. Tuatara, **14**, 82-88.

Dróżdż, J. (1966) Studies on helminths and helminthiases in Cervidae. II. The helminth fauna in Cervidae in Poland. Acta Parasitologica Polonica, **14**, 1-13.

Guildal, J. A. (1962) Endoparasites of Danish red deer (*Cervus elaphus* L.) and of Danish fallow deer (*Dama dama* (L.)). Yearbook of the Royal Veterinary and Agricultural College, Copenhagen, 49-61.

Kotrlý, A. (1964) Ecology of parasites on game of the family Cervidae and Bovidae in Czechoslovakia. Práce výzkumných ústavů lesnických ČSSR, **29**, 7-47. (Czech., Eng. summary).

Kutzer, E. & Hinaidy, H. K. (1969) Parasites of wild ruminants in Austria. Zeitschrift für Parasitenkunde, **32**, 354-368. (Ger.)

Siefke, A. (1965) Recent results of investigations upon the parasitic attack of roe - and fallow deer. Jagd - und Wildforschung, 4, 135-145. (Ger.)

Swierstra, D., Jansen, Jr., J. & Broek, E. van den (1959) Parasites of animals in the Netherlands. Tijdschrift voor Diergeneeskunde, **84**, 892-900.

Appendix V
Morris, D. (1965) *The Mammals: A Guide to the Living Species.* London; Hodder and Stoughton.

Index

Localities mentioned in Chapter Four which are outside Britain and which are below country or state level, have not been indexed.

Further Reading: post-1975 references

General

Bradley, C. (1996) *The Realm of the Fallow Buck: The Deer of Wyre Forest.* —; Christopher Bradley. pp. 168.

Brown, Baxter, M. (1985) *Richmond Park: The History of a Royal Deer Park.* London, Robert Hale. pp. 208.

Chapman, Norma (1984) *Fallow Deer.* Oswestry; Anthony Nelson: Mammal Society Series. pp.24.

Chapman, Norma (1993) Distribution and Biology of Fallow Deer. In: *Proceedings of First World Forum on Fallow Deer Farming, Mudgee, New South Wales, March 1993.* Asher, G. W. (ed.) pages 1-11.

Chapman, N. & Chapman, D. (1978) *Fallow Deer* (2nd edn.) —: British Deer Society. pp. 22.

Chapman, N. G. & Chapman, D. I. (1982) *The Fallow Deer.* Forestry Commission, Forest Record 124, H.M.S.O. pp. 19.

Chapman, N. G. & Putman, R. (1991) Fallow Deer. In: *The Handbook of British Mammals,* Third edn. Eds. G. B. Corbet & S. Harris. Oxford; Blackwell Scientific Publications.

Focardi, S. & Poli, B. M. (eds) (1996) Resources Utilization in Fallow Deer. Proceedings of Conference at Montepaldi, Italy, June 20-22 1995. Supplemento alle Ricerche di Biologia della Selvaggina, **XXV,** 1-242.

Harris, S. (1983) Donald Ivan Chapman 1935-1982. Mammal Review, **13,** 197-201.

Langbein, J. (1991) *The effects of density and age on body condition, reproductive performance, behaviour and survival of Fallow deer.* Unpub. Ph.D. Thesis, University of Southampton, England.

Putman, R. (1988) *The Natural History of Deer.* London; Christopher Helm. pp. 191.

Ueckermann, E. & Hansen, P. (1994) *Das Damwild.* Hamburg; Verlag Paul Parey. pp. 327.

Fossil and Early History

Ferguson, W. W., Porath, Y. & Paley, S. (1985) Late Bronze Period yields first osteological evidence of *Dama dama* (Artiodactyla: Cervidae) from Israel and Arabia. Mammalia, **49,** 209-214.

Leonardi, G. & Petronio, C. (1976) The Fallow deer of European Pleistocene. Geologica Romana, **XV,** 1-67.

Lister, A. M. (1986) New Results on Deer from Swanscombe, and the Stratigraphical Significance of Deer in the Middle and Upper Pleistocene of Europe. Journal of Archaeological Science, **13,** 319-338.

Masseti, M. (1995) Survey of the extant populations of the fallow deer of Rhodes (*Dama dama* L., 1758) in continental and insular Greece, with a numerical estimate of their consistence. In: Abstracts of the 2nd European Congress of Mammalogy, Southampton University, England. (Gurnell, J. ed.), page 190.

Masseti, M. (1996) The postglacial diffusion of the genus *Dama* Frisch, 1775, in the Mediterranean region. Supplemento alle Ricerche di Biologia della Selvaggina, **XXV,** 7-29.

Pfeiffer, T. (1995) The occurrence of *Dama dama* in central Europe during the Pleistocene with special consideration of the finds at Neumark-Nord. Zeitschrift für Jagdwissenschaft, **41,** 157-170.

Distribution, Past and Present

Cantor, L. (1983) *The Medieval Parks of England: A Gazetteer.* Loughborough; Loughborough University. pp. 95.

Chapman, D. (1977) Deer of Essex. Essex Naturalist (new series) No. 1, 1-50.

Chapman, N. G. & Chapman, D. I. (1980) The distribution of fallow deer: a worldwide review. Mammal Review, **10,** 61-138.

Conseil International de la Chasse & de la Conservation du Gibier (1984) Proceedings of a Symposium (Le daim, the Fallow deer, Damwild) held in Budapest, January 1984.

Gray, G. G. (1983) History and Status of European Fallow Deer (*Dama dama dama*) at Argonne National Laboratory, Illinois. The Prairie Naturalist, **15**, 113-119.

Harris, S., Morris, P., Wray, S. & Yalden, D. (1995) *A Review of British Mammals.* Peterborough; JNCC. pp. 168.

Ortiz, C. (1992) Current status of Red and Fallow deer Populations in Chile: The Need of Management. In: *The Biology of Deer.* Brown, R. D. (ed.) pages 30-36. New York; Springer-Verlag.

Schaal, A. (1981) Le Daim (*Dama dama* L.) en France. Mammalia, **45**, 512-513.

Ueckermann, E. (1980) A contribution to the history of the introduction of fallow deer in North-Rhine Westphalia. Zeitschrift für Jagdwissenschaft, **26**, 32-40.

Structure, Function and Growth

Alexander, R. McN., Dimery, N. J. & Ker, R. F. (1985) Elastic structures in the back and their role in galloping in some mammals. Journal of Zoology, **207**, 467-482.

Apollonio, M. & Vailati, G. (1966) Functional morphology of metatarsal glands in Fallow Deer. Zeitschrift für Säugetierkunde, **61**, 321-326.

Barrell, G. K. & Simpson-Morgan, M. W. (1990) Major lymph nodes of the head of the fallow deer (*Dama dama*) and lymphatic drainage of antlers. Australian Veterinary Journal, **67**, 406-407.

Ceccarelli, P., Pedini, V. & Gargiulo, A. M. (1995) The Endocrine Cells in the gastroenteric Tract of Adult Fallow Deer (*Dama dama* L.). Anatomy, Histology and Embryology, **24**, 171-174.

Chapman, D. I. & Chapman, N. G. (1979) Seasonal changes in the male accessory glands of reproduction in adult Fallow deer (*Dama dama*). Journal of Zoology, **189**, 259-273.

Chapman, D. I. & Chapman, N. G. (1980) Morphology of the male accessory organs of reproduction of immature fallow deer (*Dama dama* L.) with particular reference to puberty and antler development. Acta anatomica, **108**, 51-59.

Chapman, D. I., Chapman, N. G. & Kennaugh, J. H. (1981) Development of the preputial gland of immature fallow deer (*Dama dama* Linnaeus) with particular reference to puberty. Zeitschrift für Säugetierkunde, **46**, 322-330.

Chapman, N. G. & Twigg, G. I. (1990) Studies on the thymus gland of British Cervidae, particularly muntjac, *Muntiacus reevesi*, and fallow, *Dama dama*, deer. Journal of Zoology, **222**, 653-675.

Dimery, N., Ker, R. F. & Alexander, R. McN. (1986) Elastic properties of the feet of deer (Cervidae). Journal of Zoology, **208**, 161-169.

Dondorf, W. & Hofmann, W. (1984) Differences in size and form of the ossa metacarpalia II and V between red deer and fallow deer. Zeitschrift für Jagdwissenschaft, **30**, 155-164.

Field, R. A., Young, O. A., Asher, G. A. & Foote, D. M. (1985) Characteristics of male fallow deer muscle at a time of sex-related muscle growth. Growth, **49**, 190-201.

Fischer, K. (1991) Seasonal changes in neck girth and the fat season in male fallow deer: 2 secondary sex characteristics and their ontogenesis. In: *Transactions 20th Congress IUGB.* Csanyi, S. & Ernhaft, J. (eds) pages 547-55. Gödöllö, Hungary.

Fischer, K. (1996) The course of puberty in male fallow deer. Zeitschrift für Säugetierkunde, **61**, 165-175. (In German).

Gosch, B., Bartolomaeus & Fischer, K. (1989) Light and scanning electron microscopy of fallow deer (*Dama dama*) spermatozoa. Journal of Reproduction and Fertility, **87**, 187-192.

Gosch, B. & Fischer, K. (1989). Seasonal changes of testis volume and sperm quality in adult fallow deer (*Dama dama*) and their relationship to the antler cycle. Journal of Reproduction and Fertility, **85**, 7-17.

Henke, S. E., Demarais, S. & Pfister, J. A. (1988) Digestive capacity and diets of white-tailed deer and exotic ruminants. Journal of Wildlife Management, **52**, 595-598.

Hofmann, R. R. (1985) Digestive physiology of the deer – their morphophysiological specialisation and adaptation. Royal Society of New Zealand Bulletin, **22**, 393-407.

Jacobs, G. H., Deegan, J. F., Neitz, J., Murphy, B. P., Miller, K. V. & Marchinton, R. L. (1994) Electro-physiological measurements of spectral mechanisms in the retinas of two cervids: white-tailed deer and fallow deer. Journal of Comparative Physiology A, **174**, 551-557.

Johnson, E. & Hornby, J. (1980) Age and seasonal coat changes in long haired and normal Fallow deer (*Dama dama*). Journal of Zoology, **192**, 501-509.

Kennaugh, J. H., Chapman, D. I. & Chapman, N. G. (1977) Seasonal changes in the prepuce of adult Fallow deer (*Dama dama*) and its probable function as a scent organ. Journal of Zoology, **183**, 301-310.

Kierdorf, H., Kierdorf, U., Szuwart, T., Gath, U. & Clemen, G. (1994) Light microscopic observations on the ossification process in the early developing pedicle of fallow deer (*Dama dama*). Annals of Anatomy, **176**, 243-249.

Krzywinski, A., Niedbalska, A. & Twardowski, L. (1984) Growth and Development of Hand Reared Fallow Deer Fawns. Acta Theriologica, **29**, 349-356.

Lister, A. M. & Chapman, N. G. (1988) Variation in lateral metacarpals of fallow deer (*Dama dama*) (Mammalia, Cervidae). Journal of Zoology, **216**, 597-603.

Malzahn, E. & Pohlmeyer, K. (1991) The lymph nodes of fallow deer (*Dama dama* L., 1758). Deutsche Tierärztliche Wochenschrift, **98**, 188-191. (In German).

Musse, E., Pohlmeyer, K. & Von Rautenfeld, D. B. (1993) Investigations in the lymph vessel system of fallow deer (*Dama dama* L. 1758). Deutsche Tierärztliche Wochenschrift, **100**, 188-191. (In German).

Nugent, G. (1989) Identifying the Sex of Fallow Deer from Jawbone Measurements. Australian Wildlife Research, Australian Wildlife Research, **16**, 441-447.

Pélabon, C. (1995) Growth and lactation in a captive population of fallow deer (*Dama dama*). Mammalia, **59**, 268-273. (Entirely in French).

Pélabon, C. (1995) Variability of age estimation criteria for fallow deer (*Dama dama*) during the first days after birth. Mammalia, **59**, 141-146. (Entirely in French).

Pemberton, J. M. & Dansie, O. (1983) Live weights of Fallow deer (*Dama dama*) in British deer parks. Journal of Zoology, **199**, 171-177.

Pohlmeyer, K. & Abdulla, K. E. H. (1986) Comparative anatomical studies on skeletal muscles of fallow deer, sheep and goat. Deutsche Tierärztliche Wochenschrift, **93**, 185-240. (In German).

Saber, A. S. (1983) On the presence of anomalous muscles in the heads of the fallow deer (*Cervus dama*) and red deer (*Cervus elaphus*). Zeitschrift für Jagdwissenschaft, **29**, 184-187. (In German).

St.-Pierre, M. & Prescott, J. (1983) Notes on the development of feeding of fallow deer (*Cervus dama*) in captivity. Les Carnets de Zoologie, **43**, 25-28. (In French).

Schnare, H. & Fischer, K. (1987) Secondary Sex Characteristics and Connected Physiological Values in Male Fallow Deer (*Dama dama* L.) and Their Relationship to Changes of the Annual Photoperiod: Doubling the Frequency. The Journal of Experimental Zoology, **244**, 463-471.

Age Estimation and Teeth

Brown, W. A. B. & Chapman, N. G. (1990) The dentition of fallow deer (*Dama dama*): a scoring scheme to assess age from wear of the permanent malariform teeth. Journal of Zoology, **221**, 659-682.

Brown, W. A. B. & Chapman, N. G. (1991) Age assessment of fallow deer (*Dama dama*): from a scoring scheme based on radiographs of developing permanent molariform teeth. Journal of Zoology, **224**, 367-379.

Kierdorf, H. & Kierdorf, U. (1992) A scanning electron microscope study on the distribution of peritubular dentine in cheek teeth of Cervidae and Suidae (Mammalia, Artiodactyla). Anatomy and Embryology, **186**, 319-326.

Kierdorf, H., Kierdorf, U. & Hommelsheim (1991) Scanning Electron Microscopic Observtions on the Development and Structure of Tooth Enamel in Cervidae (*Mammalia: Ruminantia*). Anatomy, Histology and Embryology, **20**, 237–252.

Lutz, W. (1993) Contribution toward the dental and lower jaw development among fallow deer fawns in an urban region. Zeitschrift für Jagdwissenschaft, **39**, 73-86. (In German).

Moore, N. P., Cahill, J. P., Kelly, P. F. & Hayden, T. J. (1995) An assessment of five methods of age determination in an enclosed population of fallow deer (*Dama dama*). Proceedings of the Royal Irish Academy, **95B**, 27-34.

Antlers

Alvarez, F. (1994) Bone density and breaking stress in relation to consistent fracture position in fallow deer antlers. Doñana, Acta Vertebrata, **21**, 15-24.

Alvarez, F. (1995) Functional directional asymmetry in fallow deer (*Dama dama*) antlers. Journal of Zoology, **236**, 563-569.

Banwell, D. B. (1989) *Great New Zealand Deer Heads. Vol. 3.* Auckland; The Halcyon Press. 34-73.

Brown, R. D. (ed) *Antler Development in Cervidae.* Kingsville, Texas: Caesar Kleberg Wildlife Research Institute. pp. 480.

Bubenik, G. A. & Bubenik, A. B. (1990) (eds) *Horns, Pronghorns and Antlers.* New York; Springer-Verlag. pp. 562.

Chapman, D. I. (1975) Antlers – bones of contention. Mammal Review, **5**, 121-172.

Chapman, N. G. (1986) An explanation of the porous tips of the antlers of some Fallow deer (*Dama dama*). Journal of Zoology, **210**, 628-631.

Goss, R. J. (1983) *Deer Antlers.* New York; Academic Press. pp. 316.

Goss, R. J. (1990) Tumor-like growth of antlers in castrated fallow deer: an electron microscope study. Scanning Microscopy, **4**, 715-721.

Goss, R. J., Van Praagh, A. & Brewer, P. (1992) The Mechanism of Antler Casting in the Fallow Deer. The Journal of Experimental Zoology, **264**, 429-436.

Kierdorf, H. & Kierdorf, U. (1992) State of determination of the Antlerogenic Tissues with Special Reference to Double-head Formation. In: *The Biology of Deer*, Brown, R. D. (ed.) pages 525-531. New York; Springer-Verlag.

Kierdorf, U., Kierdorf, H. & Schultz, M. (1994) The macroscopic and microscopic structure of double-head antlers and pedicle bone of Cervidae. Annals of Anatomy, **176**, 251-257.

Lincoln, G. A. (1992) Biology of antlers. Journal of Zoology, **226**, 517-528.

MacKenzie, G. (1995) Skull damage in fallow deer. Australian Deer, **20**, 19-23.

Stubbe, C. & Pofahl, U. (1995) The influence of fallow deer of differing origins on the antler quality of a newly introduced population. Zeitschrift für Jagdwissenschaft, **41**, 1-7.

Rut and Male Reproduction

Alvarez, F. (1993) Risks of fighting in relation to age and territory holding in fallow deer. Canadian Journal of Zoology, **71**, 376-383.

Alvarez, F., Braza, F. & San Jose C. (1990) Coexistence of territoriality and harem defense in a rutting fallow deer population. Journal of Mammalogy, **71**, 692-695.

Apollonio, M., Fiesta-Bianchet, M., Mari, F., Mattioli, S. & Sarno, B. (1992) To lek or not to lek: mating strategies of male fallow deer. Behavioral Ecology, **3**, 25-31.

Buschhaus, N. L. & Lagory, K. E. (1990) Behavior in an Introduced Population of Fallow deer during the Rut. The American Midland Naturalist, **124**, 318-329.

Clutton-Brock, T. H., Price, O. F. & MacColl, A. D. A. (1992) Mate retention, harassment, and the evolution of ungulate leks. Behavioral Ecology, **3**, 234-242.

Fischer, K. (1983) Experiments on the reproductive capability of young female and male fallow deer (*Dama dama* L.) Zeitschrift für Jagdwissenschaft, **29**, 137-142. (In German).

Langbein, J. & Thirgood, S. (1989) Variation in Mating Systems of Fallow Deer (*Dama dama*) in Relation to Ecology. Ethology, **83**, 195-214.

Moore, N. P., Kelly, P. F., Cahill, J. P. & Hayden, T. J. (1995) Mating strategies and mating success of fallow (*Dama dama*) bucks in a non-lekking population. Behavioural Ecology and Sociobiology, **36,** 91-100.

Pemberton, J. & Balmford, A. (1987) Lekking in fallow deer. Journal of Zoology, **213,** 762-765.

Schaal, A. & Bradbury, J. W. (1987) Lek breeding in a deer species. Biology of Behaviour, **12,** 28-32.

Štěrba, O. & Klusak, K. (1984) Reproductive Biology of Fallow Deer, *Dama dama*. Acta Scientiarum Naturalium Academiae Scientiarum Bohemoslovacae Brno, **18,** 1-46.

Thirgood, S. J. (1991) Alternative mating strategies and reproductive success in fallow deer. Behaviour, **116,** 1-10.

Female Reproduction and Maternal Behaviour

Asher, G. W. (1985) Oestrous cycle and breeding season of farmed fallow deer, *Dama dama*. Journal of Reproduction and Fertility, **75,** 521-529.

Asher, G. W., Barrell, G. K. & Peterson, A. J. (1986) Hormonal changes around oestrus of farmed fallow deer, *Dama dama*. Journal of Reproduction and Fertility, **78,** 487-496.

Asher, G. W. & Morrow, C. J. (1993) Observations on gestation length of European, Mesopotamian and hybrid fallow deer. In: *Proceedings of First World Forum on Fallow Deer Farming, Mudgee, New South Wales, March 1993.* Asher, G. W. (ed) pages 169-172.

Birgersson, B. & K. Ekvall, K. (1994) Suckling time and fawn growth in fallow deer (*Dama dama*). Journal of Zoology, **232,** 641-650.

Birgersson, B., Ekvall, K. & Temrin, H. (1991) Allosuckling in fallow deer, *Dama dama*. Animal Behaviour, **42,** 326-327.

Braza, F., San Jose C. & Blom, A. (1988) Birth measurements, parturition dates, and progeny sex ratio of *Dama dama* in Doñana, Spain. Journal of Mammalogy, **69,** 607-610.

Gautheir, D. & Barrette, C. (1985) Suckling and weaning in captive white-tailed and fallow deer. Behaviour, **94,** 128-149.

Langbein, J. & Putman, R. (1992) Reproductive Success of Female Fallow Deer in Relation to Age and Condition. In: *The Biology of Deer,* Brown, R. D. (ed) pages 293-299, New York: Springer-Verlag.

Mulley, R. C., English, A. W. & Kirby, A. (1990) The reproductive performance of farmed fallow deer (*Dama dama*) in New South Wales. *Australian Veterinary Record,* **67,** 281-286.

San José, C. & Braza, F. (1992) Antipredator aspects of fallow deer behaviour during calving season at Doñana National Park (Spain). Ethology Ecology and Evolution, **4,** 139-149.

Social Organisation and Behaviour

Alvarez, F. (1993) Risks of fighting in relation to age and territory holding in fallow deer. Canadian Journal of Zoology, **71,** 376-383.

Bullock, D. J., Kerridge, F. J., Hanlon, A. & Arnold, R. W. (1993) Short-term responses of deer to recreational disturbances in two deer parks. Journal of Zoology, **230,** 327-332.

Gould, M. S. & Werts, J. M. (1979) Influence of the buck on social behavior of captive female fallow deer (*Dama dama*) during the rutting season. Behavioural Processes, **4,** 253-263.

Gradl-Grams, M. (1977) Studies of behaviour of fallow deer in captivity. Zoologischer Garten, **47,** 81-108. (In German).

Ecology

Braza, F. & Álvarez, F. (1987) Habitat use by red deer and fallow deer in Doñana National Park. Miscellania Zoologica, **11,** 363-367.

Bullock, D. J. & Vernon, S. A. (1992) What do Red and fallow deer eat in Deer Parks? In: *Management, Welfare and Conservation of Park Deer.* Proceedings of the Second Deer park Symposium, Leicester, 1992. Bullock, D. J. & Goldspink, C. (eds), pages 13-25. Potters Bar; Universities Federation for Animal Welfare.

Caldwell, J., Chapman, D. I. & Chapman, N. G. (1983) Observations on the autumn and winter diet of Fallow deer (*Dama dama*). Journal of Zoology, **201**, 559-563.

Nugent, G. (1990) Forage availability and the diet of fallow deer (*Dama dama*) in the Blue Mountains, Otago. New Zealand Journal of Ecology, **13**, 83-95.

Henke, S. E., Demarais, S., & Pfister, J. A. (1988) Digestive capacity and diets of white-tailed deer and exotic ruminants. Journal of Wildlife Management, **52**, 595-598.

Poli, B. M. (1966) Feeding and Nutrition in Fallow deer: a review. Supplemento alle Ricerche di Biologia della Selvaggina, **XXV**, 31-61.

Poli, B. M., Focardi, S. & Tinelli, A. (1996) Composition and metabolizable energy of feed used by Fallow deer (*Dama dama*) in a coastal Mediterranean ecosystem. Small Ruminant Research, **22**, 103-109.

Putman, R. (1986) *Grazing in Temperate Ecosystems: Large Herbivores and the Ecology of the New Forest.* London & Sydney; Croom Helm. pp. 210.

Putman, R. J., Culpin, S. & Thirgood, S. J. (1993) Dietary differences between male and female fallow deer in sympatry and in allopatry. Journal of Zoology, **229**, 267-275.

Schaal, A. (1982) Influence of the environment on the composition of social groups of fallow deer. La Terre et la Vie, Revue d'ecologie, **36**, 161-174.

Thirgood, S. J. (1995) The effects of sex, season and habitat availability on patterns of habitat use by fallow deer (*Dama dama*). Journal of Zoology, **235**, 645-659.

Veblen, T. T., Mermoz, M., Martin, C. & Ramilo, E. (1989) Effects of exotic deer on forest regeneration and composition in northern Patagonia. Journal of Applied Ecology, **26**, 711-724.

Wehausen, J. D. & Elliott, H. W. (1982) Range relationships and demography of fallow and axis deer on Point Reyes National Seashore, Californian Fish and Game, **68**, 132-145.

Mortality, Diseases and Parasites

Ambrosi, M., Manfredi, M. T. & Lanfranchi, P. (1993) Pattern of abomasal helminths in fallow deer farming in Umbria (central Italy). Veterinary Parasitology, **47**, 81-86.

Baker, J. R., Ashton, D. G., Jones, D. M. & Noddle, B. A. (1979) Four cases of chondrodystrophy in fallow deer. The Veterinary Record, **104**, 450-453.

Batty, A. F., Chapman, D. I. & Chapman, N. G. (1987) Prevalence of nematode parasites in wild fallow deer (*Dama dama*). The Veterinary Record, **120**, 599.

Chapman, D. I., Chapman, N. G., Atherton, J. G. & Platt, H. (1979) Yersiniosis in a free-living Fallow deer. The Veterinary Record, **105**, 573-574.

Chapman, D. I., Chapman, N. G. & Jeffcott, L. B. (1984) Deformities of the metacarpus and metatarsus in fallow deer (*Dama dama* L.). Journal of Comparative Pathology, **94**, 77-91.

Chapman, N. G. & Chapman, D. I. (1987) Cysticercosis in Fallow Deer in England. Acta Theriologica, **32**, 105-113.

Chapman, N. G. & Harris, S. (1992) Brachygnathia in fallow deer (*Dama dama*). Journal of Zoology, **227**, 323-326.

English, A. W. & Mulley, R. C. (1992) Causes of perinatal mortality in farmed fallow deer (*Dama dama*). Australian Veterinary Journal, **69**, 191-193.

Guberti, V. & Cucchi, C. (1996) Fallow deer as a resource for micro and macroparasites. Supplemento alle Ricerche di Biologia della Selvaggina, **XXV**, 171-184.

Hinaidy, H. K. (1987) Blood parasites of wildliving ruminants in Austria. Journal of Veterinary Medicine, **34**, 81-97. (In German).

Jones, T. O. (1982) Outbreak of *Pasteurella multocida* septicaemia in fallow deer (*Dama dama*). The Veterinary Record, **110**, 451-452.

Nettles, V., Prestwood, A. K. & Smith, R. D. (1977) Cerebrospinal parelaphostrongylosis in fallow deer. Journal of Wildlife Diseases, **13**, 440-444.

Sleeman, D. P. (1983) Parasites of deer in Ireland. Journal of Life Sciences, **4**, 203-210.

Wesemeier, H.-H. & Sedlaczek, J. (1995) One known *Sacrocystis* species and one found for the first time in fallow deer (*Dama dama*). Applied Parasitology, **36**, 299-302.

Westrom, D. R., Nelson, B. C. & Connolly, G. E. (1976) Transfer of *Bovicola tibialis* (Piaget) (Mallophaga: Trichodectidae) from the introduced fallow deer to the Columbian black-tailed deer in California. Journal of Medical Entomology, **13**, 169-173.

Blood constituents

Chapman, D. I. (1977) Haematology of the deer. In: *Comparative Clinical Haematology*, Archer, R. K. & Jeffcott, L. B. (eds), pages 345-364. Oxford; Blackwell Scientific Publications.

Chapman, D. I., Chapman, N. G. & Allen, B. V. (1982) Some haematological data for fallow deer (*Dama dama*) in England. Research in Veterinary Science, **33**, 205-207.

Chapman, D. I., Chapman, N. G. & Kent, J. E. (1980) Some serum constituents of fallow deer (*Dama dama* L.). Research in Veterinary Science, **29**, 105-107.

Eiben, B. & Fischer, K. (1984) Examination of various blood parameters in fallow deer (*Dama dama* L.) during the course of the year. Zeitschrift für Jagdwissenschaft, **30**, 235-242. (In German).

Ranucci, S., Morgante, M., Diverio, S., Costarelli, S., Beghelli, D. & Duranti, E. (1996). Blood constituents and clinical findings in captured fallow deer (*Dama dama*). Supplemento alle Ricerche di Biologia della Selvaggina, **XXV**, 209-217.

Schnare, H. & Fischer, K. (1987) Hematocrit, Erythrocytes and Haemoglobin in blood of adult male fallow deer (*Dama dama* L.) especially in relation to the ambient temperature. Zeitschrift für Jagdwissenschaft, **33**, 9-14.

Genetics

Bignell, J. (1993) Genetics of coat colour inheritance in fallow deer. In: *Proceedings of First World Forum on Fallow Deer Farming, Mudgee, New South Wales, March 1993*. Asher, G. W. (ed) pages 173-179.

Hertzog, S. (1989) Genetic polymorphism of transferrin in fallow deer, *Cervus dama* L. Animal Genetics, **20**, 421-426.

Lioi, M. B., Scarfi, M. R. & Di Berardino, D. (1994) The RBA-banded karyotype of the fallow deer (*Dama dama* L.). Cytogenetics and Cell Genetics, **67**, 75-80.

Pemberton, J. M. & Smith, R. H. (1985) Lack of Biochemical Polymorphism in British Fallow Deer. Heredity, **55**, 199-207.

Rubini, M., Negri, E. & Fontana, F. (1990) Standard karyotype and chromosomal evolution of the fallow deer (*Dama dama* L.). Cytobios, **64**, 155-161.

Scheiber, A. & Fakler, P. (1996) NADH Diaphorase Polymorphism in European Fallow Deer. Biochemical Genetics, **34**, 61-65.

Farming, Welfare, Management and Field Techniques

Asher, G. W. (ed) (1993) Welfare Issues. In *Proceedings of First World Forum on Fallow Deer Farming, Mudgee, New South Wales, March 1993*. pages 207-228.

Asher, G. W. (ed) (1993) World Status of Fallow Deer Farming. In: *Proceedings of First World Forum on Fallow Deer Farming, Mudgee, New South Wales, March 1993*. pages 13-63.

Asher, G. W. (1993) Oestrous synchronization, semen collection and artificial insemination of farmed red deer (*Cervus elaphus*) and fallow deer (*Dama dama*). Animal Reproduction Science, **33**, 241-265.

Bailey, R. E. & Putman, R. J. (1981) Estimation of Fallow deer (*Dama dama*) populations from fecal accumulation. Journal of Applied Ecology, **18**, 697-702.

Bamberg, F-B. (1985) Investigations of the behaviour of fallow deer in enclosures. Kronshagen; Verlag Gunter Hartmann. pp. 217. (In German).

Bamberg, F. B. (1987) The use of collar transmitters in biotelemetry in fallow deer. Zeitschrift für Jagdwissenschaft, **33**, 71-77. (In German).

Chapman, D. I. (1974) Reproductive physiology in relation to deer management. Mammal Review, **4,** 61-74.

Jones, A. R. & Price, S. E. (1992) Measuring the Responses of Fallow Deer to Disturbance. In: *The Biology of Deer.* Brown, R. D. (ed) pages 211-216. New York; Springer-Verlag.

Mayle, B. A., Doney, J., Lazarus, G., Peace, J. A., Smith, D. E. (1996) Fallow deer (*Dama dama* L.) defecation rate and its use in determining population size. Supplemento alle Ricerche di Biologia della Selvaggina, **XXV,** 63-78.

Putman, R. & Langbein, J. (1992) Effects of Stocking Density, Feeding and Herd Management on Mortality of Park Deer. In: *The Biology of Deer.* Brown, R. D. (ed) pages 180-88. New York; Springer-Verlag.

Putman, R. J., Langbein, J., Hewison, A. J. M. & Sharma, S. K. (1996) Relative roles of density-dependent and density-independent factors in population dynamics of British deer. Mammal Review, **26,** 81-101.

Rudge, A. J. B. (Ed) (1984) *The Capture and Handling of Deer.* Peterborough; Nature Conservancy Council, pp. 273.

Vincent, J.-P., Hewison, A. J. M., Angibault, J.-M. & Cargnelutti, B. (1966) Testing density estimators on a fallow deer population of known size. Journal of Wildlife Management, **60,** 18-28.

Persian Fallow Deer

Anon. (1986) The flight of the Yachmur. The Deer Farmer (New Zealand), September, 15-17.

Rudloff, R. (1996) *International Studbook of the Persian Fallow Deer.* Berlin; Tierpark Berlin.

Otway, W. (1991) Establishment of Mesopotamia Fallow Deer in New Zealand and Their Hybridization with European Fallow Deer. In: *The Biology of Deer.* Brown, R. D. (ed) page 400. New York; Springer-Verlag.

Saltz, D. (1986) Minimizing Extinction Probability due to demographic stochasticity in a reintroduced herd of Persian fallow deer *Dama dama mesopotamica.* Biological Conservation, **75,** 27-33.

Legislation

Deer Act 1991. This consolidation Act repeals the whole of The Deer Act 1993 and all or parts of eight other Acts. Anyone concerned with deer management in England and Wales should be familiar with the content of this Act. Various other Acts deal with the welfare, transport, farming and diseases of deer.

Unless otherwise indicated, publications in languages other than English have a brief summary in English.